C000292041

THE ABC OF BRITISH RAILWAYS LOCOMOTIVES

EDITED BY A. F. COOK

PART 1 - Nos. 1-9999
WESTERN REGION
STEAM LOCOMOTIVES

Ian Allan
PUBLISHING

NOTES ON THE USE OF THIS BOOK

1. This booklet lists British Railways locomotives numbered between 1 and 9999 in service at August 31st, 1950. This range of numbers covers Western Region (ex-G.W.R.) engines with the following exceptions:

    (i) Diesel and gas turbine locomotives, which are dealt with in the ABC OF BRITISH RAILWAYS LOCOMOTIVES Part 2—NOS. 10000-39999.

    (ii) British Railways Class " WD " 2-8-0 locomotives in service on the Western Region. These are listed in the ABC OF BRITISH RAILWAYS LOCOMOTIVES Part 4—60000-90999.

2. This booklet is divided into two sections, as follows :

SECTION ONE. A list of classes in order of wheel arrangement, with dimensions and sub-divisions and a summary of locomotives in the class (pp. 4-8 and 57-64).

SECTION TWO. A list of locomotives in numerical order, under appropriate class headings, and showing against each the British Railways code number of its home shed. This section concludes with a list of named engines in numerical order and is found on pp. 17-47.

3. The aim of this booklet is that **SECTION ONE** shall provide ready reference to particulars of individual locomotives in a class and that **SECTION TWO** shall be used for observation purposes.

4. In **SECTION TWO**, all named locomotives are denoted by an asterisk, and a full list of locomotive names in numerical order will be found on pp. 38-47. A key to the British Railways shed code is found on pp. 18-19 ; all locomotives will carry their appropriate shed code on a small plate at the foot of the smoke-box door. Locomotives not given a shed code in the list were not in service or not allocated at the time of compilation. For fuller details of a particular locomotive, the reader should consult **SECTION ONE**, under the appropriate class heading shown for the engine in **SECTION TWO**.

5. The following notes are a guide to the system of reference marks and other details given in the lists of dimensions shown for each class in **SECTION ONE** :

    (a) " Su " denotes a superheated class ; " SS " denotes that some locomotives of the class are superheated.

    (b) Locomotives are fitted with two inside cylinders, slide valves and Stephenson link motion, except where otherwise shown, e.g." (O) " denotes outside cylinders and " P.V. " piston valves.

    (c) The date on which a design of locomotive first appeared is indicated by " Introduced." If the oldest surviving locomotive was built at a later date, that also is indicated. Differences between sub-divisions of a class can be followed

by tracing the appropriate reference mark throughout the details given for that class.

(d) The code given in smaller bold type at the head of each class, e.g. "4MT," denotes its British Railways power classification.

(e) The order followed by the classes in **SECTION TWO** is set out at the head of page 4.

6. All locomotives are of G.W.R. origin, except where otherwise shown.

7. The following is a list of abbreviations used to indicate the pre-grouping and pre-nationalisation owners of certain Western Region locomotives :

AD	Alexandra (Newport and South Wales) Docks & Railway.	PM	Powlesland & Mason (Contractor).
BR	Barry Railway.	RR	Rhymney Railway.
BM	Brecon and Merthyr Railway.	SHT	Swansea Harbour Trust.
BPGV	Burry Port & Gwendraeth Valley Railway.	TV	Taff Vale Railway.
Cam.R.	Cambrian Railways.	V of R	Cambrian Railways (Vale • Rheidol).
Car.R.	Cardiff Railway.	WCPR	Weston, Clevedon & Portishead Railway.
CMDP	Cleobury Mortimer and Ditton Priors Light Railway.		
LMM	Llanelly & Mynydd Mawr Railway.	W & L	Cambrian Railways (Welshpool and Llanfair).
MSWJ	Midland and South Western Junction Railway.	YTW	Ystalyfera Tin Works

CURRENT EVENTS ON THE WESTERN REGION

Construction of G.W. designs continues, and is at present at a high level, due to the extensive deliveries of "9400" Class 0-6-0 tanks, of which 200 were ordered as a dying act of the G.W.R. at the end of 1947.

The last "Castle" has been built, and surprisingly enough the first withdrawal of this class has been made. This was the curiously-numbered 100 A1, *Lloyd's*, which had already received a B.R. smokebox number plate bearing the figures "100" only. It was one of the "Castles" rebuilt from "Stars," and it retained the original frames. It is now intended to withdraw by the end of 1951 all the remaining "Stars" and "Saints," except for 4061/2, and the "Castles" which were rebuilt are therefore likely to suffer a similar fate.

The "Duke" and "Bulldog" 4-4-0 classes are approaching extermination, and the only locomotives of that wheel arrangement left on the G.W. will then be the "9000" Class, which were rebuilt from the earlier classes in comparatively recent years. Withdrawal of the 2-6-2 tanks of Classes "4400" and "4500" has begun, and the former Welsh engines have also suffered heavily. Of the Barry 0-6-2 tanks withdrawn recently, a number are in use for shunting duties at Swindon works, a rather surprising fact in the light of the high degree of standardisation which is seen at that works.

SUMMARY OF WESTERN REGION STEAM LOCOMOTIVE CLASSES

WITH HISTORICAL NOTES AND DIMENSIONS

In this list the classes are arranged by wheel arrangement in the following order: 4-6-0, 4-4-0, 2-8-0, 2-6-0, 2-4-0, 0-6-0, 2-8-2T, 2-8-0T, 2-6-2T, 0-6-2T, 0-6-0T, 0-4-2T, 0-4-0T.

4-6-0	**6MT**	**1000 Class**

" County "

Introduced 1945 : Hawksworth design
Weights : Loco. 76 tons 17 cwt.
          Tender 49 tons 0 cwt.
Pressure : 280 lb. Su.
Cyls. : (O) 18½″ × 30″
Driving Wheels : 6′ 3″
T.E. : 32,580 lb.
P.V.

1000–29   **Total 30**

4-6-0	**4P**	**2900 Class**

" Saint "

Introduced 1903 : Churchward design, developed from No. 2900 (originally No. 100, introduced 1902), earlier locomotives subsequently fitted with new boilers and superheaters, remainder built as such (oldest survivor 2981, built 1905 as 4-4-2).

Weights : Loco. 72 tons 0 cwt.
          Tender 40 tons 0 cwt.
Pressure : 225 lb. Su.
Cyls. : (O) 18½″ × 30″
Driving Wheels : 6′ 8½″
T.E. : 24,395 lb.
P.V.

2906/8/12/5/20/6/7/31 – 4/6 – 40/
    3–5/7–54/79/81

                           Total 29

4-6-0	**5P**	**4000 Class**

" Star "

Introduced 1907 : Churchward design, developed from No. 4000 (originally No. 40, introduced 1906 as a 4-4-2), earlier locomotives subsequently fitted with new boilers and superheaters, remainder built as such.

Weights : Loco. 75 tons 12 cwt.
          Tender 46 tons 14 cwt.
Pressure : 225 lb. Su.
Cyls. : (4) 15″ × 26″
Driving Wheels : 6′ 8½″
T.E. : 27,800 lb.
Inside Walschaerts gear and rocking shafts, P.V.

4003/7/15/8/20–3/8/31/3–6/8–62
                           Total 39

4-6-0	**6P**	**4073 Class**

" Castle "

Introduced 1923 : Collett design, developed from "Star" (4000/16/32/7, 5083-92 converted from " Star," 111 from 4-6-2).

Weights : Loco. 79 tons 17 cwt.
          Tender 46 tons 14 cwt.
Pressure : 225 lb. Su.
Cyls. : (4) 16″ × 26″
Driving Wheels : 6′ 8½″
T.E. : 31,625 lb.
Inside Walschaerts gear and rocking shafts, P.V.

111, 4000/16/32/7/73–99, 5000–
    99, 7000–37
                           Total 170

4-6-0   5MT   4900 Class
" Hall "

*Introduced 1924 : Collett rebuild with
 6' driving wheels of " Saint " (built
 1907).
†Introduced 1928 : Modified design for
 new construction, with higher-pitched
 boiler, modified footplating and detail
 differences.
Weights : Loco. {72 tons 10 cwt.*
 {75 tons 0 cwt.†
 Tender 46 tons 14 cwt.
Pressure : 225 lb. Su.
Cyls. : (O) 18½" × 30"
Driving Wheels : 6' 0"
T.E. : 27,275 lb.

*4900

†4901–10/2-99, 5900–99, 6900–
 58   **Total 258**

4-6-0   7P   6000 Class
" King "

Introduced 1927 : Collett design.
Weights : Loco. 89 tons 0 cwt.
 Tender 46 tons 14 cwt.
Pressure : 250 lb. Su.
Cyls. : (4) 16¼" × 28"
Driving Wheels : 6' 6"
T.E. : 40,285 lb.
Inside Walschaerts gear and rocking
shafts, P.V.

6000–29   **Total 30**

4-6-0   5MT   6800 Class
" Grange "

Introduced 1936 : Collett design, vari-
 ation of " Hall " with smaller wheels,
 incorporating certain parts of with-
 drawn 4300 2-6-0 locos.
Weights : Loco. 74 tons 0 cwt.
 Tender 40 tons 0 cwt.
Pressure : 225 lb. Su.
Cyls. (O) 18½" × 30"
T.E. : 28,875 lb.
P.V.

6800–79   **Total 80**

4-6-0   5MT   6959 Class
" Modified Hall "

Introduced 1944 : Hawksworth develop-
 ment of " Hall," with larger super-
 heater, " one-piece " main frames and
 plate framed bogie.
Weights : Engine 75 tons 16 cwt.
 Tender 46 tons 14 cwt.
Pressure : 225 lb. Su.
Cyls. : (O) 18½" × 30"
Driving Wheels : 6' 0"
T.E. : 27,275 lb.
P.V.

6959–99, 7900–29

N.B.—Locos. of this class are still
 being delivered.

4-6-0   5MT   7800 Class
" Manor "

Introduced 1938 : Collett design for
 secondary lines, incorporating certain
 parts of withdrawn 4300 2-6-0 locos.
Weights : Loco. 68 tons 18 cwt.
 Tender 40 tons 0 cwt.
Pressure : 225 lb. Su.
Cyls. : (O) 18" × 30"
Driving Wheels : 5' 8"
T.E. : 27,340 lb.
P.V.

7800–29

N.B.—Locos. of this class are still
 being delivered.

4-4-0   2P   3252 Class
" Duke "

Introduced 1895 : Dean design, some
 later fitted with new boilers and
 superheaters.
Weights : Loco. 47 tons 6 cwt.
 Tender 34 tons 5 cwt., etc.
Pressure : 180 lb. SS.
Cyls. : 18" × 26"
Driving Wheels : 5' 8"
T.E. : 18,955 lb.

9083/4/9   **Total 3**

4-4-0　3P　3300 Class
"Bulldog"

Introduced 1898 : Dean design, later
fitted with new boilers and super-
heaters (oldest survivor built 1903).
Weights : Loco.　51 tons 16 cwt.
　　　　　　　Tender 40 tons　0 cwt.
Pressure : 200 lb. Su.
Cyls. : 18″ × 26″
Driving Wheels : 5′ 8″
T.E. : 21,060 lb.

3377, 3406/44/7/9/51/3/4 **Total 8**

4-4-0　2P　9000 Class

Introduced 1936 : Collett rebuild, in-
corporating " Duke " type boiler and
" Bulldog " frames, for light lines.
Weights : Loco.　49 tons 0 cwt.
　　　　　　　Tender 40 tons 0 cwt.
Pressure : 180 lb. SS.
Cyls. : 18″ × 26″
Driving Wheels : 5′ 8″
T.E. : 18,955 lb.

9000–5/8–18/20–8　　**Total 26**

2-8-0　8F　2800 Class

*Introduced 1903 : Churchward design,
earlier locos. subsequently fitted with
new boilers and superheaters.
†Introduced 1938 : Collett design, with
side window cabs and detail altera-
tions.
Weights : Loco. ⎰75 tons 10 cwt.*
　　　　　　　⎱76 tons　5 cwt.†
　　　　　　　Tender 40 tons　0 cwt.
Pressure : 225 lb. Su.
Cyls. : (O) 18½″ × 30″
Driving Wheels : 4′ 7½″
T.E. : 35,380 lb.
P.V.

*2800–2883
†2884–99, 3800–66

　　　　　　　Total 167

2-8-0　7F　R.O.D. Class

Introduced 1911 : Robinson G.C. design
(L.N.E.R. O4), built from 1917 for
Railway Operating Division, R.E.,
taken into G.W. stock from 1919, and
subsequently fitted with G.W. boiler
mountings and details.
Weights : Loco.　73 tons 11 cwt.
　　　　　　　Tender 47 tons 14 cwt.
Pressure : 185 lb. Su.
Cyls. : (O) 21″ × 26″
Driving Wheels : 4′ 8″
T.E. : 32,200 lb.
P.V.

3010–2/4–8/20/2–6/8/9/31–4/6/8/
　40–4/7/8

　　　　　　　Total 29

2-8-0　7F　4700 Class

Introduced 1919 : Churchward mixed
traffic design (4700 built with smaller
boiler and later rebuilt).
Weights : Loco.　82 tons　0 cwt.
　　　　　　　Tender 46 tons 14 cwt.
Pressure : 225 lb. Su.
Cyls. : (O) 19″ × 30″
Driving Wheels : 5′ 8″
T.E. : 30,460 lb.
P.V.

4700–8

　　　　　　　Total 9

2-6-0　4MT　4300 Class

*Introduced 1911 : Churchward design.
†Introduced 1925 : Locos. with detail
alterations affecting weight.
‡Introduced 1932 : Locos. with side
window cabs and detail alterations.
　　　　　　　　⎧62 tons 0 cwt.*
Weights : Loco.⎨64 tons 0 cwt.†
　　　　　　　　⎩65 tons 6 cwt.‡
　　　　　　　Tender 40 tons 0 cwt.
Pressure : 200 lb. Su.
Cyls. : (O) 18½″ × 30″
Driving Wheels : 5′ 8″
T.E. : 25,670 lb.
P.V.

*4303/18/26/37/58/75/7/81, 5300/
　3/5–7/9–19/21–8/30–9/41/4–8/
　50/1/3/5–62/4/5/7–72/5–82/4–6/
　8/90–9, 6300–14/6–99, 7305–21
†7300–4
‡9300–19

　　　　　　　Total 230

2-4-0   1MT   **MSWJ**

Introduced 1894 : Dubs design for M.S.W.J., reboilered by G.W.
Weights : Loco.   35 tons 5 cwt.
         Tender 30 tons 5 cwt.
Pressure : 165 lb.
Cyls. 17″ × 24″
Driving Wheels : 5′ 6″
T.E. : 13,400 lb.

1334–6   **Total 3**

0-6-0   3MT   **2251 Class**

Introduced 1930 : Collett design.
Weights : Loco.   43 tons 8 cwt.
         Tender $\begin{cases} 36 \text{ tons } 15 \text{ cwt.} \\ 47 \text{ tons } 6 \text{ cwt.} \end{cases}$
           (ex-R.O.D. tender from
           3000 Class 2-8-0)
Pressure : 200 lb. Su.
Cyls. : 17½″ × 24″
Driving Wheels : 5′ 2″
T.E. : 20,155 lb.

2200–99, 3200–19   **Total 120**

0-6-0   2MT   **2301 Class**

Introduced 1883 : Dean design, later fitted with superheaters (oldest survivor built 1884).
Weights : Loco.   36 tons 16 cwt.
         Tender 34 tons 5 cwt.
Pressure : 180 lb. Su.
Cyls. : $\begin{cases} 17″ \times 24″ \\ 17½″ \times 24″ \end{cases}$
Driving Wheels : 5′ 2″
T.E. : $\begin{cases} 17,120 \text{ lb.} \\ 18,140 \text{ lb.} \end{cases}$

2322/3/7/39/40/3/9/50/1/4/85/6,
2401/7–9/11/4/26/31/44/5/9/52/
8/60/2/8/74/82–4, 2513/5/6/32/
4/7/8/41/3/51/6/68/72/3/8/9
                  Total 48

0-6-0   2MT   **Cam.**

Introduced 1903 : Jones Cambrian "89" class, reboilered by G.W. from 1924.
Weights : Loco.   38 tons 17 cwt.
         Tender 31 tons 13 cwt.
Pressure : 160 lb. SS.
Cyls. : 18″ × 26″
Driving Wheels : 5′ 1½″
T.E. : 18,625 lb.

844/9/55/64/73/87/92–6
                  Total 11

2-8-2T   8F   **7200 Class**

Introduced 1934 : Collett rebuild with extended bunker and trailing wheels of Churchward 4200 class 2-8-0T.
Weight : 92 tons 2 cwt.
Pressure : 200 lb. Su.
Cyls. : (O) 19″ × 30″
Driving Wheels : 4′ 7½″
T.E. : 33,170 lb.   P.V.

7200–53

                  Total 54

2-8-0T $\begin{cases} 7F^* \\ 8F^† \end{cases}$ **4200 Class**

*Introduced 1910 : Churchward design.
†Introduced 1923 : 5205 class, with enlarged cyls. and detail alterations.
Weight $\begin{cases} 81 \text{ tons } 12 \text{ cwt.}^* \\ 82 \text{ tons } 2 \text{ cwt.}^† \end{cases}$
Pressure : 200 lb. Su.
Cyls. $\begin{cases} (O) \ 18½″ \times 30″^* \\ (O) \ 19″ \times 30″^† \end{cases}$
Driving Wheels : 4′ 7½″
T.E. $\begin{cases} 31,450 \text{ lb.}^* \\ 33,170 \text{ lb.}^† \end{cases}$ P.V.

*4200/1/3/6–8/11–5/7/8/21–33/5–
8/41–3/6–8/50–99, 5200–4

†5205–64   **Total 151**

2-6-2T   4MT   **3100 Class**

Introduced 1938 : Collett rebuild with higher pressure and smaller wheels of Churchward 3150 class (introduced 1906).
Weight : 81 tons 9 cwt.
Pressure : 225 lb. Su.
Cyls. : (O) 18½″ × 30″
Driving Wheels : 5′ 3″
T.E. : 31,170 lb.   P.V.

3100–4

                  Total 5

2-6-2T   4MT   **3150 Class**

Introduced 1906 : Churchward design, developed from original 3100 class, but with larger boiler, subsequently fitted with superheaters.
Weight : 81 tons 12 cwt.
Pressure : 200 lb. Su.
Cyls. : (O) 18½″ × 30″
Driving Wheels : 5′ 8″
T.E. : 25,670 lb.   P.V.

3150/1/3/4/7/60/1/3/4/7/8/70–2/4/
6–8/80/3/5–8/90

                  Total 25

2-6-2T 3MT 4400 Class

Introduced 1904 : Churchward design for light branches, subsequently fitted with superheaters.
Weight : 56 tons 13 cwt.
Pressure : 180 lb. Su.
Cyls. : (O) 17″ × 24″
Driving Wheels : 4′ 1½″
T.E. : 21,440 lb.
P.V.

4400/1/3-10 **Total 10**

2-6-2T 4MT 4500 Class

*Introduced 1906 : Churchward design for light branches, developed from 4400 class with larger wheels, earlier locos. subsequently fitted with superheaters.
†Introduced 1927 : 4575 class, with detail alterations and increased weight.
Weights : { 57 tons 0 cwt.*
{ 61 tons 0 cwt.†
Pressure : 200 lb. Su.
Cyls. : (O) 17″ × 24″
Driving Wheels : 4′ 7½″
T.E. : 21,250 lb.
P.V.

*4500-30/2-42/4-74
†4575-99, 5500-74 **Total 173**

2-6-2T 4MT
5100 & 6100 Classes

*5100 class. Introduced 1928: Collett rebuild with detail alterations and increased weight of Churchward 3100 class (introduced 1903 and subsequently fitted with superheaters).
†5101 class. Introduced 1929: Modified design for new construction.
‡6100 class. Introduced 1931: Locos. for London suburban area with increased boiler pressure.
Weight : { 75 tons 10 cwt.*
{ 78 tons 9 cwt.†‡
Pressure : { 200 lb. Su.*†
{ 225 lb. Su.‡
Cyls. : (O) 18″ × 30″
Driving Wheels : 5′ 8″
T.E. : { 24,300 lb.*†
{ 27,340 lb.‡
P.V.

*5112-4/22/5/9/32/4/6-44/7/8
†4100-79, 5101-10/50-99
‡6100-69
Total 229

2-6-2T 4MT 8100 Class

Introduced 1938 : Collett rebuild with higher pressure and smaller wheels of Churchward locos. in 5100 class (5100/11-49).
Weight : 76 tons 11 cwt.
Pressure : 225 lb. Su.
Cyls : (O) 18″ × 30″
Driving Wheels : 5′ 6″
T.E. : 28,165 lb.
P.V.

8100-9 **Total 10**

2-6-2T 4MT AD

Introduced 1920 : Hawthorn Leslie design for A.D. Railway
Weight : 65 tons 0 cwt.
Pressure : 160 lb.
Cyls. : (O) 19″ × 26″
Driving Wheels : 4′ 7″
T.E. : 23,210 lb.

1205/6 **Total 2**

2-6-2T Unclass. V of R

*Introduced 1902 : Davies and Metcalfe design for V. of R.
†Introduced 1923 : G.W. development of V. of R. design.
Weight : 25 tons 0 cwt.
Pressure : 165 lb.
Cyls. : (O) { 11″ × 17″*
{ 11½″ × 17″†
Driving Wheels : 2′ 6″
T.E. : { 9,615 lb.*
{ 10,510 lb.†
*9
† 7/8 **Total 3**

0-6-2T 5MT 5600 Class

*Introduced 1924 : Collett design for service in Welsh Valleys.
†Introduced 1927 : Locos. with detail alterations.
Weight : { 68 tons 12 cwt.*
{ 69 tons 7 cwt.†
Pressure : 200 lb. Su.
Cyls. : 18″ × 26″
Driving Wheels : 4′ 7½″
T.E. : 25,800 lb.
P.V.

*5600-99
†6600-99 **Total 200**

Top to bottom:

BPGV 0 6-0STs Nos.
2176 and 2193 *Burry
Port*; BPGV 0 6-0Ts
Nos. 2197 *Pioneer*
and 2166.

[*J. N. Westwood* (2),
A. Delicata,
P. Ransome Wallis.

Top Left : " 5700 " Class 0-6-0PT No. 6710 (for shunting).

Top right : "5700" Class 0-6-0PT No. 9700 (condensing).

Bottom left: "5700" Class 0-6-0PT No. 3727 (with later cab).

Bottom right: "5400" Class 0-6-0PT No. 5409.

[*P. Ransome Wallis,
D. G. Carpenter,
E. R. Wethersett* (2).

10

0-6-0PT. *Top left:* "1600" Class No. 1619 ; *Top right:* "6400" Class No. 6417 ; *Bottom left:* "1901" Class No. 1967 ; *Bottom right:* "1854" Class No. 1705.

[J. N. Westwood (2), H. C. Casserley, F. W. Day.

11

This Page. *Top left:* SHT 0-5-0ST No. 1147. *Top right:* TV "H" 0-5-0T No. 191. *Bottom left:* RR "S1" 0-6-0T No. 91. *Bottom right:* RR "S" 0-6-0T No. 93.

[J. N. Westwood (2), A. Delicata, P. Ransome-Wallis.

Facing Page. *Top left:* SHT 0-4-0ST No. 1142. *Top right:* "1101" Class 0-4-0T No. 1104. *Bottom left:* "1361" Class 0-5-0ST No. 1362. *Bottom right:* "1400" Class 0-4-2T No. 1445.

[F. W. Day (2), A. Delicata, S. W. Baker.

13

Above : " M " Class No. 33.

Below : " R1 " Class No. 36.
[*J. N. Westwood, P. Ransome-Wallis.*

**RR
0-6-2T**

Above : " A " Class No. 57.

Below : Reboilered " R1 " Class No. 4J.
[*A. Delicata.*

**RR
0-6-2T**

Top to bottom

Cardiff R. 0-6-2T
No. 155 ; TV "O4"
0-6-2T No. 208 ;
Barry R. "B1" 0-6-2T
No. 276; B.M. 0-6-2T
No. 433.

[*F. W. Day* (2),
A. Delicata (2).

Top to bottom :

"King" Class 4-6-0 No. 6023 *King Edward II* ; "Castle" Class 4-6-0 No. 4)84 *Aberystwyth Castle* ; "Star" Class 4-6-0 No. 4034 *Queen Adelaide*.

[P. H. Wells, M. W. Earley (2).

Top to bottom :

"Saint" Class 4-6-0 No. 2931 *Arlington Court* ; "Modified Hall" Class 4-6-0 No. 7905 *Fowey Hall* ; "County" Class 4-6-0 No. 1024 *County of Pembroke.*

[*W. Gilburt, K. H. Leech, R. E. Vincent.*

This Page

Top to bottom :

"8100" Class 2-6-2T
No. 8109 ; "5101"
Class 2-6-2T No.
4157 ; "7200" Class
2-8-2T No. 7241.

[A. Delicata (2),
F. F. Moss.

Facing Page

Top to bottom :

"4400" Class 2-6-2T
No. 4403 ; "4500"
Class 2-6-2T No.
4539 ; "3150" Class
2-6-2T No. 3154.

[F. W. Day, G. B.
Seymour, P. Ransome-
Wallis.

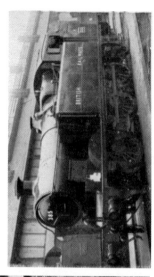

(For captions see facing page)

22

Facing Page. Top left : "9400" Class 0-6-0PT No. 8400.
Top right : "1500" Class 0-6-0PT No. 1502. Bottom left : "5600" Class 0-6-2T No. 5651. Bottom right : TV "A" Class 0-6-2T No. 385.

[R. H. G. Simpson, C. C. B. Herbert, F. F. Moss, G. B. Seymour.

This Page. "Bulldog" Class 4-4-0 No. 3447 Jackdaw. Right upper : Cam. R. 0-6-0 No. 849. Right lower : "2301" Class 0-6-0 No. 2482.

[J. N. Westwood, T. J. Saunders, W. J. Skillern.

23

Above : MSWJ 2-4-0 No. 1335.
Right upper : "9000 " Class 4-4-0 No. 9012.
Right lower : "3252 " Class 4-4-0 No. 9083 Comet.

[G. L. Hoare, A. Delicata, B. W. Brooksbank.

24

0-6-2T 3F Barry Rly.

•Introduced 1890: Hosgood Barry Railway "B1" class.
†Introduced 1924: Reboilered by G.W.R.

Weight $\begin{cases} 55 \text{ tons } 3 \text{ cwt.•} \\ 53 \text{ tons } 9 \text{ cwt.†} \end{cases}$

Pressure $\begin{cases} 160 \text{ lb.•} \\ 150 \text{ lb.†} \end{cases}$

Cyls.: $17\frac{1}{2}" \times 26"$
Driving Wheels: 4' 3"
T.E. $\begin{cases} 20,825 \text{ lb.•} \\ 19,525 \text{ lb.†} \end{cases}$

*276
†240/63/7/70/1/4   Total 7

0-6-2T 4F B & M.

Introduced 1909: Dunbar design for B. & M. Fitted with ex-Rhymney boiler by G.W.R.
Weight: 66 tons 19 cwt.
Pressure: 175 lb.
Cyls.: $18\frac{1}{2}" \times 26"$
Driving Wheels: 4' 6"
T.E.: 24,520 lb.

425   Total 1

3F

•Introduced 1926: Dunbar design for B. & M., reboilered by G.W. with taper boiler (introduced 1915).
†Reboilered by G.W.R. with ex-Rhymney boiler.
Weight: 59 tons 5 cwt.
Pressure $\begin{cases} 175 \text{ lb. Su.•} \\ 175 \text{ lb.†} \end{cases}$
Cyls.: $18" \times 26"$
Driving Wheels: 5' 0"
T.E.: 20,885 lb.

*431–5
†436   Total 6

0-6-2T 4F Cardiff Rly.

Introduced 1928: G.W. rebuild with taper boiler of Ree Cardiff Railway design, introduced 1908.
Weight: 66 tons 12 cwt.
Pressure: 175 lb. Su.
Cyls.: $18" \times 26"$
Driving Wheels: 4' 6½"
T.E.: 22,990 lb.

155   Total 1

0-6-2T 4F Rhymney Rly.

Introduced 1904: Jenkins and Robert Stephenson Rhymney "M" class (survivor built 1905).
Weight: 62 tons 11 cwt.
Pressure: 175 lb.   Cyls.: $18\frac{1}{2}" \times 26"$
Driving Wheels: 4' 6"
T.E.: 24,510 lb.
33   Total 1

4F

•Introduced 1921: Hurry Riches Rhymney "R1" class, development of "R" (introduced 1907).
†Introduced 1926: Reboilered by G.W. with superheated taper boiler (earliest survivor rebuilt 1929).
Weight $\begin{cases} 66 \text{ tons } 0 \text{ cwt.•} \\ 62 \text{ tons } 10 \text{ cwt.†} \end{cases}$
Pressure $\begin{cases} 175 \text{ lb.•} \\ 200 \text{ lb. Su.†} \end{cases}$
Cyls.: $18\frac{1}{2}" \times 26"$
Driving Wheels: 4' 6"
T.E. $\begin{cases} 24,520 \text{ lb.•} \\ 28,015 \text{ lb.†} \end{cases}$
*35–8,41–3   †31/9,40/4
                                     Total 11

4F

•Introduced 1910: Hurry Riches Rhymney "A" class, rebuilt by G.W. from round top to Belpaire boiler.
†Introduced 1914: Class "A1," built with Belpaire boiler.
‡§Introduced 1929: Reboilered by G.W. with superheated taper boiler.
Weight $\begin{cases} 64 \text{ tons } 3 \text{ cwt.•†} \\ 63 \text{ tons } 0 \text{ cwt.‡§} \end{cases}$
Pressure $\begin{cases} 175 \text{ lb. •†} \\ 175 \text{ lb. Su.‡§} \end{cases}$
Cyls. $\begin{cases} 18" \times 26" \text{•†‡} \\ 18\frac{1}{2}" \times 26" \text{§} \end{cases}$
Driving Wheels: 4' 4½"
T.E. $\begin{cases} 23,870 \text{ lb.•†‡} \\ 25,210 \text{ lb. §} \end{cases}$
*57, 72–4   †65/7/8
‡56/8–60/3/6/9, 70/5   §55
                                     Total 17

3P

•Introduced 1926: G.W. rebuild with superheated taper boiler of Hurry Riches Rhymney "P" class.
†Introduced 1928: Rebuild of Rhymney "AP" class (superheated development of "P," introduced 1921), No. 76 originally "P," but later rebuilt with larger tanks to conform to "AP."
Weight $\begin{cases} 58 \text{ tons } 19 \text{ cwt.•} \\ 63 \text{ tons } 0 \text{ cwt.†} \end{cases}$

Pressure : 175 lb. Su.
Cyls. { 18″ × 26″•
{ 18½″ × 26″†
Driving Wheels : 5′ 0″
T.E. { 20,885 lb.•
{ 21,700 lb.†

*82/3 †76–81 **Total 8**

0-6-2T 4F TV

Introduced 1924 : G.W. rebuild with
superheated taper boiler of Hurry
Riches T.V. " O4 " class (introduced
1907).
Weight : 61 tons 0 cwt.
Pressure : 175 lb. Su.
Cyls. : 17½″ × 26″
Driving Wheels : 4′ 6½″
T.E. : 21,480 lb.

203–5/7–11/5–20/36/78/9/82/4–6/
90/2/3/5/9 **Total 26**

4P

Introduced 1924 : G.W. rebuild with
superheated taper boiler of Cameron
T.V. " A " class (introduced 1914).
Two sizes of cylinder.
Weight : 65 tons 14 cwt.
Pressure : { 175 lb. Su.•
{ 200 lb. Su.†
Cyls. { 18½″ × 26″•
{ 17½″ × 26″†
Driving Wheels : 5′ 3″
T.E. : { 21,000 lb.•
{ 21,480 lb.†

*307–9/22/35/7/44/9/52/60/1/6/
70–2/80/7/8
†303–6/12/6/43/5–8/51/6/7/62/4/
5/7/8/73–9/81–6/9–91/3/4/7–9
Total 58

0-6-0ST 0F 1361 Class

Introduced 1910 : Churchward design
for dock shunting.
Weight : 35 tons 4 cwt.
Pressure : 150 lb.
Cyls. : (O) 16″ × 20″
Driving Wheels : 3′ 8″
T.E. : 14,835 lb.

1361–5 **Total 5**

0-6-0PT 1F 1366 Class

Introduced 1934 : Collett development
of 1361 class, with pannier tanks.
Weight : 35 tons 15 cwt.
Pressure : 165 lb.
Cyls. : (O) 16″ × 20″
Driving Wheels : 3′ 8″
T.E. : 16,320 lb.

1366–71 **Total 6**

0-6-0T 4F 1500 Class

Introduced 1949 : Hawksworth short-
wheelbase heavy shunting design.
Weight : 58 tons 4 cwt.
Pressure : 200 lb.
Cyls. : (O) 17½″ × 24″
Driving Wheels : 4′ 7½″
T.E. : 22,515 lb.
Walschaerts gear, P.V.

1500–29

N.B.—Locos of this class are still
being delivered.

0-6-0PT 2F 1501 Class

Introduced 1872 : Dean & G. Armstrong
saddle tanks, rebuilt with pannier
tanks from 1910 (oldest survivor built
1879).
Weight : 42 tons 17 cwt.
Pressure : 165 lb.
Cyls. : 17″ × 24″
Driving Wheels : 4′ 7½″
T.E. : 17,525 lb.

1542, 1782/9, 2716/9 **Total 15**

0-6-0PT 2F 1600 Class

Introduced 1949 : Hawksworth light
branch line and shunting design.
Weight : 41 tons 12 cwt.
Pressure : 165 lb.
Cyls. : 16½″ × 24″
Driving Wheels : 4′ 1½″
T.E. : 18,515 lo.

1600–49

N.B.—Locos. of this class are still
being delivered.

0-6-0PT 3F 1854 Class

Introduced 1890 : Dean design, rebuilt
with pannier tanks from 1909.
Weight : 46 tons 13 cwt
Pressure : 180 lb.
Cyls. : 17″ × 24″
Driving Wheels : 4′ 7½″
T.E. : 19,120 lb.

907, 1705/9, 1855/8/61/2/70
Total 8

0-6-0T   2F   1901 Class

*Introduced 1874 : Dean & G. Armstrong saddletank (survivor built 1883).
†Introduced 1910 : Rebuilt with pannier tanks (oldest survivor built 1875).
Weight : 36 tons 3 cwt.
Pressure : 165 lb.
Cyls. : 16″ × 24″
Driving Wheels : 4′ 1½″
T.E. : 17,410 lb.

*1925
†992, 1903/17/35/41/3/57/64/7/8 89/91/3/6, 2001/2/4/8–12/4/6/7

Total 26

0-6-0T   2F
2021 & 2181 Classes

*2021 class. Introduced 1897 : Dean saddletank, subsequently rebuilt with pannier tanks.
†2181 class. Introduced 1939 : 2021 class modified with increased brake power for heavy gradients.
Weight : 39 tons 15 cwt.
Pressure : 165 lb.
Cyls. : 16½″ × 24″
Driving Wheels : 4′ 1½″
T.E. : 18,515 lb.

*2021/3/5–7/30–5/8/40/2–4/8/50/l/ 3–6/60/1/3/6–70/2/3/5/6/9–83/5 6/8/9/90/2–5/7–9,2100/1/4/6–9/ 11/2/5/7/21–3/6/7/9/31 /4–6/8/ 40/1/4/6–8/50–6/9/60

†2181–90

Totals : 2021 Class 93
        2181 Class 10

0-6-0PT   3F   2721 Class

Introduced 1896 : Dean saddletank, later rebuilt with pannier tanks.
Weight : 45 tons 13 cwt.
Pressure : 180 lb.
Cyls. : 17½″ × 24″
Driving Wheels : 4′ 7½″
T.E. : 20,260 lb.

2722/43/4/54/60

Total 5

0-6-0PT   1P   5400 Class

Introduced 1931 : Collett design for light passenger work, push-and-pull fitted.
Weight : 46 tons 12 cwt.
Pressure : 165 lb.
Cyls. : 16½″ × 24″
Driving Wheels : 5′ 2″
T.E. : 14,780 lb.

5400–24

Total 25

0-6-0PT   4F   5700 Class

*Introduced 1929 : Collett design for shunting and light goods work, developed from 2721 class.
†Introduced 1930 : Locos. without vacuum brake and A.T.C. fittings, for shunting only.
‡Introduced 1933 : Locos. with condensing gear for working over L.T.E. Metropolitan line.
§Introduced 1933 : Locos. with detail alterations, modified cab (except 8700) and increased weight.
**Introduced 1948 : Steam brake locos. with increased weight.
Weight :   { 47 tons 10 cwt.*†
              50 tons 15 cwt.‡
              49 tons 0 cwt.§**
Pressure : 200 lb.
Cyls. : 17½″ × 24″
Driving Wheels : 4′ 7½″
T.E. : 22,515 lb.

*5700–99, 7700–99, 8701–49
†6700–49
‡9700–10
§3600–3799, 4600–99, 8700/50– 99, 9600–82, 9711–99
**6750–79

N.B.—Locos. of this class are still being delivered.

0-6-0PT   2P* 2F†
6400 & 7400 Classes

*6400 class. Introduced 1932 : Collett design for light passenger work, variation of 5400 class with smaller wheels.

†7400 class. Introduced 1936 : Non-push-and-pull fitted locos.

Weight : { 45 tons 12 cwt.*
{ 45 tons 9 cwt.†
Pressure : 180 lb.
Cyls. : 16½″ × 24″
Driving Wheels : 4′ 7½″
T.E. : 18,010 lb.

*6400–39

†7400–49

N.B.—Locos. of the 7400 series are still being delivered.

0-6-0PT 4F 9400 Class

*Introduced 1947 : Hawksworth taper-boiler design for heavy shunting.
†Introduced 1949 : Locos. with non-superheated boilers.
Weight : 55 tons 7 cwt.
Pressure : 160 lb. SS.
Cyls. : 17½″ × 24″
Driving Wheels : 4′ 7½″
T.E. : 1,965 lb.

*9400–9

†3400–9, 8400–99, 9410–99

N.B.—Locos. of this class are still being delivered.

0-6-0T 3F AD

Introduced 1917 : Kerr Stuart design for Railway Operating Division, R.E., purchased by A.D. Railway 1919.
Weight : 50 tons 0 cwt.
Pressure : 160 lb.
Cyls. : 17″ × 24″
Driving Wheels : 4′ 0″
T.E. : 19,650 lb.

666/7   **Total 2**

0-6-0T IF BPGV

Introduced 1906 : Avonside design for B.P.G.V.
Weight : 38 tons 0 cwt.
Pressure : 170 lb.
Cyls. : (O) 15″ × 22″
Driving Wheels : 3′ 6″
T.E. : 17,030 lb.

2196   **Total 1**

0F

Introduced 1909 : Hudswell Clarke design for B.P.G.V.
Weight : 36 tons 8 cwt.
Pressure : 160 lb.
Cyls. : (O) 15″ × 22″
Driving Wheels : 3′ 9″
T.E. : 14,960 lb.

2197   **Total 1**

IF

Introduced 1910 : Hudswell Clarke design for B.P.G.V., rebuilt by G.W.R.
Weight : 37 tons 15 cwt.
Pressure : 165 lb.
Cyls. : (O) 15″ × 22″
Driving Wheels : 3′ 9″
T.E. : 15,430 lb.

2198   **Total 1**

2F

*Introduced 1912 : Hudswell Clarke design for B.P.G.V.
†Rebuilt by G.W.R.
Weight : 37 tons 15 cwt.
Pressure : 160 lb.
Cyls. : (O) 16″ × 24″
Driving Wheels : 3′ 9″
T.E. : 18,570 lb.

*2166

†2162/5/7/8   **Total 5**

0-6-0ST IF BPGV

Introduced 1907 : Avonside design for B.P.G.V. rebuilt by G.W.R.
Weight : 38 tons 5 cwt.
Pressure : 165 lb.
Cyls. : (O) 15″ × 22″
Driving Wheels : 3′ 6″
T.E. : 16,530 lb.

2176   **Total 1**

IF

Introduced 1900 : R. A. Carr design for B.P.G.V.
Weight : 41 tons 18 cwt.
Pressure : 140 lb.
Cyls. : (O) 16″ × 24″
Driving Wheels : 3′ 8″
T.E. : 16,615 lb.

2192   **Total 1**

0F

Introduced 1901 : R. A. Carr design for
B.P.G.V.
Weight : 35 tons 12 cwt.
Pressure : 140 lb.
Cyls.: (O) 15″ × 22″
Driving Wheels : 3′ 6″
T.E. : 14,025 lb.

2193   **Total 1**

0F

Introduced 1903 : Eager design for
B.P.G.V.
Weight : 31 tons 7 cwt.
Pressure : 150 lb.
Cyls.: (O) 15″ × 20″
Driving Wheels : 3′ 6″
T.E. : 13,660 lb.

2194/5   **Total 2**

0-6-0PT   4F   Cardiff Rly.

Introduced 1920 : Hope and Hudswell
Clarke design for Cardiff Railway,
reboilered by G.W. and fitted with
pannier tanks.
Weight : 45 tons 6 cwt.
Pressure : 165 lb.
Cyls. : 18″ × 24″
Driving Wheels : 4′ 1½″
T.E. : 22,030 lb.

681-4   **Total 4**

0-6-0PT   2F   CMDP

Introduced 1905 : M. Wardle saddle
tank for C.M.D.P., reboilered by
G.W. and fitted with pannier tanks.
Weight : 39 tons 18 cwt.
Pressure : 160 lb.
Cyls. : (O) 16″ × 22″
Driving Wheels : 3′ 6″
T.E. : 18,235 lb.

28/9   **Total 2**

0-6-0T   2F   LMM

Introduced 1911 : Hudswell Clarke
design for L.M.M., reboilered by G.W.
Weight : 40 tons 12 cwt.
Pressure : 160 lb.
Cyls. : 16″ × 24″
Driving Wheels : 4′ 0″
T.E. : 17,410 lb.

803   **Total 1**

0-6-0ST   1F   LMM

Introduced 1912 : Hudswell
Clarke design for L.M.M., reboilered by G.W.
(survivor built 1917).
Weight : 34 tons 9 cwt.
Pressure : 160 lb.
Cyls. : (O) 15″ × 22″
Driving Wheels : 3′ 7½″
T.E. : 15,475 lb.

359   **Total 1**

0-6-0T   4F   Rhymney Rly.

Introduced 1930 : Hurry Riches
Rhymney " S " class (introduced
1908), rebuilt by G.W. with taper
boiler.
Weight : 54 tons 8 cwt.
Pressure : 175 lb.
Cyls. : 18″ × 26″
Driving Wheels : 4′ 4½″
T.E. : 23,870 lb.

93-6   •   **Total 4**

4F

Introduced 1920 : Hurry Riches
Rhymney " S1 " class.
Weight : 56 tons 8 cwt.
Pressure : 175 lb.
Cyls. $\begin{cases} 18″ \times 26″* \\ 18\frac{1}{2}″ \times 26″† \end{cases}$
Driving Wheels : 4′ 4½″
T.E. $\begin{cases} 23,870 \text{ lb.*} \\ 25,210 \text{ lb.†} \end{cases}$

*91/2   **†90**   **Total 3**

0-6-0ST   1F   SHT

Introduced 1912 : Peckett design for
S.H.T.
Weight : 38 tons 10 cwt.
Pressure : 160 lb.
Cyls. : 16″ × 22″
Driving Wheels : 3′ 10″
T.E. : 16,650 lb.

1146/7   **Total 2**

0-6-0T   1F   TV

Introduced 1884 : Hurry Riches T.V.
" H " class with steeply tapered
boiler for Pwllyrhebog incline, sub-
sequently rebuilt twice.
Weight : 44 tons 15 cwt.
Pressure : 140 lb.
Cyls. : 17½″ × 26″
Driving Wheels : 5′ 3″
T.E. : 15,040 lb.

193-5   **Total 3**

0-6-0T   0F   **WCP**

Introduced 1911 : Marsh rebuild of
   Stroudley L.B.S.C. A1, purchased
   W.C.P. 1925, acquired by G.W. 1940
   (loco. built 1877, rebuilt to A1X 1919).
Weight : 28 tons 5 cwt.
Pressure : 150 lb.
Cyls. : 12″ × 20″
Driving Wheels : 4′ 0″   T.E. : 7,650 lb.

5   **Total 1**

0-6-0T   Unclass.   **W & L**

Introduced 1902 : Beyer Peacock
   design for W. & L. section, Cam.
   Railways.
Weight : 19 tons 18 cwt.
Gauge : 2′ 6¼″
Pressure : 150 lb.
Cyls. : (O) 11½″ × 16″
Driving Wheels : 2′ 9″. T.E. : 8,175 lb.

822/3   **Total 2**

0-4-2T   1P
1400 & 5800 Classes

*1400 class †Introduced 1932 : Collett
   design for light branch work (originally designated 4800 class).
†5800 class introduced 1933 : Non push-
   and-pull fitted locos.
Weight : 41 tons 6 cwt.
Pressure : 165 lb.
Cyls. : 16″ × 24″
Driving Wheels : 5′ 2″. T.E. : 13,900 lb.

*1400–74   †5800–19   **Total 95**

0-4-0T   3F   **1101 Class**

Introduced 1926 : Avonside Engine Co.
   design to G.W. requirements for
   dock shunting.
Weight : 38 tons 4 cwt.
Pressure : 170 lb.
Cyls. : (O) 16″ × 24″
Driving Wheels : 3′ 9½″
T.E. : 19,510 lb.
Walschaerts gear.

1101–6   **Total 6**

0-4-0ST   0F   **Car.R**

Introduced 1898 : Kitson design for
   Car.R.
Weight : 25 tons 10 cwt.
Pressure : 160 lb.
Cyls. : (O) 14″ × 21″
Driving Wheels : 3′ 2½″   T.E. : 54014, lb.
Hawthorn Kitson valve gear.

1338   **Total 1**

0-4-0ST   0F   **P & M**

Introduced 1907 : Peckett design for
   P. & M. (oldest survivor built 1912).
Weight : 33 tons 10 cwt.
Pressure : 150 lb.
Cyls. : (O) 15″ × 21″
Driving Wheels : 3′ 7″   T.E. : 14,010 lb.

1150–2   **Total 3**

Introduced 1903 : Hawthorn Leslie
   design for P. & M., reboilered by
   G.W.R.
Weight : 26 tons 13 cwt.
Pressure : 120 lb.
Cyls. : (O) 14″ × 20″
Driving Wheels : 3′ 6″   T.E. : 9,520 lb.

1153   **Total 1**

0-4-0ST   0F   **SHT**

Introduced 1905 : Barclay design for
   S.H.T.
Weight : 28 tons 0 cwt.
Pressure : 160 lb.
Cyls. : (O) 14″ × 22″
Driving Wheels : 3′ 5″   T.E. : 14,305 lb.

1140   **Total 1**

Introduced 1906 : Peckett design for
   S.H.T. (similar to 1150-2).
Weight : 33 tons 10 cwt.
Pressure : 150 lb.
Cyls. : (O) 15″ × 21″
Driving Wheels : 3′ 7″. T.E. : 14,010 lb.

1141/3/5   **Total 3**

Introduced 1909 : Hawthorn Leslie
   design for S.H.T.
Weight : 26 tons 17 cwt.
Pressure : 150 lb.
Cyls. : (O) 14″ × 22″
Driving Wheels : 3′ 6″   T.E. : 13,090 lb.

1144   **Total 1**

Introduced 1911 : Hudswell Clarke
   design for S.H.T.
Weight : 28 tons 15 cwt.
Pressure : 160 lb.
Cyls. : (O) 15″ × 22″
Driving Wheels : 3′ 4″   T.E. : 16,830 lb.

1142   **Total 1**

0-4-0ST   Unclass.   **YTW**

Introduced 1900 : Peckett design
   supplied to Ystalyfera Tin Works.
Weight : 23 tons 0 cwt.
Pressure : 146 lb.
Cyls. : (O)14½″ × 22″
Driving Wheels : 3′ 2″   T.E.: 13,000 lb.

1   **Total 1**

STREAM-LINED DIESEL RAIL-CARS

* Buffet and lavatory facilities.
† Lavatory facilities.
‡ Parcels cars.
§ Experimentally geared to haul trailer car, became prototype of subsequent designs.

|| Twin-coach units with buffet and lavatory facilities. Adjoining statistics apply per 2-car unit. When new, some of these units worked as 3-car rakes by the addition of an ordinary 70 ft. corridor coach.

Car No.	Date	Engines	Total b.h.p.	Seats	Car No.	Date	Engines	Total b.h.p.	Seats
1	1934	1	121	69	18§	1937	2	242	70
2-4*	1934	2	242	44	19-32	1940	2	210	48
5-7	1935	2	242	70	33	1941	2	210	48
8, 9	1936	2	242	70	34‡	1941	2	210	—
10-12†	1936	2	242	63	35-36||	1941	4	420	104
13-16	1936	2	242	70	37-38||	1942	4	420	104
17‡	1936	2	242	—					

SERVICE LOCOS
Petrol
0-4-0 : 15, 23, 24, 26 and 27
Total 5

WESTERN REGION POWER CLASSIFICATION

The power classification of Western Region locomotives under the former G.W. scheme was as follows :

Unclassified
V. of R. 2-6-2T, " 1361," " 1366," " 1901," " 5400," B.P.G.V. 2194/5/7/8, W.C.P. 5, W. & L. 822/3, " 1400," " 5800," Car.R. 1338, P. & M. 1150, S.H.T. 1140/1/4.

A
M.S.W.J. 2-4-0, " 2301," Cam.R. 0-6-0, " 1501," " 1600," " 1854," " 2021," " 2181," " 6400," " 7400," B.P.G.V. 2162/5-8/76/92/3/6, C.M.D.P. 0-6-0T, L.M.M. 359 and 803, S.H.T. 1146, T.V. 193-5, P. & M. 1153, S.H.T. 1142.

B
" Duke," " Bulldog," " 9000," " 2251," B.R. " B," B. & M. 4' 6", R.R. " P " and " AP " 0-6-2Ts, A.D. 0-6-0T, " 1101."

C
" Saint," " 4400," " 4500," A.D. 2-6-2T, Car.R. 155, R.R. " A " and " Al," T.V. " A " and " O4 " 0-6-2Ts, " 1500," " 5700," " 9400," Car.R. 681-4, R.R. " S " and " Sl."

D
" County," " Star," " Castle," " Hall," " Grange," " Manor," R.O.D., " 4700," " 4300," " 3100," " 3150," " 5100," " 6100," " 8100," " 5600," B. & M. 4' 6", R.R. " M " and " Rl " 0-6-2Ts.

E
" 2800," " 7200," " 4200."

Special
" King."

ROUTE AVAILABILITY

The route availability of Western Region locomotives is denoted by letters, as follows, in ascending order of restriction :

Not " coloured "
M.S.W.J. 2-4-0, " 2301," " 4400," V. of R. 2-6-2T, B.R. " B," " 1361," " 1366," " 1600," " 1901," " 2021," B.P.G.V. 2176/94-8, L.M.M. 359 and 803, W.C.P. 5, W. & L. 822/3, " 1400," " 5800," Car.R. 1338, P. & M. 1150, S.H.T. 1140.

Yellow
" Duke," " 9000," " 2251," Cam.R. 0-6-0, " 4500," A.D. 2-6-2T, " 1501," " 5700 " (except 9700-10), " 6400," " 7400," B.P.G.V. 2162/5-8/92/3, Car.R. 681-4, C.M.D.P. 0-6-0T, T.V. 193-5, P. & M. 1153, S.H.T. 1142/4.

Blue
" Manor," " Duke," " 2800," R.O.D., " 4300 " (except 9300-19), " 5100," " 6100," " 8100," B. & M. 5', R.R. " A " and " AP," T.V. " 04," " 1854," " 2721," A.D. 0-6-0T, S.H.T. 1141.

Red
" County," " Saint," " Star," " Castle," " Hall," " Grange," " 4700," 2-6-0 9300-19, " 7200," " 4200," " 3100," " 3150," " 5600," Car.R. 155, R.R. " M " and " RI," T.V. " A " 0-6-2Ts, " 1500," " 9400," R.R. " S " and " SI " 0-6-0T, " 1101."

NAMED LOCOMOTIVES
IN THE 1–9999 SERIES

YTW 0–4–0T

1 Hercules

WCP 0–6–0T

5 Portishead

CLASS 4073 " CASTLE " 4–6–0

111 Viscount Churchill

LMM 0–6–0T

359 Hilda

W & L 0–6–0T

822 The Earl | 823 Countess

CLASS 1000 " COUNTY " 4–6–0

1000 County of Middlesex	1015 County of Gloucester
1001 County of Bucks	1016 County of Hants
1002 County of Berks	1017 County of Hereford
1003 County of Wilts	1018 County of Leicester
1004 County of Somerset	1019 County of Merioneth
1005 County of Devon	1020 County of Monmouth
1006 County of Cornwall	1021 County of Montgomery
1007 County of Brecknock	1022 County of Northampton
1008 County of Cardigan	1023 County of Oxford
1009 County of Carmarthen	1024 County of Pembroke
1010 County of Carnarvon	1025 County of Radnor
1011 County of Chester	1026 County of Salop
1012 County of Denbigh	1027 County of Stafford
1013 County of Dorset	1028 County of Warwick
1014 County of Glamorgan	1029 County of Worcester

BPGV RLY. 0–6–0T

2192 Ashburnham	2196 Gwendraeth
2193 Burry Port	2197 Pioneer
2194 Kidwelly	

CLASS 2900 " SAINT " 4–6–0

2906 Lady of Lynn	2927 Saint Patrick
2908 Lady of Quality	2931 Arlington Court
2912 Saint Ambrose	2932 Ashton Court
2915 Saint Bartholomew	2933 Bibury Court
2920 Saint David	2934 Butleigh Court
2926 Saint Nicholas	2936 Cefntilla Court

2937 Clevedon Court	2949 Stanford Court
2938 Corsham Court	2950 Taplow Court
2939 Croome Court	2951 Tawstock Court
2940 Dorney Court	2952 Twineham Court
2943 Hampton Court	2953 Titley Court
2944 Highnam Court	2954 Tockenham Court
2945 Hillingdon Court	2979 Quentin Durward
2947 Madresfield Court	2981 Ivanhoe
2948 Stackpole Court	

CLASS 3300 " BULLDOG " 4-4-0

3406 Calcutta	3451 Pelican
3444 Cormorant	3453 Seagull
3447 Jackdaw	3454 Skylark
3449 Nightingale	

CLASS 4073 " CASTLE " 4-6-0

4000 North Star

CLASS 4000 "STAR" 4-6-0

4003 Lode Star	4015 Knight of St. John
4007 Swallowfield Park	

CLASS 4073 " CASTLE " 4-6-0

4016 The Somerset Light
    Infantry (Prince Albert's)

CLASS 4000 " STAR " 4-6-0

4018 Knight of the Grand Cross	4021 British Monarch
4020 Knight Commander	4031 Queen Mary

CLASS 4073 " CASTLE " 4-6-0

4032 Queen Alexandra

CLASS 4000 "STAR" 4-6-0

4033 Queen Victoria	4035 Queen Charlotte
4034 Queen Adelaide	4036 Queen Elizabeth

CLASS 4073 " CASTLE " 4-6-0

4037 The South Wales Borderers

CLASS 4000 "STAR" 4-6-0

4038 Queen Berengaria	4044 Prince George
4039 Queen Matilda	4045 Prince John
4040 Queen Boadicea	4046 Princess Mary
4041 Prince of Wales	4047 Princess Louise
4042 Prince Albert	4048 Princess Victoria
4043 Prince Henry	4049 Princess Maud

NAMED LOCOMOTIVES

4050 Princess Alice	4057 Princess Elizabeth
4051 Princess Helena	4058 Princess Augusta
4052 Princess Beatrice	4059 Princess Patricia
4053 Princess Alexandra	4060 Princess Eugenie
4054 Princess Charlotte	4061 Glastonbury Abbey
4055 Princess Sophia	4062 Malmesbury Abbey
4056 Princess Margaret	

CLASS 4073 " CASTLE " 4–6–0

4073 Caerphilly Castle	4087 Cardigan Castle
4074 Caldicot Castle	4088 Dartmouth Castle
4075 Cardiff Castle	4089 Donnington Castle
4076 Carmarthen Castle	4090 Dorchester Castle
4077 Chepstow Castle	4091 Dudley Castle
4078 Pembroke Castle	4092 Dunraven Castle
4079 Pendennis Castle	4093 Dunster Castle
4080 Powderham Castle	4094 Dynevor Castle
4081 Warwick Castle	4095 Harlech Castle
4082 Windsor Castle	4096 Highclere Castle
4083 Abbotsbury Castle	4097 Kenilworth Castle
4084 Aberystwyth Castle	4098 Kidwelly Castle
4085 Berkeley Castle	4099 Kilgerran Castle
4086 Builth Castle	

CLASS 4900 " HALL " 4–6–0

4900 Saint Martin	4924 Eydon Hall
4901 Adderley Hall	4925 Eynsham Hall
4902 Aldenham Hall	4926 Fairleigh Hall
4903 Astley Hall	4927 Farnborough Hall
4904 Binnegar Hall	4928 Gatacre Hall
4905 Barton Hall	4929 Goytrey Hall
4906 Bradfield Hall	4930 Hagley Hall
4907 Broughton Hall	4931 Hanbury Hall
4908 Broome Hall	4932 Hatherton Hall
4909 Blakesley Hall	4933 Himley Hall
4910 Blaisdon Hall	4934 Hindlip Hall
4912 Berrington Hall	4935 Ketley Hall
4913 Baglan Hall	4936 Kinlet Hall
4914 Cranmore Hall	4937 Lanelay Hall
4915 Condover Hall	4938 Liddington Hall
4916 Crumlin Hall	4939 Littleton Hall
4917 Crosswood Hall	4940 Ludford Hall
4918 Dartington Hall	4941 Llangedwyn Hall
4919 Donnington Hall	4942 Maindy Hall
4920 Dumbleton Hall	4943 Marrington Hall
4921 Eaton Hall	4944 Middleton Hall
4922 Enville Hall	4945 Milligan Hall
4923 Evenley Hall	4946 Moseley Hall

4947 Nanhoran Hall	4974 Talgarth Hall
4948 Northwick Hall	4975 Umberslade Hall
4949 Packwood Hall	4976 Warfield Hall
4950 Patshull Hall	4977 Watcombe Hall
4951 Pendeford Hall	4978 Westwood Hall
4952 Peplow Hall	4979 Wootton Hall
4953 Pitchford Hall	4980 Wrottesley Hall
4954 Plaish Hall	4981 Abberley Hall
4955 Plaspower Hall	4982 Acton Hall
4956 Plowden Hall	4983 Albert Hall
4957 Postlip Hall	4984 Albrighton Hall
4958 Priory Hall	4985 Allesley Hall
4959 Purley Hall	4986 Aston Hall
4960 Pyle Hall	4987 Brockley Hall
4961 Pyrland Hall	4988 Bulwell Hall
4962 Ragley Hall	4989 Cherwell Hall
4963 Rignall Hall	4990 Clifton Hall
4964 Rodwell Hall	4991 Cobham Hall
4965 Rood Ashton Hall	4992 Crosby Hall
4966 Shakenhurst Hall	4993 Dalton Hall
4967 Shirenewton Hall	4994 Downton Hall
4968 Shotton Hall	4995 Easton Hall
4969 Shrugborough Hall	4996 Eden Hall
4970 Sketty Hall	4997 Elton Hall
4971 Stanway Hall	4998 Eyton Hall
4972 Saint Brides Hall	4999 Gopsal Hall
4973 Sweeney Hall	

CLASS 4073 " CASTLE " 4–6–0

5000 Launceston Castle	5019 Treago Castle
5001 Llandovery Castle	5020 Trematon Castle
5002 Ludlow Castle	5021 Whittington Castle
5003 Lulworth Castle	5022 Wigmore Castle
5004 Llanstephan Castle	5023 Brecon Castle
5005 Manorbier Castle	5024 Carew Castle
5006 Tregenna Castle	5025 Chirk Castle
5007 Rougemont Castle	5026 Criccieth Castle
5008 Raglan Castle	5027 Farleigh Castle
5009 Shrewsbury Castle	5028 Llantilio Castle
5010 Restormel Castle	5029 Nunney Castle
5011 Tintagel Castle	5030 Shirburn Castle
5012 Berry Pomeroy Castle	5031 Totnes Castle
5013 Abergavenny Castle	5032 Usk Castle
5014 Goodrich Castle	5033 Broughton Castle
5015 Kingswear Castle	5034 Corfe Castle
5016 Montgomery Castle	5035 Coity Castle
5017 St. Donats Castle	5036 Lyonshall Castle
5018 St. Mawes Castle	5037 Monmouth Castle

5038 Morlais Castle	5069 Isambard Kingdom Brunel
5039 Rhuddlan Castle	5070 Sir Daniel Gooch
5040 Stokesay Castle	5071 Spitfire
5041 Tiverton Castle	5072 Hurricane
5042 Winchester Castle	5073 Blenheim
5043 Earl of Mount Edgcumbe	5074 Hampden
5044 Earl of Dunraven	5075 Wellington
5045 Earl of Dudley	5076 Gladiator
5046 Earl of Cawdor	5077 Fairey Battle
5047 Earl of Dartmouth	5078 Beaufort
5048 Earl of Devon	5079 Lysander
5049 Earl of Plymouth	5080 Defiant
5050 Earl of St. Germans	5081 Lockheed-Hudson
5051 Earl Bathurst	5082 Swordfish
5052 Earl of Radnor	5083 Bath Abbey
5053 Earl Cairns	5084 Reading Abbey
5054 Earl of Ducie	5085 Evesham Abbey
5055 Earl of Eldon	5086 Viscount Horne
5056 Earl of Powis	5087 Tintern Abbey
5057 Earl Waldegrave	5088 Llanthony Abbey
5058 Earl of Clancarty	5089 Westminster Abbey
5059 Earl St. Aldwyn	5090 Neath Abbey
5060 Earl of Berkeley	5091 Cleeve Abbey
5061 Earl of Birkenhead	5092 Tresco Abbey
5062 Earl of Shaftesbury	5093 Upton Castle
5063 Earl Baldwin	5094 Tretower Castle
5064 Bishop's Castle	5095 Barbury Castle
5065 Newport Castle	5096 Bridgwater Castle
5066 Wardour Castle	5097 Sarum Castle
5067 St. Fagans Castle	5098 Clifford Castle
5068 Beverston Castle	5099 Compton Castle

CLASS 4900 " HALL " 4–6–0

5900 Hinderton Hall	5915 Trentham Hall
5901 Hazel Hall	5916 Trinity Hall
5902 Howick Hall	5917 Westminster Hall
5903 Keele Hall	5918 Walton Hall
5904 Kelham Hall	5919 Worsley Hall
5905 Knowsley Hall	5920 Wycliffe Hall
5906 Lawton Hall	5921 Bingley Hall
5907 Marble Hall	5922 Caxton Hall
5908 Moreton Hall	5923 Colston Hall
5909 Newton Hall	5924 Dinton Hall
5910 Park Hall	5925 Eastcote Hall
5911 Preston Hall	5926 Grotrian Hall
5912 Queen's Hall	5927 Guild Hall
5913 Rushton Hall	5928 Haddon Hall
5914 Ripon Hall	5929 Hanham Hall

5930 Hannington Hall	5965 Woollas Hall
5931 Hatherley Hall	5966 Ashford Hall
5932 Haydon Hall	5967 Bickmarsh Hall
5933 Kingsway Hall	5968 Cory Hall
5934 Kneller Hall	5969 Honington Hall
5935 Norton Hall	5970 Hengrave Hall
5936 Oakley Hall	5971 Merevale Hall
5937 Stanford Hall	5972 Olton Hall
5938 Stanley Hall	5973 Rolleston Hall
5939 Tangley Hall	5974 Wallsworth Hall
5940 Whitbourne Hall	5975 Winslow Hall
5941 Campion Hall	5976 Ashwicke Hall
5942 Doldowlod Hall	5977 Beckford Hall
5943 Elmdon Hall	5978 Bodinnick Hall
5944 Ickenham Hall	5979 Cruckton Hall
5945 Leckhampton Hall	5980 Dingley Hall
5946 Marwell Hall	5981 Frensham Hall
5947 Saint Benet's Hall	5982 Harrington Hall
5948 Siddington Hall	5983 Henley Hall
5949 Trematon Hall	5984 Linden Hall
5950 Wardley Hall	5985 Mostyn Hall
5951 Clyffe Hall	5986 Arbury Hall
5952 Cogan Hall	5987 Brocket Hall
5953 Dunley Hall	5988 Bostock Hall
5954 Faendre Hall	5989 Cransley Hall
5955 Garth Hall	5990 Dorford Hall
5956 Horsley Hall	5991 Gresham Hall
5957 Hutton Hall	5992 Horton Hall
5958 Knolton Hall	5993 Kirby Hall
5959 Mawley Hall	5994 Roydon Hall
5960 Saint Edmund Hall	5995 Wick Hall
5961 Toynbee Hall	5996 Mytton Hall
5962 Wantage Hall	5997 Sparkford Hall
5963 Wimpole Hall	5998 Trevor Hall
5964 Wolseley Hall	5999 Wollaton Hall

CLASS 6000 " KING " 4–6–0

6000 King George V	6011 King James I
6001 King Edward VII	6012 King Edward VI
6002 King William IV	6013 King Henry VIII
6003 King George IV	6014 King Henry VII
6004 King George III	6015 King Richard III
6005 King George II	6016 King Edward V
6006 King George I	6017 King Edward IV
6007 King William III	6018 King Henry VI
6008 King James II	6019 King Henry V
6009 King Charles II	6020 King Henry IV
6010 King Charles I	6021 King Richard II

6022 King Edward III	6026 King John
6023 King Edward II	6027 King Richard I
6024 King Edward I	6028 King George VI
6025 King Henry III	6029 King Edward VIII

CLASS 6800 " GRANGE " 4–6–0

6800 Arlington Grange	6840 Hazeley Grange
6801 Aylburton Grange	6841 Marlas Grange
6802 Bampton Grange	6842 Nunhold Grange
6803 Bucklebury Grange	6843 Poulton Grange
6804 Brockington Grange	6844 Penhydd Grange
6805 Broughton Grange	6845 Paviland Grange
6806 Blackwell Grange	6846 Ruckley Grange
6807 Birchwood Grange	6847 Tidmarsh Grange
6808 Beenham Grange	6848 Toddington Grange
6809 Burghclere Grange	6849 Walton Grange
6810 Blakemere Grange	6850 Cleeve Grange
6811 Cranbourne Grange	6851 Hurst Grange
6812 Chesford Grange	6852 Headbourne Grange
6813 Eastbury Grange	6853 Morehampton Grange
6814 Enbourne Grange	6854 Roundhill Grange
6815 Frilford Grange	6855 Saighton Grange
6816 Frankton Grange	6856 Stowe Grange
6817 Gwenddwr Grange	6857 Tudor Grange
6818 Hardwick Grange	6858 Woolston Grange
6819 Highnam Grange	6859 Yiewsley Grange
6820 Kingstone Grange	6860 Aberporth Grange
6821 Leaton Grange	6861 Crynant Grange
6822 Manton Grange	6862 Derwent Grange
6823 Oakley Grange	6863 Dolhywel Grange
6824 Ashley Grange	6864 Dymock Grange
6825 Llanvair Grange	6865 Hopton Grange
6826 Nannerth Grange	6866 Morfa Grange
6827 Llanfrechfa Grange	6867 Peterston Grange
6828 Trellech Grange	6868 Penrhos Grange
6829 Burmington Grange	6869 Resolven Grange
6830 Buckenhill Grange	6870 Bodicote Grange
6831 Bearley Grange	6871 Bourton Grange
6832 Brockton Grange	6872 Crawley Grange
6833 Calcot Grange	6873 Caradoc Grange
6834 Dummer Grange	6874 Haughton Grange
6835 Eastham Grange	6875 Hindford Grange
6836 Estevarney Grange	6876 Kingsland Grange
6837 Forthampton Grange	6877 Llanfair Grange
6838 Goodmoor Grange	6878 Longford Grange
6839 Hewell Grange	6879 Overton Grange

NAMED LOCOMOTIVES
CLASS 4900 "HALL" 4-6-0

6900 Abney Hall	6930 Aldersey Hall
6901 Arley Hall	6931 Aldborough Hall
6902 Butlers Hall	6932 Burwarton Hall
6903 Belmont Hall	6933 Birtles Hall
6904 Charfield Hall	6934 Beachamwell Hall
6905 Claughton Hall	6935 Browsholme Hall
6906 Chicheley Hall	6936 Breccles Hall
6907 Davenham Hall	6937 Conyngham Hall
6908 Downham Hall	6938 Corndean Hall
6909 Frewin Hall	6939 Calveley Hall
6910 Gossington Hall	6940 Didlington Hall
6911 Holker Hall	6941 Fillongley Hall
6912 Helmster Hall	6942 Eshton Hall
6913 Levens Hall	6943 Farnley Hall
6914 Langton Hall	6944 Fledborough Hall
6915 Mursley Hall	6945 Glasfryn Hall
6916 Misterton Hall	6946 Heatherden Hall
6917 Oldlands Hall	6947 Helmingham Hall
6918 Sandon Hall	6948 Holbrooke Hall
6919 Tylney Hall	6949 Haberfield Hall
6920 Barningham Hall	6950 Kingsthorpe Hall
6921 Borwick Hall	6951 Impney Hall
6922 Burton Hall	6952 Kimberley Hall
6923 Croxteth Hall	6953 Leighton Hall
6924 Grantley Hall	6954 Lotherton Hall
6925 Hackness Hall	6955 Lydcott Hall
6926 Holkham Hall	6956 Mottram Hall
6927 Lilford Hall	6957 Norcliffe Hall
6928 Underley Hall	6958 Oxburgh Hall
6929 Whorlton Hall	

CLASS 6959 "MODIFIED HALL" 4-6-0

6959 Peatling Rall	6974 Bryngwyn Hall
6960 Raveningham Hall	6975 Capesthorne Hall
6961 Stedham Hall	6976 Graythwaite Hall
6962 Soughton Hall	6977 Grundisburgh Hall
6963 Throwley Hall	6978 Haroldstone Hall
6964 Thornbridge Hall	6979 Helperly Hall
6965 Thirlestaine Hall	6980 Llanrumney Hall
6966 Witchingham Hall	6981 Marbury Hall
6967 Willesley Hall	6982 Melmerby Hall
6968 Woodcock Hall	6983 Otterington Hall
6969 Wraysbury Hall	6984 Owsden Hall
6970 Whaddon Hall	6985 Parwick Hall
6971 Athelhampton Hall	6986 Rydal Hall
6972 Beningbrough Hall	6987 Shervington Hall
6973 Bricklehampton Hall	6988 Swithland Hall

NAMED LOCOMOTIVES

6989 Wightwick Hall	6995 Benthall Hall
6990 Witherslack Hall	6996 Blackwell Hall
6991 Acton Burnell Hall	6997 Bryn-Ivor Hall
6992 Arborfield Hall	6998 Burton Agnes Hall
6993 Arthog Hall	6999 Capel Dewi Hall
6994 Baggrave Hall	

CLASS 7000 " CASTLE " 4–6–0

7000 Viscount Portal	7019 Fowey Castle
7001 Sir James Milne	7020 Gloucester Castle
7002 Devizes Castle	7021 Haverfordwest Castle
7003 Elmley Castle	7022 Hereford Castle
7004 Eastnor Castle	7023 Penrice Castle
7005 Lamphey Castle	7024 Powis Castle
7006 Lydford Castle	7025 Sudeley Castle
7007 Great Western	7026 Tenby Castle
7008 Swansea Castle	7027 Thornbury Castle
7009 Athelney Castle	7028 Cadbury Castle
7010 Avondale Castle	7029 Clun Castle
7011 Banbury Castle	7030 Cranbrook Castle
7012 Barry Castle	7031 Cromwell's Castle
7013 Bristol Castle	7032 Denbigh Castle
7014 Caerhays Castle	7033 Hartlebury Castle
7015 Carn Brea Castle	7034 Ince Castle
7016 Chester Castle	7035 Ogmore Castle
7017 G. J. Churchward	7036 Taunton Castle
7018 Drysllwyn Castle	7037 Swindon

CLASS 7800 " MANOR " 4–6–0

7800 Torquay Manor	7815 Fritwell Manor
7801 Anthony Manor	7816 Frilsham Manor
7802 Bradley Manor	7817 Garsington Manor
7803 Barcote Manor	7818 Granville Manor
7804 Baydon Manor	7819 Hinton Manor
7805 Broome Manor	7820 Dinmore Manor
7806 Cockington Manor	7821 Ditcheat Manor
7807 Compton Manor	7822 Foxcote Manor
7808 Cookham Manor	7823 Hook Norton Manor
7809 Childrey Manor	7824 Iford Manor
7810 Draycott Manor	7825 Lechlade Manor
7811 Dunley Manor	7826 Longworth Manor
7812 Erlestoke Manor	7827 Lydham Manor
7813 Freshford Manor	7828 Odney Manor
7814 Fringford Manor	7829 Ramsbury Manor

CLASS 6959 " MODIFIED HALL " 4–6–0

7900 St. Peter's Hall	7903 Foremarke Hall
7901 Dodington Hall	7904 Fountains Hall
7902 Eaton Mascot Hall	7905 Fowey Hall

NAMED LOCOMOTIVES

7906	Fron Hall	7918	Rhose Wood Hall
7907	Hart Hall	7919	Runter Hall
7908	Henshall Hall	7920	Coney Hall
7909	Heveningham Hall	7921	Edstone Hall
7910	Hown Hall	7922	Salford Hall
7911	Lady Margaret Hall	7923	Speke Hall
7912	Little Linford Hall	7924	Thornycroft Hall
7913	Little Wyrley Hall	7925	Westol Hall
7914	Lleweni Hall	7926	Willey Hall
7915	Mere Hall	7927	Willington Hall
7916	Mobberley Hall	7928	Wolf Hall
7917	North Aston Hall	7929	Wyke Hall

CLASS 3252 " DUKE " 4-4-0

9083	Comet	9084	Isle of Jersey

ABBREVIATIONS

The following is a list of abbreviations used to indicate the pre-grouping and pre-nationalisation owners of certain Western Region locomotives :

AD	Alexandra (Newport and South Wales) Docks & Railway.	PM	Powlesland & Mason (Contractor).
BR	Barry Railway.	RR	Rhymney Railway.
BM	Brecon and Merthyr Railway.		
BPGV	Burry Port & Gwendraeth Valley Railway.	SHT	Swansea Harbour Trust.
		TV	Taff Vale Railway.
Cam.R.	Cambrian Railways.		
Car.R.	Cardiff Railway.	V of R	Cambrian Railways (Vale of Rheidol).
CMDP	Cleobury Mortimer and Ditton Priors Light Railway.	WCPR	Weston, Clevedon & Portishead Railways.
LMM	Llanelly & Mynydd Mawr Railway.	W & L	Cambrian Railways (Welshpool and Llanfair).
MSWJ	Midland and South Western Junction Railway.	YTW	Ystalyfera Tin Works.

THE ABC OF BRITISH RAILWAYS LOCOMOTIVES

EDITED BY A. F. COOK AND O. J. MORRIS

**PART 2—Nos. 10000-39999
BRITISH RAILWAYS
NON-STEAM AND S.R.
STEAM LOCOMOTIVES**

LONDON:

Ian Allan Ltd

THE NEW STANDARD B.R. CAB

To be fitted to all new B.R. designs

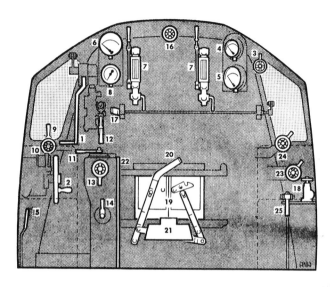

1. Regulator lever.
2. Reversing gear handle.
3. Train heating supply valve.
4. Train heating pressure gauge.
5. Boiler pressure gauge.
6. Steam chest pressure gauge.
7. Boiler water level gauge.
8. Vacuum brake gauge.
9. Small ejector steam supply valve.
10. Large ejector steam supply valve.
11. Vacuum brake lever.
12. Steam brake lever.
13. Blower valve.
14. Steam sanding valve.

15. Cylinder drain cocks lever.
16. Steam manifold cut-off valve.
17. Whistle control handle.
18. Coal slacking hose water cock.
19. Double firedoors.
20. Firedoors operating lever
21. Firehole half-door.
22. Anti-glare screen.
23. Live steam injector steam supply valve.
24. Exhaust steam injector steam supply valve.
25. Injector water control.

NEW STANDARD LOCOMOTIVES

FURTHER details have been released by the Railway Executive of the initial six standard locomotive designs, all two-cylinder, of which the first examples are expected to be in service by the spring of 1951. The principal aims are interchangeability of duties, maximum radius of action, and maximum mileage between repairs. The larger locomotives and all tenders will be fitted with roller bearings, and coupled axle-boxes will incorporate manganese liners to give better wearing capacity. The largest possible firegrate area will be provided in each design, to cope with the quality of fuel which has to be used in these days. As far as practicable, fittings and general details will be standardised.

There will first be two new mixed traffic Pacific types, a medium and a light. The 1951 batch of the former will be numbered 70000-24; of these 15 will be for the Eastern Region (G.E. Section) and 10 for the Western Region, their power being roughly comparable with that of " West Country " Pacifics, " Castle " and L.M.R. Class " 6 " 4-6-0s, and E.R. " V2 " 2-6-2s. The first light Pacifics will be numbered 72000-9, and are to be allocated to Scotland; they are intended to undertake similar duties to those of the W.R. " Counties " and L.M.R. " 5XP " 4-6-0s, as well as the heavier tasks now given to Class " 5 " and " B1 " 4-6-0s, which may indicate such routes as the Highland main line. Both Pacifics, designed at Derby, will be built at Crewe.

Two types of mixed traffic 4-6-0s also will be built, a heavy and a light. Of the former, designed at Doncaster, 30 will be constructed at Derby, five for the Scottish and 25 for the London Midland Region, numbered 73000-29; of the latter, designed at Brighton and built at Swindon, there will at first be 20, numbered 75000-19, half each for the Western and London Midland Regions. The six new standard types are completed by 2-6-4 and 2-6-2 tank designs, the 2-6-4 designed at Brighton and built both there and at Derby, and the 2-6-2 designed and built at Swindon. Of the 2-6-4 tanks, 54 will be built, 21 for the Scottish, 20 for the London Midland, 10 for the Southern and 3 for the North Eastern Region; they will be numbered 80000-53. Of the 2-6-2 tanks the order is for 20, half each for the Southern and Western Regions, numbered 82000-19.

Interesting reflections on this 159-locomotive programme are that none of the new engines are to be built at Doncaster or Darlington, and that only 15 of the engines are for the Eastern and 3 for the North Eastern Region, as compared with 20 for the Southern, 30 for the Western, 36 for the Scottish and 55 for the London Midland Regions.

GAS TURBINE LOCOMOTIVES

THE appearance on the Western Region of Britain's first gas turbine locomotive, No. 18000, is a reminder that the supremacy of steam on the railways is now to be challenged from yet another quarter. For a good many years past straight electric power has been a competitor, though this form of traction in Great Britain has had to depend on steam power for the generation of its electricity, and the high cost of its installation hitherto has been justified only on busy suburban passenger lines. Then there opened the era of the internal combustion engine on the railways, first with petrol-engined railcars in France.

But petrol is a very expensive fuel for railway operation, and it was not until the Germans had adapted for railway traction the diesel engine, which works with oil fuel of a considerably cruder and cheaper quality, that the internal combustion engine took its place as a really powerful rival of the steam locomotive. In the United States it has made such enormous strides that in no more than fifteen years all but 50 per cent. of the passenger services and the shunting, and nearly 40 per cent. of the long-distance freight working, have now been turned over from steam to diesel-electric traction. The Germans and Americans have both associated electricity with the diesel engine in developing this form of motive power ; diesel engines driving electric generators, which in their turn supply current to traction motors, provide a much more flexible method of transmission than any attempt to transmit 1,000 to 2,000 horsepower directly by gears, as is done in the much smaller and less powerful diesel-mechanical railcars of the Western Region.

And now, as I said at the beginning, steam has to face yet another competitor in the form of the gas turbine. This is not entirely steam's fault ; on the contrary, in recent years great strides have been made in improving the efficiency of the steam locomotive. The trouble lies largely with the high price and poor quality of present-day coal. Diesel oil is a far cheaper fuel, and the crude oil used in the gas turbine is much cheaper still. Indeed, the oil last-mentioned is one of the by-products from the manufacture of high grade fuels like petrol ; thus, the greater the scale on which petrol is refined, so much the more crude fuel, suitable for the gas turbine, becomes available. In the U.S.A. to-day it is a glut on the market, and has dropped to one-quarter of its wartime price. If, as the gas turbine experts hope, it becomes possible one day to work the gas turbine on a locomotive direct from pulverised coal, working costs might be cut still more.

Two years of concentrated research by the well-known engineering firm of Brown Boveri in Switzerland produced the first gas turbine locomotive, in 1941. Apart from a period when it was loaned to the French National Railways, this machine has since been putting in good service on the Swiss Federal Railways, mainly over the few remaining non-electrified branches in that country. Early in 1946, American locomotive designers took up the same idea, and it took them four years to perfect the first U.S.A. gas turbine locomotive. Their accumulated experience with diesel-electric locomotives proved helpful, and when the " Big Blow," as the first American example has been nicknamed, entered service on the Union Pacific Railroad, it was seen to have a strong outward resemblance to a modern diesel locomotive.

It has been tried successfully on all the principal U.P. main lines, over summits as high as Sherman Hill, 8,013 ft. above the sea, but has put in most of its time on the desert route between Salt Lake City and Los Angeles, over which it is in competition exclusively with diesels. No. 18000, the new Swiss-built gas turbine locomotive for the Western Region of British Railways, thus is the third of this type to take the rails ; and the fourth is likely to be the rather larger locomotive, No. 18100, now under construction for the W.R. by Metropolitan-Vickers. Both these latter are to be tried against the London Midland express passenger diesels, Nos. 10000 and 10001, which have been authorised for this purpose to work between Paddington and Plymouth.

How does a gas-turbine locomotive work ? The principle is that air is drawn through intakes to a compressor, where it is compressed to about 40 or 45 lb. per sq. in. The compressed air then passes through a heat exchanger, in which its temperature is raised to about 500 deg. F. Part of this heated air is then passed into a combustion chamber, into which the fuel oil, finely divided in the form of spray, is introduced and ignited, and the temperature of this part of the compressed air thus is raised to some 3,300 deg. F. while its volume is greatly increased. The remainder of the air, by-passing the combustion chamber, mixes with the expanded and highly heated air, and the resultant product, at a temperature of about 1,100 deg. F., reaches the turbine. After driving the turbine, the hot gases pass through the heat exchanger to heat the incoming air, before they are discharged through the locomotive roof.

The turbine of the new W.R. locomotive develops a total of 10,300 h.p., but of this no less than 7,800 h.p. is needed to drive the air compressor, so that less than one-quarter of the turbine's output, 2,500 h.p., is available for traction. This is used to drive an electric generator, through reduction gearing, and the current so produced is used, in its turn, through four traction motors to

drive the locomotive, the outer axles of each six-wheel bogie being motor-driven. The locomotive is thus of the A1A-A1A type. At 20 m.p.h. the tractive effort available is 33,000 lb., at 60 m.p.h. 13,000 lb., and at 90 m.p.h., the maximum rated continuous speed, 8,800 lb. In running order the locomotive weighs 113 tons, of which 75 tons rests on the four motor-driven axles and is available for adhesion ; it is 63 ft. long. Sufficient fuel can be carried for a run of 250 miles in normal loading conditions.

For starting up the gas turbine, a diesel engine of 150 h.p. is installed, which drives an auxiliary generator. To get the locomotive under way, the diesel engine first is started by means of a small auxiliary motor, fed with current from the locomotive's storage batteries. As the diesel engine and the auxiliary generator work up into speed the current so produced is used to start up the main generator. This in its turn starts the air compressor, which accelerates until the air is compressed to the stage when ignition becomes possible. The turbine itself now takes over, and accelerates from 1,300 to 3,500 r.p.m. Up to this point diesel fuel oil has been used, but it is now shut off, and the injection of crude oil begins. This sounds a rather complicated sequence, but actually no more than 4 minutes is needed to start up from cold. The driving control in the cab has eleven positions, each corresponding to a certain predetermined power output.

Various problems connected with the gas turbine locomotive remain yet to be solved. One is the length of time that the turbine blades will stand up to the impact of high pressure and highly heated gases without needing replacement or repair. The Americans estimate that their " Big Blow " will need overhaul three times as often as a diesel-electric locomotive of comparable power, but the former is much the simpler machine of the two, and should normally cost considerably less to build and to maintain. Moreover, the fuel needed for the diesel engine costs three times as much as the " Bunker C " oil used by the gas turbine. A minor trouble with the Union Pacific's " Big Blow " has been the locomotive's " scream " while warming up. " Within 50 feet of the locomotive, as she warms up," an American paper said recently, " all talk is drowned out. Though this is not so serious in a freight yard, six ' X-50s ' warming up in a downtown station would create bedlam."

BOILERS AND CABS

BRITISH Railways inherited some 20,000 locomotives, of which the most modern represented four schools of thought. It is interesting to compare the details of these four schools. To the foreigner they are all typically English, but inspection reveals many differences in practice. In this article, we will confine ourselves to a consideration of the differences in boilers and cab fittings.

The tapered boiler was standard on the G.W.R. for all but the smallest locomotives from early in the Churchward period. Through Maunsell it passed to the S.R., and later, through Stanier to the L.M.S.R., so that at nationalisation it was practically standard for all modern engines, except the smallest, of three groups. The L.N.E.R. adhered to the parallel boiler for all locomotives with narrow fireboxes, that is for all but the largest locomotives and the two " V4 " light 2-6-2s. The parallel boiler is heavier than a taper boiler with the same size of firebox, but is cheaper to construct. The 1948 Exchanges showed no superiority in efficiency in the G.W. and L.M.S. locomotives compared with their L.N.E. parallel-boiler counterparts, but it was rumoured that the L.N.E.R. found the L.M.S. taper boiler for the " 8F " 2-8-0 much more expensive to construct than its own " B1 " and " O1 " boiler, even when built in numbers.

There are differences in the method of arranging the taper. It is usual to have all the taper on the top, the bottom edge of the barrel being horizontal. The Southern Pacifics have the converse arrangement, which results, amongst other things, in the smokebox being sufficiently high to clear the steeply-inclined inside valves. On the L.N.E. locomotives and on the L.M.S. " Princess Coronation " Pacifics the taper is divided between top and bottom. The front ring of the barrel is often parallel, although this may not be readily apparent from the shape of the casing.

Combined with the L.N.E.R. preference for parallel boilers was their universal use of round top fireboxes. This type of firebox was also used on two notable Southern classes—the " King Arthurs " and " Schools "—but apart from this the Belpaire firebox has been used on all the standard types of the G.W.R., L.M.S.R. and S.R. For the M.o.S. Austerity locomotives, in the design of which maximum simplicity was sought, the round top firebox and parallel boiler were used, a significant fact considering that the designs were prepared under the direction of an L.M.S. engineer, and derived much inspiration from the L.M.S. " 8F."

The G.W. boilers have combined top feed and safety valves on the barrel, both these fittings being of Swindon design. Steam is

collected by an open pipe over the firebox, and controlled by a smokebox regulator. The L.M.S.R., following Stanier's early experiments with the Swindon arrangement, returned to the traditional British practice of dome regulator and safety valves on the firebox, but retained top feed valves set well forward on the barrel. The S.R. has top and under-water feed on different classes, but on the whole followed tradition. On the Bulleid Pacifics, however, the safety valves are at the front of the barrel, and sometimes deliver a column of water when the engine stops abruptly. Apart from experiments with multiple-valve smokebox regulators, L.N.E.R. practice was conventional, with under-water feed, dome-regulator and safety valves on the firebox.

In the application of superheaters there has been general conformity of practice except on the G.W.R. The Robinson type of equipment, originating on the G.C.R., was extensively used on the L.M.S.R. and L.N.E.R., and the S.R., after some years of experience with the Eastleigh pattern, introduced the Maunsell type, generally similar to the Robinson. The principal differences in these types is in the shape of the header, and in the method of fastening the elements. The number of elements is usually between 18 and 42, this representing the range between an 0-8-0 and a Pacific, and there is usually one element in each large tube, with two loops.

As in other respects, Swindon was distinctive in its superheater layout, and followed a general policy of using smaller superheaters than the other companies, the intention being to heat the steam just sufficiently to prevent condensation. The arrangement of the Swindon superheater is also different, as there are three elements in each large tube, but each element has only one loop. The more recent Swindon boilers have superheaters of more conventional proportions, and the subsidiary trials carried out on the W.R. after the 1948 exchanges, using Welsh coal, showed an advantage in efficiency to the " King " with enlarged superheater.

The superheater snifting valve is a conspicuous boiler mounting, and produces important differences in the boiler outlines of the four groups. In the early days of superheating, dampers, were provided to cover the ends of the flues, to reduce the force of the draught when steam was shut off. This lessened the risk of the elements being burned when no steam was circulating to cool them. The dampers were later superseded by snifting valves, which are held shut by steam pressure, but are lifted from their seats by air pressure when the pumping action of the pistons during coasting creates a partial vacuum in the steam pipes. This permits air to enter the superheater and leave by the exhaust, reducing also the risk of smokebox ashes being drawn into the blastpipe. Modern

heat-resisting steels have eliminated the risk of burned elements, and it is now usual to fit combined pressure-relief and anti-vacuum valves to the cylinders. The L.N.E.R. nevertheless continued the use of dome-shaped snifting valves behind the chimney, whilst on the L.M.S.R. similar valves are fitted to the steam chest (the " clicking " which they produce when bouncing on their seats is a characteristic sound of an L.M.S. locomotive coasting). On the S.R. Maunsell superheaters the snifting valves take the form of small vertical cylinders on each side of the smokebox below the chimney. Experiments on the S.R. have shown that the pressure in the superheater rarely falls sufficiently low for the snifting valves to perform their intended function, and they are being removed as locomotives pass through shops.

At the rear of the firebox, known to enginemen by the anomalous description of the " front," are the controls. Here also Swindon is distinctive, as it retains the right hand position of the driver, which was once general, but has now been largely superseded on modern locomotives by the more logical left hand position. The G.W. tapered boiler and wide cab give the driver a much wider view than on many other large locomotives, and the change to left hand drive has not been considered necessary.

The regulator handle may move across the firebox or fore-and-aft. The latter arrangement was standard for most locomotives on the L.N.E.R. under Gresley, although retained only for Pacifics since, and is also used on the S.R. Pacifics and " Leaders." It enables the driver to pull hard (if necessary) on the handle, without leaving his seat or twisting his body, but it requires a more complicated gland where the regulator rod enters the firebox.

The reversing wheel is normally arranged with the screw parallel to the boiler, so that the driver moves the handle across in front of him. In many cabs this cannot be done, except at the risk of bruised legs, unless the driver leaves his seat. The larger Gresley locomotives have a vertical reversing column, a more convenient arrangement, but one which involves an extra ball crank in the rodding. The only recent locomotives with power reverse are those of Mr. Bulleid. The difficulty of making small adjustments of cut-off, and of locking the gear in position whilst running, have been found to outweigh the advantages of power reverse.

On the L.M.R. steam brakes are standard on all modern locomotives. They are controlled from the vacuum brake by the old Midland type of brake handle, which is nearly vertical, and moves across the cab. Provision is not made for independent control of the locomotive brake, and a vacuum must be maintained even when working a non-fitted train. In Gresley days vacuum brakes on the locomotives were gradually adopted as standard on the

L.N.E.R., but on post-Gresley engines the steam brake is used, with separate control, in addition to the automatic operation from the vacuum train brake. On the S.R. there are both vacuum and steam brakes on different classes, with independent control of the steam brake, but on the W.R. vacuum on the locomotive is standard. The brake handle is similar to the L.M.S. type, with a separate control for the ejector. On the usual vacuum brake ejectors the brake handle rotates about a spindle crossways to the cab. The W.R. retains the motion-driven pump in place of a small ejector, although this fitting was formerly used on the L.M.S.R. and S.R.

The comfort of the engineman has improved greatly with the advent of side window cabs, extended cab roofs and side wind-screens, the latter being a notable detail which originated on the L.N.E.R. Another innovation used only on the L.N.E.R. was the bucket seat for the crew. Despite these improvements, many pre-nationalisation cabs give the impression that the designer has made a few concessions to the enginemen, rather than that their comfort and convenience have been the predominating factors in cab design.

CURRENT EVENTS ON THE SOUTHERN REGION

New construction of steam locomotives in S.R. shops has been confined to L.M.R. "4MT" 2-6-4 tank locomotives, which are replacing L.B.S.C. "I3" locomotives on certain duties. There remains one Pacific to be built, and despite the uncertainty which has surrounded its construction, this is likely to appear eventually as a standard "lightweight."

The experimental Diesel-mechanical shunting locomotive has been completed at Ashford, and the two express Diesel-electric locomotives are well in hand.

The last Stroudley "D1" 0-4-2 tank locomotives have been withdrawn from ordinary service, the two remaining locomotives of the class being used for stationary duties. The interesting 0-8-0 tank *Hecate*, which was acquired by the S.R. from the Kent and East Sussex Railway, has ended its career as shed shunter at Nine Elms. The last of the unrebuilt Billinton "C2" 0-6-0 locomotives has also been withdrawn.

NOTES ON THE USE OF THIS BOOK

1. The remainder of this book lists and describes British Railways locomotives numbered between 10000 and 39999 in service at November 15th, 1950. This range of numbers covers all British Railways internal combustion and electric locomotives and steam locomotives of the former Southern Railway, now Southern Region. For details of "4MT" 2-6-4 tanks and "WD" 2-8-0s operating on the S.R., the reader should consult Pts. 3 and 4 respectively of the *A.B.C. of British Railways Locomotives*.

2. The remaining pages provide, in the following order :
  (i) A list of British Railways Motive Power Depots with their code numbers (pages 13–16).
  (ii) A list of locomotives, in numerical order and showing against each its classification and the code of its home shed, which can be identified from (i) above (pages 25–33). Steam locomotives bear their appropriate shed code number on a small plate at the foot of the smokebox door. Locomotives not given a code number in this list were not in service at the time of compilation. In this list named locomotives are noted by an asterisk, and a full list of names will be found on pages 34–40.
  (iii) A summary list of the classes included in this range of numbers, beginning with B.R. internal combustion and electric locomotives (in which, pages 49–52, the classes are listed in the numerical order of the locomotives) and concluding with S.R. steam locomotives (in which, pages 53–64, the classes are listed in alphabetical order).

The aim of this booklet is that the numerical list shall be used for observation purposes, while the class summaries, which provide details of dimensions, sub-divisions within the class, etc., will provide more comprehensive information on individual engines.

3. The following notes are a guide to the system of reference marks and other details given in the lists of dimensions shown for each class in the alphabetical list of classes.

(a) In the lists of dimensions " Su " indicates a superheated locomotive.

(b) Locomotives are fitted with two inside cylinders, slide valves and Stephenson link motion, except where otherwise shown, e.g. (O) indicates outside cylinders and " P.V." piston valves.

(c) The letter " S " following a number indicates a Service Locomotive. On the S.R. (only) this marking appears on the locomotive.

(d) (W) before a number indicates an Isle of Wight locomotive. The " W " is no longer painted on the locomotives, but may still be seen on the bunker numberplate of some of them.

(e) The date on which a design of locomotive first appeared is indicated by " Introduced." If the oldest surviving locomotive was built at a later date, that also is indicated. Differences between sub-divisions of a class can be followed by tracing the appropriate reference mark throughout the details given for that class.

(f) The code given in smaller bold type at the head of each class, e.g. " 4MT " denotes its British Railways power classification.

4. In accordance with the usual British practice the wheel arrangement of Diesel and petrol locomotives are defined by the Whyte system (i.e., 0-6-6-0) and electric locomotives by the letter system (i.e., Co+Co). Service locomotives are not included in this section.

Left Upper: 0-4-0 Diesel Electric Locomotive No. 10800
Above: Class M7 0-4-4T No. 30133. Below: Class R1 0-4-4T No. 31703
Left Lower: Class H 0-4-4T No. 31182.

[L. Beard, W. Gilbert, H. C. Cosserley, R. H. Tunstall.]

55

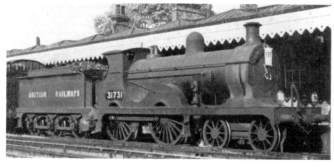

This Page.

Top to Bottom : Class D1 4-4-0 No. 31470 ; Class L 4-4-0 No. 31774 ; Class L1 4-4-0 No. 31785.

[W. Beckerlegge, H. C. Casserley (2).

Facing Page. *Top to Bottom :* Class D15 4-4-0 No. 30469 ; Class B4X 4 4-0 No. 32071 ; Class E 4-4-0 No. 31516 ; Class D 4-4-0 No. 31731.

[W. Gilburt, W. Beckerlegge, C. C. B. Herbert, R. E. Vincent.

Class MN 4-6-2 No. 35017 *Belgian Marine*.   [*P. Ransome-Wallis*.

Above :   Class WC 4-6-2 No. 34005 *Barnstaple*.   [*G. O. P. Pearce*.

Below :   Class LN 4-6-0 No. 30856 *Lord St. Vincent*.   [*W. Gilburt*.

Above : Class 700 0-6-0 No. 30700.   *Below :* Class C2X 0-6-0 No. 32532.

[*W. Gilburt.*

Above : Class W 2-6-4T No. 31918.   [*A. F. Cook.*

Facing Page. *Top to Bottom :* Class K 2-6-0 No. 62350 ; Class Q1 0-6-0 No. 33019 ; Class Q 0-6-0 No. 30544 ; Class 0395 0-6-0 No. 30578.

[*W. Gilburt* (2), *H. C. Casserley* (2)

Top to Bottom : Class
0415 4-4-2T No.
30583 ; Class Z
0-8-0T No. 30952 ;
Class 0298 2-4-0T No.
30586 (with longer
frames and square
splashers).

[M. W. Earley, P.
Ransome-Wallis.

Facing Page.

Top to Bottom : Class
G16 4-8-0T No.
30492 ; Class J 0-6-4T
No. 31596 ; Class
J1 4-6-2T No. 32325 ;
Class I3 4-4-2T No.
32086.

[R. H. Tunstall, P.
Ransome-Wallis, W.
Beckerlegge, W.
Gilburt.

Top to bottom : E4 0-6-2T No. 32464 ; E1/R 0-6-2T No. 32124 ; E1 0-6-0T No. 32606 ; A1X 0-6-0T No. 32662.
Facing Page : *Top to bottom :* R1 0-6-0Ts Nos. 31154 & 31339 ; G6 0-6-0T No. DS3152 ; D3 0-4-4T No. 32365 ; O2 0-4-4T No. W16.
[*W. Gilburt, H. Casserley, P. R.-Wallis, C. Herbert. G. Seymour, E. Smith, R. Tunstall, R. Bowler.*

Above : 0-6-0T No. 756 A. S. Harris. (new No. 30756).
Right upper : Class C14 0-4-0T No. 30589 ; Right lower : 0-4-0ST No.
30458 Ironside. Below : Class T 0-6-0T No. 31604.

[P. Ransome-Wallis, P. J. Truscott, C. C. Herbert (2).

SUMMARY OF BRITISH RAILWAYS
NON-STEAM LOCOMOTIVE CLASSES
WITH HISTORICAL NOTES AND DIMENSIONS
INTERNAL COMBUSTION LOCOMOTIVES

Co+Co Diesel Electric
LONDON MIDLAND REGION

Introduced 1947 : English Electric Co. and H. A. Ivatt, main line passenger design for L.M.S.R.
Weight : 121 tons 10 cwt.
Driving Wheels : 3′ 6″.
T.E. : 41,400 lb.
Engine : English Electric Co. 16 cyls. 1,600 h.p.
Motors : Six nose-suspended motors, single reduction gear drive.

10000/1   **Total 2**

4-8-4 Diesel Mechanical

Under construction : H. G. Ivatt and Fell design for L.M.S.R.
Engines : Four 500 h.p.
Transmission : Fell patent differential drive and fluid couplings.

10100

1-Co+Co-1
Diesel Electric

English Electric Co. and Bulleid main line passenger design for S.R.
Engine : English Co. 16 cyls. 1,600 h.p.

10201/2

Bo+Bo Diesel Electric

Introduced 1950 : N.B. Loco. Co., B.T.H. Co. and H. A. Ivatt, branch line design for L.M.S.R.
Weight : 69 tons 16 cwt.
Driving Wheels : 3′ 6″.
T.E. : 34,500 lb.
Engine : Davey Paxman 16 cyls. 827 h.p.
Motors : Four nose-suspended motors, single reduction gear drive.

10800   **Total 1**

0-6-0 Diesel Mechanical

Introduced 1950 : Bulleid S.R. design for shunting and transfer work.
Weight : 49 tons 9 cwt.
Driving Wheels : 4′ 6″.
T.E. : 33,500 lb. (max. in low gear).
Engine : Davey Paxman 12 cyls. 500 h.p.
Transmission : S.S.S. Powerflow three-speed gearbox and fluid coupling.

11001

          Total 1

0-6-0   Diesel Electric
LONDON MIDLAND REGION

Introduced 1936 : English Electric–Hawthorn Leslie design for L.M.S.R.
Weight : $\begin{cases} 51 \text{ tons.*} \\ 47 \text{ tons.†} \end{cases}$
Driving Wheels : 4′ 0½″.
T.E. : 30,000 lb.
Engine : English Electric 6 cyl. 350 h.p.
Motors : Two nose-suspended motors, single reduction gear drive.

12000*/1*   12002†
          Total 3

0-6-0   Diesel Electric
LONDON MIDLAND REGION

Introduced 1939 : English Electric and Stanier design for L.M.S.R., development of previous design with jack-shaft drive.
Weight . 54 tons 16 cwt.
Driving Wheels : 4′ 3″.
T.E. : 33,000 lb.
Engine : English Electric, 6 cyls. 350 h.p.
Motors : Single motor ; jackshaft drive

12003–32

          Total 30

0-6-0   Diesel Electric
LONDON MIDLAND REGION

Introduced 1945 : English Electric and Fairburn design for L.M.S.R., development of previous design with double reduction gear drive.

Weight : 50 tons.
Driving Wheels : 4′ 0¼″.
T.E. : 33,000 lb.
Engine : English Electric, 6 cyls. 350 h.p.
Engine : Two nose-suspended motors, double reduction gear drive.

12033–82

N.B.—Locos of this class are still being delivered.

0-6-0 Diesel Electric DES I
EASTERN REGION

Introduced 1944 : English Electric and Thompson design for L.N.E.R., (L.N.E.R. version of L.M.S. 12033 series).

Weight : 51 tons.
Driving Wheels : 4′ 0″.
T.E. : 32,000 lb.
Engine : English Electric, 6 cyl. 350 h.p.
Motors : Two nose-suspended motors, double reduction gear.

15000–3

Total 4

0-6-0 Diesel Electric DES 2
EASTERN REGION

Introduced 1949 : Brush design for E.R.

Weight : 51 tons.
Driving Wheels : 4′ 0″.
T.E. : 32,000 lb.
Engine : Petter 4 cyl. 360 h.p.

15004   Total I

0-4-0   Petrol (Class YII)
EASTERN REGION

Introduced 1921 : Motor, Rail and Tram Car Co., design (purchased by N.B.R. and L.N.E.R.).
Weight : 8 tons.
Driving Wheels : 3′ 1″.
Engine : 4 cyl. 40 h.p. petrol.
Drive : Chains and two speed gear box.

15097–9

Total 3

0-6-0   Diesel Electric
WESTERN REGION

Introduced 1936: Hawthorn Leslie and English Electric design for G.W.R. (G.W.R. version of L.M.S.R. Nos. 12000/1).
Weight: 51 tons 10 cwt.
Driving Wheels: 4′ 1″.
T.E.: 30,000 lb.
Engine: English Electric 6 cyl. 350 h.p.
Motors: Two nose-suspended motors, single reduction gear drive.

15100   Total I

0-6-0   Diesel Electric
WESTERN REGION

Introduced 1948 : English Electric and Hawksworth design for Western Region (W.R. version of L.M.S. 12033 series).
Weight : 46 tons 9 cwt.
Driving Wheels : 4′ 0¼″.
T. E.: 33,500 lb.
Engine: English Electric 6 cyl. 350 h.p.
Motors: Two nose-suspended motors, single reduction gear drive.

15101–6

Total 6

0-6-0   Diesel Electric
Introduced 1949 : Brush design for W.R.

15107   Total I

0-6-0   Diesel Electric
SOUTHERN REGION
Introduced 1937 : English Electric and
Bulleid designs for S.R.
Weight : 55 tons 5 cwt.
Driving Wheels : 4′ 6″.
T.E. : 30,000 lb.
Engine : English Electric 6 cyl. 350 h.p.
Motors : Two nose-suspended motors,
single reduction gear drive.

15201–3

                         Total 3

0-6-0   Diesel Electric
SOUTHERN REGION
Introduced 1949 : English Electric and
Bulleid design for S.R. (S.R. version
of L.M.S.R. 12033 series, but designed
for higher speeds).
Weight : 49 tons.
Driving Wheels : 4′ 6″.
T.E. : 24,000 lb.
Engine : English Electric 6 cyl. 350 h.p.
Motors : Two nose-suspended motors,
double reduction gear drive.

15211–25

                        Total 16

A-1-A+A-1-A
Gas Turbine
Introduced 1949 : Brown Boveri
(Switzerland) design for W.R.
Weight : 115 tons.
Driving Wheels : 4′ 0½″.
T.E. : 31,500 lb. to 21 m.p.h.
Engine : 2,500 h.p. gas turbine.
Motors : Four independently mounted
motors with spring drive.

18000

                        Total 1

Co+Co   Gas Turbine
Under construction : Metropolitan-
Vickers and Hawksworth design for
G.W.R.
Weight : 120 tons.
Driving Wheels : 3′ 8″.
T.E. : 60,000 lb.
Motors : Six nose-suspended motors
with single reduction gear drive.

18001

> NOTE—There are a number of Diesel
> locomotives in the Service or Depart-
> mental stock of the Regions, but these
> have not been included in this section

ELECTRIC LOCOMOTIVES

Co + Co   Class CC
SOUTHERN REGION
*Introduced 1941 : Raworth & Bulleid
design for S.R.
†Introduced 1948 : Later design with
detail differences.
Weight : $\begin{cases} 99 \text{ tons } 14 \text{ cwt.*} \\ 104 \text{ tons } 14 \text{ cwt.†} \end{cases}$
Driving Wheels : 3′ 7″.
T.E. : $\begin{cases} 40,000 \text{ lb.*} \\ 45,000 \text{ lb.†} \end{cases}$
Voltage : 660 D.C.
Current Collection : Overhead and
third rail, with flywheel-driven genera-
tor for gaps in third rail.

20001/2*

20003†   **Total 3**

Bo + Bo   Class EMI
EASTERN REGION
*Introduced 1941: Metropolitan-Vickers
and Gresley design for L.N.E.R.

Remainder. Introduced 1950.
Production design with detail
alterations.

Weight : 87 tons 18 cwt.
Driving Wheels : 4′ 2″.
T.E. : 45,000 lb.
Voltage : 1,500 D.C.
Current Collection : overhead.

26000*
26001–57

**NOTE: Locomotives of this class
are still being delivered.**

Bo + Bo   Class EB1

EASTERN REGION

EB1 Introduced 1946 : L.N.E.R. rebuild of N.E.R. Raven freight design (Introduced 1914) for banking work on Manchester-Wath line.
Weight : 74 tons 8 cwt.
Driving Wheels : 4′ 0″.
T.E. : 37,600 lb.
Voltage : 1,500 D.C.
Current collection : overhead.
26510   **Total 1**

Bo + Bo   Class ES1

NORTH-EASTERN REGION

Built 1902 : Brush & Thomson-Houston shunting design for N.E.R.

Weight : 46 tons.
Voltage : 600 D.C.
T.E. : 25,000 lb.
26500/1   **Total 2**

Co + Co

EASTERN REGION

Under construction : Metropolitan Vickers and L.N.E.R. design, development of E.M.I. with six axles and higher speed range.
Weight: 102 tons.
Driving Wheels: 4′ 2″
T.E.: 45,000 lb.
Voltage: 1,500 D.C.
Current Collection: Overhead.
27 locomotives. Numbers not yet allocated.

SOUTHERN REGION SERVICE LOCOMOTIVES.

No.	Old No.	Class	Station
†49 S	—	Shunter	{ Broad Clyst Sleep. Depot
*74 S	—	Bo-Bo	{ Durnsford R Power Stn.
*75 S	—	Bo	{ Waterloo & City Rly.
77 S	0745	C14	{ Redbridge Sleep. Depot
†343 S	—	Shunter	{ Eastleigh Carr. Works
†346 S	—	Inspection Car	Engin'r's Dept.
‡377 S	2635	AIX	Brighton Wks.
§400 S	—	0-4-0	S'hamptonDks.
515 S	{ L.B.S.C. 650 I.W. 9 }	AIX	{ Lancing Carr. Wks.
600 S	—	0-4-0 diesel	
680 S	{ L.B.S.C. 654 SEC. 751. }	A 1	,,
701 S	2284	D 1	Fratton**
DS 1169	—	0-4-0 Diesel	Engineer's Dt.
DS 1173	2217	0-4-0 Diesel	Engineer's Dt.
DS 3152	30272	G 6	Meldon Quarry

* Electric   ‡ Repainted 1947 in Stroudley livery   † Petrol
** Ex-oil Pumping Engine   § Fowler Diesel

SUMMARY OF SOUTHERN REGION STEAM LOCOMOTIVE CLASSES

IN ALPHABETICAL ORDER

WITH HISTORICAL NOTES AND DIMENSIONS

0-6-0T OP Class A1 & A1X

*A1 Introduced 1872 : Stroudley L.B.S.C. "Terrier," later fitted with Marsh boiler, retaining original type smokebox (survivor built 1875).

†A1X Introduced 1911 : Rebuild of A1 with Marsh boiler and extended smokebox.

‡A1X Loco. with increased cylinder diameter.

N.B. Western Region No. 5 is also of this class.

Weight : $\begin{cases} 27 \text{ tons } 10 \text{ cwt.*} \\ 28 \text{ tons } 5 \text{ cwt.†‡} \end{cases}$

Pressure : 150 lb. Cyls. $\begin{cases} 12'' \times 20''† \\ 14\frac{3}{16}'' \times 20''‡ \end{cases}$

Driving Wheels : 4' 0".

T.E. : $\begin{cases} 7,650 \text{ lb.*†} \\ 10,695 \text{ lb.‡} \end{cases}$

*680S

†377S, 515S, 32640/4/6/7/55/9/61 /2/70/7/8.

‡32636

Totals : A1   1
A1X 14

4-4-0   1P   Class B1

Introduced 1910 : Wainwright rebuild with domed boiler and extended smokebox of Stirling S.E.R. domeless Class B (originally introduced 1898).

Weight : Loco. 45 tons 2 cwt.

Pressure : 170 lb.   Cyls. : 18" × 26"

Driving Wheels : 7' 0".

T.E. : 14,490 lb.

31443.

Total 1

0-4-0T   OF   Class B4

*Introduced 1891 : Adams L.S.W. design for dock shunting.

†Introduced 1908 : Drummond K14 locos., with smaller boiler and detail alterations.

‡Adams locos. fitted with Drummond boiler.

§Drummond loco. fitted with Adams boiler.

Weight : $\begin{cases} 33 \text{ tons } 9 \text{ cwt.*‡} \\ 32 \text{ tons } 18 \text{ cwt.†§} \end{cases}$

Pressure : 140 lb. Cyls (O) : 16" × 22"

Driving Wheels : 3' 9¾".

T.E. : 14,650 lb.

*30086/7/9/93/4/6, 30102.

†30082/3   ‡30088   §30084

Total 11

4-4-0 $\begin{cases} \text{1P B4} \\ \text{3P B4X} \end{cases}$ Classes B4 & B4X

*B4 Introduced 1899 : R. J. Billinton L.B.S.C. design.

†B4X Introduced 1922 : L. B. Billinton design, incorporating parts from B4

Weights : Loco. $\begin{cases} 51 \text{ tons } 10 \text{ cwt.*} \\ 58 \text{ tons } 1 \text{ cwt.†} \end{cases}$

Pressure : $\begin{cases} 180 \text{ lb.*} \\ 180 \text{ lb. Su.†} \end{cases}$

Cyls. : $\begin{cases} 19'' \times 26''.* \\ 20'' \times 26''.† \end{cases}$

Driving Wheels : 6' 9".

T.E. : $\begin{cases} 17,730 \text{ lb.*} \\ 19,645 \text{ lb.†} \end{cases}$

P.V. (B4X).

*32054/62/3/8.

†32043/5/50/2/5/6/60/7/70–3.

Totals : Class B4   4
Class B4X 12

75

4-6-2   6MT   Class BB

(see Class WC & BB)

0-6-0   3F   Class C

Introduced 1900 : Wainwright S.E.C. design.
Weight : Loco. 43 tons 16 cwt.
Pressure : 160 lb.   Cyls. : 18½″ × 26″
Driving Wheels : 5′ 2″.
T.E. : 19,520 lb.

31004/18/33/7/8/54/9/61/3/8/71/
86/90, 31102/12/3/50/91, 31218
/9/21/3/5/7/9/34/42–5/52/3/5/6
/60/7/8/70–2/7/80/7/91/3/4/7/8,
31317, 31461/80/1/6/95/8,
31508/10/3/72/3/5/6/8–85/8–90
/2/3, 31681–4/6–95, 31711–25.

Total 104

0-6-0   3F   Class C2X

C2X Introduced 1908 : Marsh rebuild of R. J. Billinton L.B.S.C. C2 with larger C3-type boiler, extended smokebox, etc.
Weights : Loco. 45 tons 5 cwt.
Pressure : 170 lb.†
Cyls. : 17½″ × 26″.
Driving Wheels : 5′ 0″.
T.E. 19,175 lb.†

32434/7/8/40–51, 32521–9/32/4–
41/3–54.

Total 45

0-6-0   3F   Class C3

Introduced 1906 : Marsh L.B.S.C. design.
Weight : Loco. 47 tons 10 cwt.
Pressure : 170 lb.   Cyls. : 17½″ × 26″
Driving Wheels : 5′ 0″.
T.E. : 19,175 lb.

32300–3/6.   **Total 5**

0-4-0T   OF   Class C14

Introduced 1913 : Urie rebuild as shunting locos. of Drummond L.S.W. motor-train 2–2–0T (originally introduced 1906).

Weight : 25 tons 15 cwt.
Pressure : 150 lb.
Cyls. (O) : 14″ × 14″.
Driving Wheels : 3′ 0″.
T.E. : 9,720 lb.
Walschaerts gear.

77S, 30588/9.   **Total 3**

4-4-0 $\begin{cases} \text{I P D} \\ \text{2P DI} \end{cases}$ Classes D & DI

*D Introduced 1901 : Wainwright S.E.C. design, with round-top fire-box, some later fitted with extended smokebox.
†DI Introduced 1921 : Maunsell rebuild of Class D, with superheated Belpaire boiler, and long-travel piston valves.
Weights : $\begin{cases} 50 \text{ tons*} \\ 52 \text{ tons 4 cwt.†} \end{cases}$
Pressure : $\begin{cases} 175 \text{ lb.*} \\ 180 \text{ lb. Su.†} \end{cases}$
Cyls. : 19″ × 26″.
Driving Wheels : 6′ 8″.
T.E. : $\begin{cases} 17,450 \text{ lb.*} \\ 17,950 \text{ lb.†} \end{cases}$

*31057/75/92,   31477/88/90/3/6,
31501/49/74/7/86/91, 31728–34
/7/40/4/6/8/50.

†31145, 31246/7, 31470/87/9/92/
4, 31502/5/9/45, 31727/35/6/9/
41/3/5/9.

Total : Class D   27
Class DI   20

0-4-2T   IP

Classes DI & DI/M

*DI/M Introduced 1909 : Stroudley L.B.S.C. DI fitted for push-and-pull working (reclassified DI/M by S.R.)
†DI Introduced 1947 : DI fitted for oil pumping.
Weight : 43 tons 10 cwt.
Pressure : 170 lb.   Cyls. : 17″ × 24″.
Driving Wheels : 5′ 6″.
T.E. : 15,185 lb.

*32359
†701S.

Total :   DI I   DI/M I

0-4-4T 1P Class D3

Introduced 1892 : R. J. Billinton L.B.S.C. design, later reboilered by Marsh and fitted from 1934 for push-and-pull working.

Weight : 52 tons.

Pressure : 170 lb.   Cyls. : $17\frac{1}{2}'' \times 26''$

Driving Wheels : 5′ 6″.

T.E. : 17,435 lb.

32364/5/8/72/6/8–80/4–6/8/90/1/3/4.　　　　　　　Total 16

4-4-0 3P Class D15

Introduced 1912 : Drummond L.S.W. design, superheated by Urie from 1915.

Weight Loco. 61 tons 11 cwt.

Pressure : 180 lb. Su.

Cyls. : $20'' \times 26''$.

Driving Wheels : 6′ 7″.

T.E. : 20,140 lb.

Walschaerts gear, P.V.

30463–72.　　　　　　　Total 10

4-4-0 $\left\{ \begin{matrix} \text{1P} & \text{E} \\ \text{2P} & \text{E1} \end{matrix} \right.$ Classes E & E1

*E Introduced 1905 : Wainwright S.E.C. design with Belpaire boiler.

†E Introduced 1912 : Rebuilt with superheater in original boiler.

‡E1 Introduced 1919 : Maunsell rebuild of E, with larger superheated Belpaire boiler and long-travel piston valves.

Weight : Loco. $\left\{ \begin{matrix} \text{52 tons 5 cwt.*} \\ \text{53 tons 10 cwt.†} \\ \text{53 tons 9 cwt.‡} \end{matrix} \right.$

Pressure : $\left\{ \begin{matrix} \text{180 lb.*} \\ \text{160 lb Su.†} \\ \text{180 lb. Su.‡} \end{matrix} \right.$

Cyls. : $\left\{ \begin{matrix} 19'' \times 26''.* \\ 20\frac{1}{2}'' \times 26''.† \\ 19'' \times 26''.‡ \end{matrix} \right.$

T.E. : $\left\{ \begin{matrix} \text{18,410 lb.*} \\ \text{19,050 lb.†} \\ \text{18,410 lb.‡} \end{matrix} \right.$

Driving Wheels : 6′ 6″.

*31157/9/66/75/6, 31273, 31315, 31491, 31514–6/47/87.

†31036, 31275.

‡31019/67, 31160/5/79, 31497, 31504/6/7/11.

　　　　　Total : Class E 15
　　　　　　　　　Class E1 10

0-6-0T 2F Class E1

Introduced 1874 : Stroudley L.B.S.C. design, reboilered by Marsh.

Weight : 44 tons 3 cwt.

Pressure : 170 lb.   Cyls. : $17'' \times 24''$

Driving Wheels : 4′ 6″.

T.E. : 18,560 lb.

32113/28/9/33/8/9/45/7/51/6/60, 32606/89/91/4,
　(W) 1–4.

　　　　　　　　　Total 19

0-6-2T 2 MT Class E1/R

Introduced 1927 : Maunsell rebuild of Stroudley E1, with radial trailing axle and larger bunker for passenger service in West of England.

Weight : 50 tons 5 cwt.

Pressure : 170 lb.   Cyls. : $17'' \times 24''$

Driving Wheels : 4′ 6″.

T.E. : 18,560 lb.

32094–6, 32124/35, 32608/10/95–7.

　　　　　　　　　Total 10

0-6-0T 3F Class E2

*Introduced 1913 : L. B. Billinton L.B.S.C. design.

†Introduced 1915 : Later locos. with tanks extended further forward.

Weight : $\left\{ \begin{matrix} \text{52 tons 15 cwt.*} \\ \text{53 tons 10 cwt.†} \end{matrix} \right.$

Pressure : 170 lb.   Cyls. : $17\frac{1}{2}'' \times 26''$

Driving Wheels : 4′ 6″.

T.E. : 21,305 lb.

*32100–4.

†32105–9.

　　　　　　　　　Total 10

0-6-2T   3F   Class E3

Introduced 1894 : R. J. Billinton L.B.S.C. design, development of Stroudley " West Brighton " (introduced 1891), reboilered and fitted with extended smokebox, 1918 onwards ; cylinder diameter reduced from 18″ by S.R.

Weight : 56 tons 10 cwt.

Pressure : $\begin{cases} 160 \text{ lb.} \\ 170 \text{ lb.*} \end{cases}$

Cyls. : 17½″ × 26″

Driving Wheels : 4′ 6″

T.E. : $\begin{cases} 20,055 \text{ lb.} \\ 21,305 \text{ lb.*} \end{cases}$

*32165–70.
32453–6/8–61/2.

Total 15

0-6-2T   2 MT
Classes E4 & E4X

*E4 Introduced 1910   R. J. Billinton L.B.S.C. design, development of E3 with larger wheels, reboilered with Marsh boiler and extended smokebox, cylinder diameter reduced from 18″ by S.R.

†E4X Introduced 1909 : E4 reboilered with larger 12 4–4–2T type boiler.

Weights: $\begin{cases} 57 \text{ tons 10 cwt.*} \\ 59 \text{ tons 5 cwt.†} \end{cases}$

Pressure : 170 lb.   Cyls. : 17½″ × 26″

Driving Wheels : 5′ 0″

T.E. : 19,175 lb.

*32463–5/7–76/9–82/4–8/90–9, 32500–20/56–66/77–82.
†32466/77/8/89.

Totals E4   70
E4X   4

0-6-2T   2 MT
Classes E5 & E5X

*‡E5 Introduced 1902 : R. J. Billinton L.B.S.C. design, development of E4 with larger wheels and firebox, cylinder diameter reduced from 18″ by S.R.

†E5X Introduced 1911 : E5 reboilered with larger C3-type boiler.

Weights: $\begin{cases} 60 \text{ tons.*} \\ 64 \text{ tons 5 cwt.†} \end{cases}$

Pressure : $\begin{cases} 160 \text{ lb.} \\ 175 \text{ lb.‡} \\ 170 \text{ lb.†} \end{cases}$

Cyls. : 17½″ × 26″

Driving Wheels : 5′ 6″

T.E. : $\begin{cases} 16,410 \text{ lb.} \\ 17,945 \text{ lb.‡} \\ 17,435 \text{ lb.†} \end{cases}$

*‡32399,   32400/2/4–6,   32568/ 71/3–5/83–5/7/8/90–4.
†32401, 32570/6/86.

Totals : E5   21   E5X 4

0-6-2T   4F
Classes E6 & E6X

*‡E6 Introduced 1904 : R. J. Billinton L.B.S.C. design, development of E5 with smaller wheels.

†E6X Introduced 1911 : E6 reboilered with larger C3-type boiler.

Weights: $\begin{cases} 61 \text{ tons.*} \\ 63 \text{ tons.†} \end{cases}$

Pressure : $\begin{cases} 160 \text{ lb.*} \\ 175 \text{ lb.‡} \\ 170 \text{ lb.†} \end{cases}$

Cyls. : 18″ × 26″

Driving Wheels : 4′ 6″

T.E. : $\begin{cases} 21,215 \text{ lb.} \\ 23,205 \text{ lb.‡} \\ 22,540 \text{ lb.†} \end{cases}$

*‡32408–10/2–8.
†32407/11.

Totals : E6   10   E6X   2

0-6-0T   2F   Class G6

*Introduced 1894 : Adams L.S.W. design, later additions by Drummond, but with Adams type boiler.

†Introduced 1925 : Fitted with Drummond type boiler.

Weight : 47 tons 13 cwt.
Pressure : 160 lb.   Cyls. : 17½″ × 24″
Driving Wheels : 4′ 10″
T.E. : 17,235 lb.

*30162, 30238/58/60/6/8/70/7,
30349/53, D.S. 1152
†30160, 30259/74.

Total 14

4-8-0T 7F Class G16

Introduced 1921 : Urie L.S.W. "Hump"
loco.
Weight : 95 tons 2 cwt.
Pressure : 180 lb. Su.
Cyls. (O) : 22″ × 28″
Driving Wheels : 5′ 1″
T.E. : 33,990 lb.
Walschaerts gear, P.V.

30492-5 Total 4

0-4-4T 1P Class H

Introduced 1904. Wainwright S.E.C.
design.
*Introduced 1949. Fitted for push-and-
pull working.
Weight : 54 tons 8 cwt.
Pressure : 160 lb.   Cyls. : 18″ × 26″
Driving Wheels : 5′ 6″
T.E. : 17,360 lb.

31005,   31162/77/84/93,
31239/59/61/3/5/6/9/74/6/8/9/
95, 31305–11/20/1/4/6–9,
31500/3/12/8/9/21/2/30–3/40–
4/6/50–4.

*31016, 31158/61/4/82, 31319/22,
31517/20/3/48

Total 64

4-4-2 3P Class H1

*Introduced 1905 : Marsh L.B.S.C.
design, later superheated and re-
cylindered.
†Introduced 1947 : Rebuilt experimen-
tally with sleeve valves.
Weight : Loco. 68 tons 5 cwt.
Pressure : 200 lb. Su.
Cyls. : (O) 19″ × 26″.*
Driving Wheels : 6′ 7½″
T.E. : 20,070 lb.*

*32037/8   †32039

Total 3

Classes G16–H15

4-4-2 4P Class H2

Introduced 1911 : Marsh L.B.S.C.
design, superheated development of
H1 with large cylinders.
Weight : Loco. 68 tons 5 cwt.
Pressure : 200 lb. Su.
Cyls. : (O) 21″ × 26″
Driving Wheels : 6′ 7½″
T.E. : 24,520 lb.
P.V. :

32421/2/4–6.

Total 5

4-6-0 4 MT Class H15

*Introduced 1914 : Urie L.S.W. design,
fitted with " Maunsell " superheater
from 1927, replacing earlier types
(30490 built saturated).
†Introduced 1915 : Urie rebuild with
two outside cylinders of Drummond
E14, 4 cyl.4-6-0 introduced 1907, retaining original boiler retubed and
fitted with superheater.
‡Introduced 1924 : Maunsell locos.
with N15 type boiler and smaller
tenders.
§Introduced 1924 : Maunsell rebuild of
Drummond F13 4-cyl. 4-6-0 introduced 1905, with detail differences
from rebuild of E14.
¶Introduced 1927 : Urie loco. (built
1914 saturated) rebuilt with later
N15 class boiler, with smaller
firebox.

Weight : Loco. { 81 tons 5 cwt.*
                { 82 tons 1 cwt.†
                { 79 tons 19 cwt.‡¶
                { 80 tons 11 cwt.§
Pressure : { 180 lb. Su.*‡¶
           { 175 lb. Su.†§
Cyls. : 21″ × 28″
Driving Wheels : 6′ 0″
T.E. : { 26,240 lb.*‡¶
       { 25,510 lb.†§
Walschaerts gear, P.V.

*30482–90
†30335
‡30473–8, 30521–4
§30330–4
¶30491

Total 26

Classes H16–K10

4-6-2T 5F Class H16

Introduced 1921 : Urie L.S.W. design for heavy freight traffic.
Weight : 96 tons 8 cwt.
Pressure : 180 lb. Su.
Cyls. : (O) 21″ × 28″
Driving Wheels : 5′ 7″
T.E. : 28,200 lb.
Walschaerts valve gear, P.V.

30516–20   **Total 5**

4-4-2T 2P Class IIX

*Introduced 1925 : Maunsell rebuild with 13 class non-superheater boiler of Marsh L.B.S.C. II class (introduced 1906).
†Introduced 1929 : Maunsell rebuild of later II locos, with shorter coupled wheelbase (introduced 1907).
Weight : 71 tons 18 cwt.
Pressure : 180 lb.   Cyls. : 17½″ × 26″
Driving Wheels : 5′ 6″
T.E. : 18,450 lb.

*32595/6, 32602/3
†32002/5/8/9

                                  Total 8

4-4-2T 3P Class 13

*Introduced 1907 : Marsh L.B.S.C. design with slide valves, rebuilt 1919 with superheater and extended smokebox.
†Introduced 1908 : Marsh L.B.S.C. design with piston valves and smaller wheels, 32026-30/75/6 originally saturated, remainder built superheated.
‡Introduced 1912 : L. B. Billinton modification of 1908 design, built superheated with larger cylinders.
Weight : $\begin{cases} 75 \text{ tons 10 cwt.*} \\ 76 \text{ tons†‡} \end{cases}$
Pressure : 180 lb. Su.
Cyls. : $\begin{cases} 19″ × 26″* \\ 20″ × 26″† \\ 21″ × 26″‡ \end{cases}$
Driving Wheels : $\begin{cases} 6′ 9″* \\ 6′ 7½″†‡ \end{cases}$
T.E. : $\begin{cases} 17,730 \text{ lb.*} \\ 20,015 \text{ lb.†} \\ 22,065 \text{ lb.‡} \end{cases}$

*32021
†32022/3/6–30/75–9/81.
‡32082–4/6/9–91

                                  Total 21

0-6-4T 3 MT Class J

Introduced 1913 : Wainwright S.E.C. design.
Weight : 70 tons 4 cwt.
Pressure : 160 lb. Su.
Cyls. : 19½″ × 26″
Driving Wheels : 5′ 6″
T.E. : 20,370 lb.
P.V.

31595/6/8   **Total 3**

4-6-2T 4P

Classes J1 & J2

*J1 Introduced 1910 : Marsh L.B.S.C. design.
†J2 Introduced 1912 : L. B. Billinton development of J1 with Walschaerts valve gear and detail differences.
Weight : 89 tons.
Pressure : 170 lb. Su.
Cyls. : (O) 21″ × 26″
Driving Wheels : 6′ 7″
T.E. : 20,840 lb.
P.V. :

*32325   †32326

                Total : Class J1 1
                          Class J2 1

2-6-0 4 MT Class K

Introduced 1913 : L. B. Billinton L.B.S.C. design.
Weight : Loco. 63 tons 15 cwt.
Pressure : 180 lb. Su.
Cyls. . (O) 21″ × 26″
Driving Wheels : 5′ 6″
T.E. : 26,580 lb.
P.V. :

32337–53   **Total 17**

4-4-0 1 MT Class K10

Introduced 1901.   Drummond L.S.W. design, development of C8 express 4-4-0 for mixed traffic work.
Weight : Loco. 46 tons 14 cwt.
Pressure : 175 lb.   Cyls. : 18½″ × 26″
Driving Wheels : 5′ 7″
T.E. : 19 755 lb.

30384/90   **Total 2**

4-4-0   2P   Class L

Introduced 1914 : Wainwright S.E.C. design, with detail alterations by Maunsell.
Weight : Loco. 57 tons 9 cwt.
Pressure : 160 lb. Su.
Cyls. : 20½″ × 26″
Driving Wheels : 6′ 8″
T.E. : 18,575 lb.
P.V.

31760–81   **Total 22**

4-4-0   2P   Class L1

Introduced 1926 : Post-grouping devel-opment of L, with long-travel valves, **side** window cab and detail alterations
Weight : Loco. 57 tons 16 cwt.
Pressure : 180 lb. Su.
Cyls. : 19½″ × 26″
Driving Wheels : 6′ 8″
T.E. : 18,910 lb.
P.V.

31753–9/82–9

                            Total 15

4-4-0   1 MT   Class L11

Introduced 1903.   Drummond L.S.W. design, development of K10 with T9-type boiler, with larger firebox.
Weight : Loco. 50 tons 11 cwt.
Pressure : 175 lb.   Cyls. : 18½″ × 26″
Driving Wheels : 5′ 7″
T.E. : 19,755 lb.

30134/48/54–9/63–5/1/70–5, 30405/6/8/9/11–4/36–8/41/2.
                            Total 30

4-4-0   2P   Class L12

Introduced 1904 : Drummond L.S.W. design, development of T9 with larger boiler barrel, superheated from 1915.
Weight : Loco. 55 tons 5 cwt.
Pressure : 175 lb. Su.
Cyls. : 19″ × 26″
Driving Wheels : 6′ 7″
T.E. : 17,675 lb.

30415–34   **Total 20**

0-6-6-0T   Uncl.
"Leader" Class

Introduced 1949 : Bulleid double-bogie design, with chain-coupled wheels.
Weight : 130 tons. (approx.)
Pressure : 280 lb Su.
Cyls. : (6) 12¼″ × 15″
Driving Wheels : 5′ 1″
T.E. : 26,350 lb.
Sleeve valves with modified Bulleid valve gear.

36001

Nos. 36002–5 of this class are stored in varying stages of construction.

4-6-0   6P   Class LN

*Introduced 1926 : Maunsell design. cylinders and tender modified by Bulleid from 1938, and fitted with multiple-jet blast pipe and large chimney.
†Introduced 1929 : Loco. fitted experi-mentally with smaller driving wheels.
‡Introduced 1929 : Loco. fitted experi-mentally with longer boiler barrel.
Weights : Loco. { 83 tons 10 cwt.*†
                  { 84 tons 16 cwt.‡
Pressure : 220 lb. Su.
Cyls. : (4) 16½″ × 26″
Driving Wheels : { 6′ 7″*‡
                  { 6′ 3″†
T.E. { 33,510 lb.*‡
     { 35,300 lb.†
Walschaerts gear, P.V.

*30850–8/61–5.
†30859   ‡30860
                            Total 16

0-4-4T   2P   Class M7

*Introduced 1897 : Drummond L.S.W. M7 design.
†Introduced 1903 : Drummond X14 design, with increased front over-hang, steam reverser and detail alterations, now classified M7 (30254 originally M7).
‡Introduced 1925 : X14 design fitted for push-and-pull working.
Weights : { 60 tons 4 cwt.*
           { 60 tons 3 cwt.†
           { 62 tons 0 cwt.‡
Pressure : 175 lb.   Cyls. : 18½″ × 26″
Driving Wheels : 5′ 7″
T.E. : 19,755 lb.

Classes MN–O1

*30022–6/31–44, 30112, 30241–53/5/6, 30318–24/56/7, 30667–71/3–6.

†30029/30, 30123/4/7/30/2/3, 30254, 30374–8, 30479.

‡30021/7/8/45–60, 30104–11/25/8/9/31, 30328/79, 30480/1.

Total 103

4-6-2   7P   Class MN

*Introduced 1941 : Bulleid design.
†Introduced 1948 : Loco. rebuilt with mechanical stoker.
Weight : Loco. 94 tons 15 cwt.
Pressure : 280 lb. Su.
Cyls. : 18″ × 24″
Driving Wheels : 6′ 2″
T.E. : 37,515 lb.
Bulleid valve gear, P.V.
*35001–4/6–30
†35005

Total 30

2-6-0 4 MT Classes N & NI

*N Introduced 1917 : Maunsell S.E.C. mixed traffic design.
†NI Introduced 1922 : 3-cylinder development of N.
Weight : Loco. { 61 tons 4 cwt.*
                  { 64 tons 5 cwt.†
Pressure : 200 lb. Su.
Cyls. : { (O) 19″ × 28″*
          { (3) 16″ × 28″†
Driving Wheels : 5′ 6″
T.E. : { 26,035 lb.*
         { 27,695 lb.†
Walschaert gear, P.V.
*31400–14, 31810–21/3–75
†31822/76–80

Totals : Class N   80
Class NI   6

4-6-0   5P   Class N15

*Introduced 1918 : Urie L.S.W. design.
†Introduced 1928 : Urie Locos modified with cylinders of reduced diameter.
‡Introduced 1925 : Maunsell locos. with long-travel valves, increased boiler pressure, smaller fireboxes, and tenders from Drummond G14 4–6–0's.
§Introduced 1925 : Later locos. with detail alterations and increased weight.

‖Introduced 1925 : Locos. with modified cabs to suit Eastern Section and new bogie tenders.
¶Introduced 1926 : Locos. with detail alterations and six-wheeled tenders for Central Section.
Weight : Loco. { 80 tons 7 cwt.*†
                  { 79 tons 18 cwt.‡
                  { 80 tons 19 cwt.§‖
                  { 81 tons 17 cwt.¶
Pressure : { 180 lb. Su.*†
             { 200 lb Su.‡§‖¶
Cyls. : { (O) 22″ × 28″*
          { (O) 21″ × 28″†
          { (O) 20½″ × 28″‡§‖¶
Driving Wheels : 6′ 7″
T.E. : { 26,245 lb.*
         { 23,915 lb.†
         { 25,320 lb. §‡‖¶
Walschaerts gear, P.V.
NOTE : Nos. 30736/7/41/52/5 are fitted with multiple Jet blastpipe and large diameter chimney.
*30755   †30736–54
‡30453–7   §30448–52
‖30763–92   ¶30793–30806

Total 74

4-6-0   4P   Class N15X

Introduced 1934 : Maunsell rebuild of L. B. Billinton L.B.S.C. Class L 4–6–4T (introduced 1914).
Weight : Loco 73 tons 2 cwt.
Pressure : 180 lb. Su.
Cyls. : (O) 21″ × 28″
Driving Wheels : 6′ 9″
T.E. : 23,325 lb.
Walschaerts gear, P.V.
32327–33

Total 7

0-6-0   IF   Class O1

*Introduced 1903 : Wainwright rebuild with domed boiler and new cab of Stirling S.E.R. Class O 0–6–0 (Introduced 1878, oldest survivor built 1882).
†Introduced 1903 : Locos. with smaller driving wheels.
Weight : Loco. 41 tons I cwt.
Pressure : 150 lb.   Cyls. : 18″ × 26″
Driving Wheels : { 5′ 2″*
                    { 5′ 1″†
T.E. : { 17,325 lb.*
         { 17,610 lb.†

*31044/64–6/93, 31108, 31248/58,
  31369/70/3/9/81/3/90/1/5,
  31425/30/2/4,
†31041/8,

Total 23

0-4-4T 1P Class O2

*Introduced 1889 : Adams L.S.W.
  design.
†Introduced 1923 : Fitted with West-
  inghouse brake for I.O.W., bunkers
  enlarged from 1932.
‡Fitted with Drummond-type boiler.
§Fitted for push-and-pull working.
Weight : $\begin{cases} 46 \text{ tons } 18 \text{ cwt.}*‡ \\ 48 \text{ tons } 8 \text{ cwt.†} \end{cases}$
Pressure : 160 lb. Cyls. : 17½″ × 24″
Driving Wheels : 4′ 10″
T.E. : 17,235 lb.

*30177/9/92/3/7/9, 30200/12/6/
  24/9–32/6.
† (W)14–34 †§ (W)35/6.
‡30203/4/13/21/3/5/33.
‡§30182/3, 30207.

Total 48

0-6-0T 0F Class P

Introduced 1909 : Wainwright S.E.C.
  design for push-and-pull work, now
  used for shunting.
Weight : 28 tons 10 cwt.
Pressure : 160 lb. Cyls. : 12″ × 18″
Driving Wheels : 3′ 9¼″
T.E. : 7,810 lb.

31027, 31178, 31323/5, 31555–8.

Total 8

0-6-0 4F Class Q

Introduced 1938 : Maunsell design, later
  fitted with multiple-jet blast pipe and
  large chimney.
Weight : Loco. 49 tons 10 cwt.
Pressure : 200 lb. Su.
Cyls. : 19″ × 26″
Driving Wheels : 5′ 1″
T.E. : 26,160 lb.
P.V.
30530–49

Total 20

0-6-0 5F Class Q1

Introduced 1942 : Bulleid " Austerity "
  design.
Weight : Loco. 51 tons 5 cwt.
Pressure : 230 lb. Su.
Cyls. : 19″ × 26″
Driving Wheels : 5′ 1″
T.E. : 30,080 lb.
P.V.

33001–40

Total 40

0-4-4T 1P Classes R & R1

*R Introduced 1891 : Kirtley L.C.D.
  design, since rebuilt with H. class
  boiler.
†R1 Introduced 1900 : Locos. built for
  S.E.C. with enlarged bunkers, since
  rebuilt with H class boiler.
‡Fitted for push-and-pull working.
Weight : $\begin{cases} 48 \text{ tons } 15 \text{ cwt.}* \\ 52 \text{ tons } 3 \text{ cwt.†} \end{cases}$
Pressure : 160 lb. Cyls. : 17½″ × 24″
Driving Wheels : 5′ 6″
T.E. : 15,145 lb.

*31661/71/3/4.
†31696/8, 31705/8.
*‡31658–60/2/3/5–7/70/5.
†‡31697, 31700/3/4/6/10.

Total : Class R 15
Class R1 10

0-6-0T 2F Class R1

*Introduced 1888 : Stirling S.E. design,
  later rebuilt with domed boiler.
†Introduced 1938 : Fitted with Urie
  type short chimney for Whitstable
  branch, and fitted with or retaining
  original Stirling-type cab.
Weight : $\begin{cases} 46 \text{ tons } 15 \text{ cwt.}* \\ 46 \text{ tons } 8 \text{ cwt.†} \end{cases}$
Pressure : 160 lb. Cyls. : 18″ × 26″
Driving Wheels : $\begin{cases} 5′ 2″* \\ 5′ 1″† \end{cases}$
T.E. : $\begin{cases} 18,480 \text{ lb.}* \\ 18,780 \text{ lb.†} \end{cases}$

*31047, 31128/54/74, 31335/7/40
†31010/69, 31107/47, 31339.

Total 12

Classes S-T9

0-6-0ST 2F Class S

Introduced 1917 : Maunsell rebuild of
Wainwright S.E.C. C Class (built
1900) with saddle-tank.
Weight : 53 tons 10 cwt.
Pressure : 170 lb. Cyls. : $18\frac{1}{2}'' \times 26''$
Driving Wheels : 5' 2"
T.E. : 19,520 lb.

31685   **Total 1**

4-4-0 2P Class S11

Introduced 1903 : Drummond L.S.W.
design, development of T9 with larger
boiler barrel and smaller wheels for
West of England, superheated from
1920.
Weight : Loco. 53 tons, 15 cwt.
Pressure : 175 lb. Su.
Cyls : $19'' \times 26''$
Driving Wheels : 6' 0"
T.E. : 19,390 lb.

30395–30404   **Total 10**

4-6-0 6F Class S15

*Introduced 1920 : Urie L.S.W. design,
development of N15 for mixed traffic
work.
†Introduced 1927 : Post-grouping locos.
with higher pressure, smaller grate,
modified footplating and other detail
differences. 30833-7 with 6-wheel
tenders for Central Section.
‡Introduced 1936 : Later locos. with
detail differences and reduced weight.
Weight : Loco. $\begin{cases} 79 \text{ tons } 16 \text{ cwt.*} \\ 80 \text{ tons } 14 \text{ cwt.†} \\ 79 \text{ tons } 5 \text{ cwt.‡} \end{cases}$
Pressure : $\begin{cases} 180 \text{ lb. Su.*} \\ 200 \text{ lb. Su.†‡} \end{cases}$
Cyls. : $\begin{cases} (O) \ 21'' \times 28''* \\ (O) \ 20\frac{1}{2}'' \times 28''†‡ \end{cases}$
Driving Wheels : 5' 7"
T.E. : $\begin{cases} 28,200 \text{ lb.*} \\ 29,855 \text{ lb.†‡} \end{cases}$
Walschaerts gear, P.V.
*30496–30515   †30823–37
‡30838–47

                       Total 45

0-6-0T 2F Class T

Introduced 1879 : Kirtley L.C.D. design
(oldest survivor built 1890).
Weight : 40 tons 15 cwt.
Pressure : 160 lb. Cyls. : $17\frac{1}{4}'' \times 24''$
Driving Wheels : 4' 6"
T.E. : 18,510 lb.

31602/4

                       Total 2

0-4-4T 1P Class T1

Introduced 1894 : Adams L.S.W.
design, originally designated F6, but
later assimilated into Class T1 (introduced 1888).

Weight : 57 tons 2 cwt.
Pressure : 160 lb. Cyls. : $18'' \times 26''$
Driving Wheels : 5' 7"
T.E. : 17,100 lb.

30007/20, 30367

                       Total 3

4-4-0 2P Class T9

*Introduced 1899 : Drummond L.S.W.
design, fitted with superheater and
larger cylinders by Urie from 1922.
†Introduced 1899 : Locos. with detail
differences (originally fitted with firebox watertubes).
‡Introduced 1900 : Locos. with wider
cab and splashers, and without
coupling rod splashers (originally
fitted with firebox watertubes.)
Weight : Loco. $\begin{cases} 51 \text{ tons } 18 \text{ cwt.*} \\ 51 \text{ tons } 16 \text{ cwt.†} \\ 51 \text{ tons } 7 \text{ cwt.‡} \end{cases}$
Pressure : 175 lb. Su.
Cyls. : $19'' \times 26''$
Driving Wheels : 6' 7"
T.E. : 17,675 lb.

*30113–22, 30280–9
†30702–19/21–33
‡30300–5/7/10–4/36–8 **Total 66**

84

4-6-0   4P   Class T14

Introduced 1911 : Drummond L.S.W. design, fitted with superheater by Urie from 1915, and with Maunsell superheater, raised footplating and detail alterations from 1930.
Weight : Loco. 76 tons 10 cwt.
Pressure : 175 ib. Su.
Cyls. : (4) 15″ × 26″
Driving Wheels : 6′ 7″
T.E. : 22,030 lb.
Walschaerts gear and rocking arms.
30446/61   **Total 2**

2-6-0   4 MT
Classes U & UI

*U Introduced 1928 : Rebuild of Maunsell S.E.C. Class K (" River ") 2–6–4T (introduced 1917).
†U Introduced 1928 : Locos. built as Class U, with smaller splashers and detail alterations.
†UI Introduced 1928 : 3-cylinder development of Class U (prototype, 31890, rebuilt from 2–6–4T, originally built 1925).
Weight : Loco. $\begin{cases} 63 \text{ tons*} \\ 62 \text{ tons 6 cwt.†} \\ 65 \text{ tons 6 cwt.‡} \end{cases}$
Pressure : 200 lb. Su.
Cyls. : $\begin{cases} (O) \ 19″ \times 28″*† \\ (3) \ 16″ \times 28″‡ \end{cases}$
Driving Wheels : 6′ 0″
T.E. : $\begin{cases} 23,865 \text{ lb.*†} \\ 25,385 \text{ lb.‡} \end{cases}$
Walschaerts gear, P.V.
*31790–31809   †31610–39
‡31890–31910

                Total : Class U   50
                         Class UI   21

0-6-0T   3F   Class USA

Introduced 1942 : U.S. Army Transportation Corps design, purchased by S.R. 1946, and fitted with modified cab and bunker and other detail alterations.
Weight : Loco. 46 tons 10 cwt.
Pressure : 210 lb.
Cyls. : (O) 16½″ × 24″
Driving Wheels : 4′ 6″
T.E. : 21,600 lb.
Walschaerts gear, P.V.
30061–74   **Total 14**

Classes T14–WC & BB

4-4-0   5P   Class V

*Introduced 1930 : Maunsell design.
†Introduced 1938 : Fitted with multiple jet blastpipe and larger chimney by Bulleid.
Weight : Loco. 67 tons 2 cwt.
Pressure : 220 lb. Su.
Cyls. : (3) 16½″ × 26″
Driving Wheels : 6′ 7″
T.E. : 25,135 lb.
Walschaerts gear, P.V.
*30902–6/8/10–2/6/22/3/5–8/32/ 5/6.
†30900/1/7/9/13–5/7–21/4/29–31/ 3/4/7–9.
               Total 40

2-6-4T   5F   Class W

Introduced 1931 : Maunsell design, developed from Class N1 2–6–0.
Weight : 90 tons 14 cwt.
Pressure : 200 lb. Su.
Cyls. : (3) 16½″ × 28″
Driving Wheels : 5′ 6″
T.E. : 29,450 lb.
Walschaerts gear, P.V.
31911–25   **Total 15**

4-6-2   6 MT
Classes WC & BB

*Introduced 1945 : Bulleid " West Country " Class.
†Introduced 1946 : Bulleid " Battle of Britain " Class.
‡Introduced 1948 : Locos. with larger tenders.
Weight : Loco. 86 tons 0 cwt.
Pressure : 280 lb. Su.
Cyls. : (3) 16⅜″ × 24″
Driving Wheels : 6′ 2″
T.E. : 31,050 lb.
Bulleid valve gear, P.V.
   *34001–48   †34049–70
†‡34071–90, 34109/10
*‡34091–34108

N.B.—Locos. of this class are still being delivered.

0-8-0T   7F   **Class Z**

Introduced 1929 : Maunsell design for heavy shunting.
Weight : 71 tons 12 cwt.
Pressure : 180 lb. Cyls : (3) 16″ × 18″
Driving Wheels : 4′ 8″
T.E. : 29,375 lb.
Walschaerts gear, P.V.
30950–7   **Total 8**

0-6-0   4F   **Class 700**

Introduced 1897 : Drummond L.S.W. design, superheated from 1921.
Weight : Loco. 46 tons 14 cwt.
Pressure : 180 lb. Su.
Cyls. : 19″ × 26″
Driving Wheels : 5′ 1″
T.E. : 23,540 lb.
30306/8/9/15–7/25–7/39/46/50/2/5/68, 30687–30701.
           Total 30

0-6-0T   IF   **Class 756**

Introduced 1907 : Hawthorn Leslie design for P.D.S.W.J.
Weight : 35 tons 15 cwt.
Pressure : 170 lb.
Cyls. : (O) 14″ × 22″
Driving Wheels : 3′ 10″
T.E. : 13,545 lb.
30756   **Total 1**

0-6-2T   IMT   **Class 757**

Introduced 1907 : Hawthorn Leslie design for P.D.S.W.J.
Weight : 49 tons 19 cwt.
Pressure : 170 lb.
Cyls. : (O) 16″ × 24″
Driving Wheels : 4′ 0″
T.E. : 18,495 lb.
30757–8   **Total 2**

2-4-0WT   0F   **Class 0298**

Introduced 1874 : Beattie L.S.W. design, rebuilt by Adams (1884-92), Urie (1921-2) and Maunsell (1931-5).
Weight : 37 tons 16 cwt.
Pressure : 160 lb.
Cyls. : (O) 16¼″ × 20″
Driving Wheels : 5′ 7″
T.E. : 11,050 lb.
30585–7   **Total 3**

0-6-0   IF   **Class 0395**

*Introduced 1881 : Adams L.S.W. design.
†Introduced 1885 : Adams " 496 '' class, with longer front overhang.
‡Introduced 1928 : Reboilered with ex-S.E.C. Class M3 4–4–0 boiler.
§Fitted with Drummond type boiler.
Weight : Loco. { 37 tons 12 cwt.*
                 { 38 tons 14 cwt.†
Pressure : { 140 lb.*
           { 150 lb.†
Driving Wheels : 5′ 1″
T.E. : { 15,535 lb.*
      { 16,645 lb.†

*30568–72/4–8
†30566/79/81
*‡30573
*§30567
††30565/80
†§30564

           Total 18

4-4-2T   IP   **Class 0415**

Introduced 1882 : Adams L.S.W. design later reboilered (oldest survivor built 1883).
Weight : 55 tons 2 cwt.
Pressure : 160 lb.
Cyls. : (O) 17½″ × 24″
Driving Wheels : 5′ 7″
T.E. : 14,920 lb.
30582–4   **Total 3**

0-4-0ST   0F   **Class 0458**

Introduced 1890 : Hawthorn Leslie design for Southampton Docks Co., absorbed by L.S.W., 1892.
Weight : 21 tons 2 cwt.
Pressure : 120 lb.
Cyls. : (O) 12″ × 20″
Driving Wheels : 3′ 2″
T.E. : 7,730 lb.
30458   **Total 1**

NAMED ENGINES

CLASS B4 0–4–0T

30086	Havre	30096	Normandy
30089	Trouville	30102	Granville
30093	St. Malo		

CLASS N15 " KING ARTHUR " 4–6–0

30448	Sir Tristram	30453	King Arthur
30449	Sir Torre	30454	Queen Guinevere
30450	Sir Kay	30455	Sir Launcelot
30451	Sir Lamorak	30456	Sir Galahad
30452	Sir Meliagrance	30457	Sir Bedivere

CLASS 0458 0–4–0ST

30458	Ironside

CLASS N15 " KING ARTHUR " 4–6–0

30736	Excalibur	30746	Pendragon
30737	King Uther	30747	Elaine
30738	King Pellinore	30748	Vivien
30739	King Leodegrance	30749	Iseult
30740	Merlin	30750	Morgan le Fay
30741	Joyous Gard	30751	Etarre
30742	Camelot	30752	Linette
30743	Lyonnesse	30753	Melisande
30744	Maid of Astolat	30754	The Green Knight
30745	Tintagel	30755	The Red Knight

CLASS 756 0–6–0T

30756	A. S. Harris

CLASS 757 0-6-2T

30757	Earl of Mount Edgcumbe	30758	Lord St. Levan

NAMED LOCOMOTIVES
CLASS N15 " KING ARTHUR " 4-6-0

30763	Sir Bors de Ganis		30785	Sir Mador de la Porte
30764	Sir Gawain		30786	Sir Lionel
30765	Sir Gareth		30787	Sir Menadeuke
30766	Sir Geraint		30788	Sir Urre of the Mount
30767	Sir Valence		30789	Sir Guy
30768	Sir Balin		30790	Sir Villiars
30769	Sir Balan		30791	Sir Uwaine
30770	Sir Prianius		30792	Sir Hervis de Revel
30771	Sir Sagramore		30793	Sir Ontzlake
30772	Sir Percivale		30794	Sir Ector de Maris
30773	Sir Lavaine		30795	Sir Dinadan
30774	Sir Gaheris		30796	Sir Dodinas le Savage
30775	Sir Agravaine		30797	Sir Blamor de Ganis
30776	Sir Galagars		30798	Sir Hectimere
30777	Sir Lamiel		30799	Sir Ironside
30778	Sir Pelleas		30800	Sir Meleaus de Lile
30779	Sir Colgrevance		30801	Sir Meliot de Logres
30780	Sir Persant		30802	Sir Durnore
30781	Sir Aglovale		30803	Sir Harry le Fise Lake
30782	Sir Brian		30804	Sir Cador of Cornwall
30783	Sir Gillemere		30805	Sir Constantine
30784	Sir Nerovens		30806	Sir Galleron

CLASS LN " LORD NELSON " 4-6-0

30850	Lord Nelson		30858	Lord Duncan
30851	Sir Francis Drake		30859	Lord Hood
30852	Sir Walter Raleigh		30860	Lord Hawke
30853	Sir Richard Grenville		30861	Lord Anson
30854	Howard of Effingham		30862	Lord Collingwood
30855	Robert Blake		30863	Lord Rodney
30856	Lord St. Vincent		30864	Sir Martin Frobisher
30857	Lord Howe		30865	Sir John Hawkins

CLASS V " SCHOOLS " 4-4-0

30900	Eton		30903	Charterhouse
30901	Winchester		30904	Lancing
30902	Wellington		30905	Tonbridge

NAMED LOCOMOTIVES

30906	Sherborne	30923	Bradfield
30907	Dulwich	30924	Haileybury
30908	Westminster	30925	Cheltenham
30909	St. Paul's	30926	Repton
30910	Merchant Taylors	30927	Clifton
30911	Dover	30928	Stowe
30912	Downside	30929	Malvern
30913	Christ's Hospital	30930	Radley
30914	Eastbourne	30931	King's Wimbledon
30915	Brighton	30932	Blundells
30916	Whitgift	30933	King's Canterbury
30917	Ardingly	30934	St. Lawrence
30918	Hurstpierpoint	30935	Sevenoaks
30919	Harrow	30936	Cranleigh
30920	Rugby	30937	Epsom
30921	Shrewsbury	30938	St. Olave's
30922	Marlborough	30938	Leatherhead

CLASS H1 4-4-2

32037	Selsey Bill	32039	Hartland Point
32038	Portland Bill		

CLASS N15X " REMEMBRANCE " 4-6-0

32327	Trevithick	32331	Beattie
32328	Hackworth	32332	Stroudley
32329	Stephenson	32333	Remembrance
32330	Cudworth		

CLASS H2 4-4-2

32421	South Foreland	32425	Trevose Head
32422	North Foreland	32426	St. Alban's Head
32424	Beachy Head		

CLASSES WC & BB 4-6-2
" WEST COUNTRY " and " BATTLE OF BRITAIN "

34001	Exeter	34005	Barnstaple
34002	Salisbury	34006	Bude
34003	Plymouth	34007	Wadebridge
34004	Yeovil	34008	Padstow

NAMED LOCOMOTIVES

34009	Lyme Regis		34054	Lord Beaverbrook
34010	Sidmouth		34055	Fighter Pilot
34011	Tavistock		34056	Croydon
34012	Launceston		34057	Biggin Hill
34013	Okehampton		34058	Sir Frederick Pile
34014	Budleigh Salterton		34059	Sir Archibald Sinclair
34015	Exmouth		34060	25 Squadron
34016	Bodmin		34061	73 Squadron
34017	Ilfracombe		34062	17 Squadron
34018	Axminster		34063	229 Squadron
34019	Bideford		34064	Fighter Command
34020	Seaton		34065	Hurricane
34021	Dartmoor		34066	Spitfire
34022	Exmoor		34067	Tangmere
34023	Blackmore Vale		34068	Kenley
34024	Tamar Valley		34069	Hawkinge
34025	Whimple		34070	Manston
34026	Yes Tor		34071	601 Squadron
34027	Taw Valley		34072	257 Squadron
34028	Eddystone		34073	249 Squadron
34029	Lundy		34074	46 Squadron
34030	Watersmeet		34075	264 Squadron
34031	Torrington		34076	41 Squadron
34032	Camelford		34077	603 Squadron
34033	Chard		34078	222 Squadron
34034	Honiton		34079	141 Squadron
34035	Shaftesbury		34080	74 Squadron
34036	Westward Ho!		34081	92 Squadron
34037	Clovelly		34082	615 Squadron
34038	Lynton		34083	605 Squadron
34039	Boscastle		34084	253 Squadron
34040	Crewkerne		34085	501 Squadron
34041	Wilton		34086	219 Squadron
34042	Dorchester		34087	145 Squadron
34043	Combe Martin		34088	213 Squadron
34044	Woolacombe		34089	602 Squadron
34045	Ottery St. Mary		34090	Sir Eustace Missenden, Southern Railway
34046	Braunton			
34047	Callington		34091	Weymouth
34048	Crediton		34092	City of Wells
34049	Anti-Aircraft Command		34093	Saunton
34050	Royal Observer Corps		34094	Mortehoe
34051	Winston Churchill		34095	Brentor
34052	Lord Dowding		34096	Trevone
34053	Sir Keith Park		34097	Holsworthy

NAMED LOCOMOTIVES

34099	Templecombe	34105	Swanage
34099	Lynmouth	34106	Lydford
34100	Appledore	34107	Blandford
34101	Hartland	34108	Wincanton
34102	Lapford	34109	Sir Trafford
34103	Calstock		Leigh-Mallory
34104	Bere Alston	34110	66 Squadron

CLASS MN " MERCHANT NAVY " 4–6–2

35001	Channel Packet	35015	Rotterdam Lloyd
35002	Union Castle	35016	Elders Fyffes
35003	Royal Mail	35017	Belgian Marine
35004	Cunard White Star	35018	British India Line
35005	Canadian Pacific	35019	French Line CGT
35006	Peninsular & Oriental	35020	Bibby Line
	S.N. Co.	35021	New Zealand Line
35007	Aberdeen	35022	Holland-America Line
	Commonwealth	35023	Holland-Afrika Line
35008	Orient Line	35024	East Asiatic Company
35009	Shaw Savill	35025	Brocklebank Line
35010	Blue Star	35026	Lamport & Holt Line
35011	General Steam Navigation	35027	Port Line
35012	United States Line	35028	Clan Line
35013	Blue Funnel	35029	Ellerman Lines
35014	Nederland Line	35030	Elder Dempster Lines

CLASS E1 0–6–0T

W 1	Medina	W 3	Ryde
W 2	Yarmouth	W 4	Wroxall

CLASS O2 0–4–4T

W14	Fishbourne	W22	Brading	W30	Shorwell
W15	Cowes	W23	Totland	W31	Chale
W16	Ventnor	W24	Calbourne	W32	Bonchurch
W17	Seaview	W25	Godshill	W33	Bembridge
W18	Ningwood	W26	Whitwell	W34	Newport
W19	Osborne	W27	Merstone	W35	Freshwater
W20	Shanklin	W28	Ashey	W36	Carisbrooke
W21	Sandown	W29	Alverstone		

The ABC of

BRITISH RAILWAYS
LOCOMOTIVES

Edited by

A. F. COOK

PART 3 — Nos. 40000 - 59999

**LONDON MIDLAND
AND SCOTTISH** (Ex-L.M.S.)
**REGION STEAM
LOCOMOTIVES**

LONDON

Ian Allan Ltd

FOREWORD

THIS booklet lists all British Railways locomotives numbered between 40000 and 59999. This series of numbers includes all London Midland Region and Scottish (ex-L.M.S.) Region steam locos., i.e. steam locomotives of the former L.M.S.R. Under the general British Railways numbering scheme, the numbers of L.M.S.R. steam locomotives were increased by 40000, with certain exceptions which were to be completely renumbered. Renumbering is being carried out only as locomotives visit main works, and thus it may be some time before all locomotives bear the numbers shown in this book.

Former L.M.S.R. diesel and diesel-electric locomotives were to be renumbered, in common with all British Railways locomotives of similar propulsion, between 10000 and 29999, and details of them will be found in the ABC OF BRITISH RAILWAYS' LOCOMOTIVES Nos. 10000-39999.

CHIEF MECHANICAL ENGINEERS
BRITISH RAILWAYS (L. M. Region)

H. G. Ivatt .. 1948—

L.M.S.

George Hughes	1923—1925	Sir William Stanier ... 1932—1944
Sir Henry Fowler ...	1925—1931	Charles E. Fairburn ... 1944—1945
E. H. J. Lemon		H. G. Ivatt ... 1945—1947
(Sir Ernest Lemon)	1931—1932	

LOCOMOTIVE SUPERINTENDENTS AND C.M.E.'S—L.M.S. CONSTITUENT COMPANIES†

CALEDONIAN RAILWAY		HIGHLAND RAILWAY	
Robert Sinclair		William Stroudley	
(First loco. engineer)‡	1847—1856	(First loco. engineer) ...	1866—1869
Benjamin Connor ...	1856—1876	David Jones ...	1869—1896
George Brittain ...	1876—1882	Peter Drummond ...	1896—1911
Dugald Drummond ...	1882—1890	F. G. Smith ...	1912—1915
Hugh Smellie ...	1890	C. Cumming ...	1915—1923
J. Lambie ...	1890—1895		
J. F. McIntosh ...	1895—1914	**L. & Y.R.**	
William Pickersgill ...	1914—1923	Sir John Hawkshaw (Consultant),*	
FURNESS RAILWAY		Hurst and Jenkins successively to 1868	
R. Mason	1890—1897	W. Hurst ...	1868—1876
W. F. Pettigrew ...	1897—1918	W. Barton Wright ...	1876—1886
D. J. Rutherford ...	1918—1923	John A. F. Aspinall	1886—1899
Previous to Mason, F.R. locomotives were designed by contract with " outside " builders.		H. A. Hoy...	1899—1904
		George Hughes ...	1904—1922
GLASGOW AND SOUTH WESTERN RLY.		**L.N.W.R.**	
		Francis Trevithick and J. E. McConnell, first loco engineers, 1846, with Alexander Allan largely responsible for design at Crewe.*	
Patrick Stirling ...	1853—1866		
James Stirling ...	1866—1877		
Hugh Smellie ...	1877—1890		
James Manson ...	1890—1912		
Peter Drummond ...	1912—1918	John Ramsbottom ...	1857—1871
R. H. Whitelegg ...	1918—1923	Francis William Webb ...	1871—1903

* Date of entry into office unknown.

† The status and title of Chief Mechanical Engineer were created by the L.Y.R. for J. A. F. Aspinall in 1886.

‡ Exclusive of previous service with amalgamated company.

LOCOMOTIVE SUPERINTENDENTS
AND C.M.E.'S (continued)

L.N.W.R. (contd.)

George Whale	1903—1909
Charles John Bowen-Cooke	1909—1920
Capt. Hewitt Pearson Montague Beames	1920—1921
George Hughes	1922
The L. & Y. amalgamated with L.N.W.R. in 1921.	

L.T. & S.R.

Thomas Whitelegg ...	1880—1910
Robert Harben Whitelegg ...	1910—1912
(LTSR absorbed by M.R., control of locos. transferred to Derby as from Aug., 1912.)	

MARYPORT & CARLISLE

Hugh Smellie	1870—1878
J. Campbell	1878—
William Coulthard ...	* —1904
J. B. Adamson	1904—1923

MIDLAND RAILWAY

Matthew Kirtley (First loco. engineer) ...	1844—1873
Samuel Waite Johnson ...	1873—1903
Richard Mountford Deeley	1903—1909
Henry Fowler	1909—1923

NORTH LONDON RAILWAY
(Worked by L. & N.W. by agreemen dated Dec., 1908.)

William Adams ...	1853—1873
J. C. Park	1873—1893
Henry J. Pryce	1893—1908

NORTH STAFFORDSHIRE RAILWAY

L. Clare	1876—1882
L. Longbottom	1882—1902
J. H. Adams	1902—1915
J. A. Hookham ...	1915—1923
W. Angus was Loco. Supt. at Stoke prior to 1876. No earlier records can be traced.	

WIRRAL

Eric G. Barker	1892—1902
T. B. Hunter	1903—1923
Barker of the Wirral Railway is noteworthy for originating the 4-4-4 tank type in this country (1896).	

SOMERSET AND DORSET JOINT RAILWAYS

Until leased by Mid. and L. & S.W. (as from 1st Nov., 1875) locomotives were bought from outside builders, principally George England of Hatcham Iron Works, S.E. After the above date, Derby and its various Loco. Supts. and CMEs have acted for S. & D.J., aided by a resident Loco. Supt. stationed at Highbridge works.

* Date of actual entry into office not known.

NOTES ON THE USE OF THIS BOOK

1. This book is divided into two sections, namely:—

SECTION ONE. A list of classes, with dimensions and sub-divisions of each, and a summary of the locomotives in each (pp. 5-8, 73-81).

SECTION TWO. A list of locomotives in numerical order, under appropriate headings of classification and wheel arrangement, and showing against each locomotive the British Railways code number of its home shed (pp. 23-56).

2. The aim of the book is that SECTION ONE shall provide a ready reference to particulars of individual locomotives in a class; and that SECTION TWO shall be used for observation purposes.

3. A key to the shed codes used in SECTION TWO is found on pp. 19-22. Any locomotive not given a shed allocation was not in service at the time of compilation. Throughout SECTION TWO named locomotives are denoted by an asterisk; a full list of named locomotives in numerical order appears on pages 57-61. For details of dimensions, etc., of an individual locomotive, the reader should

consult SECTION ONE, where classes are dealt with in the order of wheel arrangement set out at the head of page 5.

4. The following notes are a guide to the system of reference marks and other details given in the lists of dimensions shown for each class in Section One:—

(a) In the lists of dimensions " Su " indicates a superheated locomotive, and " SS " indicates that some locomotives of the class are superheated.

(b) Locomotives are fitted with two inside cylinders, slide valves and Stephenson link motion, except where otherwise shown, e.g. (O) indicates outside cylinders and " P.V." piston valves.

(c) The date on which each design of locomotive first appeared is indicated by " Introduced." If the oldest surviving locomotive was built at a later date, that also is indicated.

5. Tender weights are not included in the lists of dimensions, owing to the numerous variations in weight within individual classes.

6. Where locomotives have been renumbered other than by the addition of 40,000 to their former L.M.S. numbers, the details of the former L.M.S. numbers are given in Section Two. In Section One only the new numbers are shown, so that the new numbers of locomotives affected by this scheme must be obtained from the numerical list in Section Two before reference is made to the class summary.

7. The numbers of locomotives in service and their shed allocations have been checked to September 9th, 1950.

CURRENT EVENTS ON THE L.M. REGION

Further experimental variations of the Class " 5 " 4-6-0 have been introduced—ten with Skefco roller bearings on all axles, ten with these bearings on the driving coupled axle only, and ten with Timken bearings on the driving axle. In the Timken bearings the rollers are tapered, whereas those of the Skefco bearings are barrelled.

Delivery of the first L.M.S. types to be built in the works of other regions has begun. Brighton is constructing Class " 4 " 2-6-4 tanks and Doncaster and Darlington Class " 4 " 2-6-0s. All these works have built another L.M.S. design in recent years, the Class " 8 " 2-8-0. The new 2-8-0s have single chimneys, difficulties having been experienced with steaming in the earlier double-chimney locomotives of the class.

The last L.N.W. 4-6-0 has been withdrawn, the last Highland " Clan " 4-6-0 and the last " Loch " 4-4-0 from the same railway. The remaining Highland tender engines of the " Clan Goods," " Barney " 0-6-0 and " Ben " 4-4-0 Classes are reduced to a total of eleven, and the only Highland tank engines are the two small Drummond 0-4-4T's.

SUMMARY OF FORMER L.M.S. LOCO-MOTIVE CLASSES

WITH HISTORICAL NOTES AND DIMENSIONS

In this list the classes are arranged by wheel arrangement in the following order: 4-6-2, 4-6-0, 4-4-0, 2-8-0, 2-6-0, 2-4-0, 0-10-0, 0-8-0, 0-6-0, 4-6-2T, 4-4-2T, 2-6-4T, 2-6-2T, 2-4-2T, 2-4-0T, 2-6-6-2T, 0-8-4T, 0-8-2T, 0-6-2T, 0-6-0T, 0-6-0ST, 0-4-4T, 0-4-2ST, 0-4-0T, 0-4-0ST.

" Princess Royal " Class
4-6-2   7P

*Introduced 1933. Stanier L.M.S. taper boiler design.

†Introduced 1935. Experimental turbine-driven locomotive (" Turbomotive "). (*NOTE : Cyl. and T.E. figures given below do not apply to this locomotive.*)

‡Introduced 1935. Development of original design with alterations to valve gear, boiler and other details.

Weight : Loco. { 110 tons 11 cwt.†
               { 104 tons 10 cwt.*‡

Pressure : 250 lb. Su.
Cyls. : (4) 16¼″×28″.
Dr. Wheels : 6′ 6″.   T.E. : 40,285 lb.
Walschaerts Valve Gear and rocking shafts, P.V.

*46200/1   †46202
‡46203–12   **Total 13**

" Princess Coronation " Class
4-6-2   7P

*Introduced 1938. Stanier L.M.S. enlargement of " Princess Royal " class. All except Nos. 46230-4/9-48 originally streamlined (introduced 1937. Streamlining removed from 1946).

†Introduced 1947. Ivatt development with roller bearings and detail alterations.

Weight : { 105 tons 5 cwt.*
          { 106 tons 8 cwt.†

Pressure : 250 lb. Su.
Cyls. : (4) 16¼″×28″.
Dr. Wheels : 6′ 9″.   T.E. : 40,000 lb.
Walschaerts Valve Gear and rocking shafts, P.V.

*46220–55
†46256/7   **Total 38**

" Royal Scot " Class
4-6-0   6P

*Introduced 1927. Fowler L.M.S. parallel boiler design.

†Introduced 1935. Stanier taper boiler rebuild with simple cyls. of experimental high pressure loco. No. 6399 *Fury*.

‡Introduced 1943. Stanier rebuild of Fowler locos. with taper boiler, new cyls. and double chimney.

Weight : Loco. { 84 tons 18 cwt.*
                { 84 tons 1 cwt.†
                { 83 tons‡

Pressure : 250 lb. Su.
Cyls. : (3) 18″×26″.
Dr. Wheels : 6′ 9″.   T.E. : 33,150 lb.
Walschaerts Valve Gear.   P.V.

*46110/3/30/4/7/40/2/8/51/6/8/ 63-5
†46170
‡46100-9/11/2/4-29/31-3/5/6/8/9/ 41/3-7/9/50/2-5/7/9-62/6-9
                                Total 71

" Patriot " Class
4-6-0   5XP & 6P

*5XP. Introduced 1930. Fowler 3-cyl. rebuild of L.N.W. " Claughton " Class (introduced 1912), retaining original wheels and other details.

†5XP. Introduced 1933. New locos. to Fowler design (45502-41 were officially considered as rebuilds).

‡6P. Introduced 1946. Ivatt rebuild of Fowler locos. with large taper boiler, new cylinders and double chimney.

Weight : Loco. { 80 tons 15 cwt. (5XP).
                { 82 tons 0 cwt, (6P).

Pressure : $\begin{cases} 200 \text{ lb. Su. (5XP).} \\ 250 \text{ lb. Su. (6P).} \end{cases}$

Cyls. : $\begin{cases} (3) \ 18'' \times 26'' \ (5XP). \\ (3) \ 17'' \times 26'' \ (6P). \end{cases}$

Dr. Wheels : 6' 9".

T.E. : $\begin{cases} 26,520 \text{ lb. (5XP).} \\ 29,570 \text{ lb. (6P).} \end{cases}$

Walschaerts Valve Gear P.V.

*45500/1
†45502-11/3/5-20/4/33/7-9/41-4/
6-51
‡45512/4/21-3/5-32/4-6/40/5

Total 52

"Jubilee" Class
4-6-0   5XP & 6P

*5XP. Introduced 1934. Stanier L.M.S. taper boiler development of the "Patriot" class.
†Introduced 1936. Boiler fitted with double chimney. Double chimney fitted to No. 45742 in 1940.
‡6P. Introduced 1942. Rebuilt with larger boiler and double chimney.

Weight : Loco. $\begin{cases} 79 \text{ tons 11 cwt.*†} \\ 82 \text{ tons 0 cwt.‡} \end{cases}$

Pressure : $\begin{cases} 225 \text{ lb. Su.*†} \\ 250 \text{ lb. Su.‡} \end{cases}$

Cyls. : 17" × 26".
Dr. Wheels : 6' 9".

T.E. : $\begin{cases} 26,610 \text{ lb.*†} \\ 29,570 \text{ lb.‡} \end{cases}$

Walschaerts Valve Gear. P.V.

*45552-45734/8-41
†45742
‡45735/6

Total 191

4-6-0   5MT

1. Introduced 1934. Stanier L.M.S. taper boiler design.
Experimental locomotives :—
2. Introduced 1947. Stephenson link motion (outside), Timken roller bearings, double chimney.
3. Introduced 1948. Caprotti Valve Gear.
4. Introduced 1948. Caprotti Valve Gear, Timken roller bearings.
5. Introduced 1948. Caprotti Valve Gear, Timken roller bearings, double chimney.
6. Introduced 1948. Timken roller bearings.
7. Introduced 1948. Timken roller bearings, double chimney.
8. Introduced 1949. Fitted with steel firebox.
9. Introduced 1950. Skefco roller bearings.
10. Introduced 1950. Skefco roller bearings on driving coupled axle only.

11. Introduced 1950. Timken roller bearings on driving coupled axle only.
12. Introduced 1950. Caprotti valve gear, Skefco roller bearings.

Weights : Loco. $\begin{cases} 72 \text{ tons 2 cwt.} & 1, 8. \\ 75 \text{ tons 6 cwt.} & 2, 6, 7, 9. \\ 74 \text{ tons 0 cwt.} & 3, 4, 5. \end{cases}$

Pressure : 225 lb. Su.
Cyls. : (O) 18½" × 28".
Dr. Wheels : 6' 0". T.E. :- 25,455 lb.
Walschaerts Valve Gear, and P.V. except where otherwise described.

1 :	44658/67/98/9,		44700-17/
	28-37/68-99,	44800-45499
2 :	44767	3 :	44738-47
4 :	44748-54	5 :	44755-7
6 :	44758-64	7 :	44765-6
8 :	44718-27	9 :	44678-85
10 :	44688-97	11 :	44668-77
12 :	44686/7		

N.B. Locomotives of this class are still being delivered.

4-6-0   5P

Introduced 1924. Development of Hughes superheated L. & Y. Class 8. with longer wheelbase, larger fireboxes and parts originally made for 4-6-4T.
Weight : Loco. 77 tons 18 cwt.
Pressure : 180 lb. Su.
Cyls. : (4) 16½" × 26".
Dr. Wheels : 6' 3".
T.E. : 28,880 lb.
Walschaerts Valve Gear and rocking shafts, P.V.

50455   **Total 1**

4-6-0   4MT

Introduced 1916. Pickersgill Caledonian "60" Class.
Weight : Loco. 75 tons 0 cwt.
Pressure : 180 lb. Su.
Cyls. : (O) 20" × 26".
Dr. Wheels : 6' 1". T.E. : 21,795 lb.
P.V.

54650/4   **Total 2**

4-6-0   4MT

Introduced 1925. Post-Grouping development of Caledonian "60" Class.
Weight : Loco. 74 tons 15 cwt.
Pressure : 180 lb. Su.
Cyls. : (O) 20½" × 26".
Dr. Wheels : 6' 1". T.E. : 22,900 lb.
P.V.

54630/4-6/8-40/7-9   **Total 10**

4-6-0   **4MT**

Introduced 1918. Cumming Highland
" Clan Goods " Class.
Weight : Loco. 56 tons 9 cwt.
Pressure : 175 lb. Su.
Cyls. : (O) 20½"×26".
Dr. Wheels : 5' 3".   T.E. : 25,800 lb.
Walschaerts Valve Gear, P.V.

57950/1/4-6   **Total 5**

4-4-0 (3-Cyl. Compd.)   **4P**

*Introduced 1905. Development by
   Deeley of Johnson Midland compound,
   later superheated by Fowler.
†Introduced 1914. Fowler superheated
   rebuild of Johnson locos. (originally
   built 1902).
‡Introduced 1924. Post-Grouping locos.
   with modified dimensions and (except
   61045-64) reduced boiler mountings.
Weight : Loco. 61 tons 14 cwt.
Pressure : 200 lb. Su.
Cyls. : L.P. (2) 21"×26".
         H.P. (1) 19"×26".
Dr. Wheels : {7' 0"*†
             {6' 9"‡
T.E. (of L.P. cyls. at {21,840 lb.*†
   80% boiler   {
   pressure)   {22,650 lb.‡
P.V. (H.P. cyl. only).

*41000/1/3/4
†41005-7/9/11/2/4-6/9-21/3/5/8/
30/2/5/7/8/40/1/3/4
‡40900-39, 41045-41199

                       Total 221

4-4-0   **3P**

Introduced 1901. Johnson Midland
design rebuilt by Fowler from 1916
with larger cyls., superheater, etc.
Weight : Loco. 55 tons 7 cwt.
Pressure : 175 lb. Su.
Cyls. : 20½"×26".
Dr. Wheels : 6' 9".   T.E. : 20,065 lb.
P.V.

40726/8/9/41/3/7/58/62

                       Total 8

4-4-0   **3P**

*Introduced 1910. McIntosh Caledonian
   " Dunalastair IV Superheater " or
   " 139 " class.
†Introduced 1915. Superheated rebuild of McIntosh Caledonian " Dunalastair IV " or " 140 " class (originally introduced 1904).
Weight : Loco. 61 tons 5 cwt.

Pressure : 180 lb. Su.
Cyls. : 20½"×26".
Dr. Wheels : 6' 6".   T.E. : 20,915 lb.
P.V.

*54440/1/3-60
†54438/9   **Total 22**

4-4-0   **3P**

Introduced 1916. Pickersgill Cale-
donian " 113 " and " 928 " classes.
Weight : Loco. 61 tons 5 cwt.
Pressure : 180 lb. Su.
Cyls. : 20"×26".
Dr. Wheels : 6' 6".   T.E. : 20,400 lb.
P.V.

54461-76   **Total 16**

4-4-0   **3P**

Introduced 1920. Pickersgill Cale-
donian " 72 " class.
Weight : Loco. 61 tons 5 cwt.
Pressure : 180 lb. Su.
Cyls. : 20½"×26".
Dr. Wheels : 6' 6".   T.E. : 21,435 lb. P.V.

54477-54508   **Total 32**

4-4-0   **2P**

*Introduced 1909. Fowler rebuild of
   Johnson Midland loco. (introduced
   1882).
†Introduced 1912. Fowler rebuild of
   Johnson locos. with superheater and
   piston valves.
‡Introduced 1914. Locos. built new to
   superheated design for S. & D.J.R.
   (taken into L.M.S. stock, 1930).
Weight : Loco. 53 tons 7 cwt.
Pressure : 160 lb. SS.
Cyls. : {18"×26".*
        {20½"×26".†‡
Dr. Wheels : {6' 6½".*
             {7' 0½".†‡
T.E. : {15,960 lb.*
      {17,585 lb.†‡

*40383
†40332/7/51/3/6/9/62/4/70/7/95-
7, 40401/2/4-7/9-26/30/2-4/6/8/
9/43/4/7/8/50/2-5/8/61-4/70-2/7
/8/80/2/4-9/91/3/5/7/9, 40501-2/7
/7-9/11/3/4/8-32/4-43/6 - 53/6 -
60/2
‡40322-6   **Total 132**

4-4-0   **2P**

*Introduced 1928. Post-Grouping devel-
   opment of Midland design, with
   modified dimensions and reduced
   boiler mountings.

†Introduced 1928. Locos. built for S. & D.J.R. (taken into L.M.S. stock, 1930).
‡Fitted experimentally in 1933 with Dabeg feed water heater.
Weight : Loco. 54 tons 1 cwt.
Pressure : 180 lb. Su.
Cyls. : 19″ × 26″.
P.V.
Dr. Wheels : 6′ 9″.   T.E. : 17,730 lb.

*40563-90/2-9, 40600-32/6-8/40-52/4-40700
†40634/5
‡40653
†‡40633   Total 136

4-4-0 "Ben" Class   2P
Introduced 1898. Drummond Highland "Small Ben," later rebuilt with C.R. boiler.
Weight : Loco. 46 tons 17 cwt.
Pressure : 190 lb.
Cyls : 18½″ × 26″.
Dr. Wheels . 6′ 0″.   T.E. : 18,400 lb.
54398/9, 54404   Total 3

2-8-0   8F
Introduced 1935. Stanier L.M.S. taper boiler design.
Weight : Loco. 72 tons 2 cwt.
Pressure : 225 lb. Su.
Cyls. : 18½″ × 28″.
Dr. Wheels : 4′ 8½″.   T.E. : 32,440 lb.
Walschaerts Valve Gear, P.V.

48000-12/6-8/20/4/6/7/9/33/5-7/9/45/6/50/3-7/60-5/7/9/70/3-85/8-90/2-9, 48100-48225/46-97, 48301-48479/90-5, 48500-59, 48600-48772   Total 663

2-8-0   7F
*Introduced 1914. Fowler design for S. & D.J. with 4′ 9″ boiler (some rebuilt from 1925 series).
†Introduced 1925. Fowler design with 5′ 3″ boiler.
(All taken into L.M.S. stock, 1930).
Weight : Loco. { 64 tons 15 cwt.*
                { 68 tons 11 cwt.†
Pressure : 190 lb. Su.
Cyls. : 21″ × 28″.
Dr. Wheels : 4′ 8½″.   T.E. : 35,295 lb.
Walschaerts Valve Gear, P.V.
*53800-5/9/10
†53806-8   Total 11

2-6-0   5MT
*Introduced 1926. Hughes L.M.S. design built under Fowler's direction. With Walschaerts Valve Gear and P.V.
†Introduced 1931. Locos. rebuilt experimentally with Lentz R.C. poppet valves.
Weight : Loco. 66 tons 0 cwt.
Pressure : 180 lb. Su.
Cyls. : (O) 21″ × 26″.
Dr. Wheels . 5′ 6″.   T.E. : 26,580 lb.
*42700-42817/9-21/3/6-8/30-99, 42900-44
†42818/22/4/5/9   Total 245

2-6-0   5MT
Introduced 1933. Stanier L.M.S. taper boiler design.
Weight : Loco. 69 tons 2 cwt.
Pressure : 225 lb. Su.
Cyls. : (O) 18″ × 28″.
Dr. Wheels : 5′ 6″.   T.E. : 26,290 lb.
Walschaerts Valve Gear, P.V.
42945-84   Total 40

2-6-0   4MT
*Introduced 1947. Ivatt L.M.S. taper boiler design with double chimney.
†Introduced 1949. With single chimney.
Weight : Loco. 59 tons 2 cwt.
Pressure : 225 lb. Su.
Cyls. : (O) 17½″ × 26″.
Dr. Wheels : 5′ 3″.   T.E. : 24,170 lb.
Walschaerts Valve Gear, P.V.
*43000-26/8-49
†43027/50-99, 43100-61
N.B. Locos. of this class are still being delivered.

2-6-0   2MT
Introduced 1946. Ivatt L.M.S. taper boiler design.
Weight : Loco. 47 tons 2 cwt.
Pressure : 200 lb. Su.
Cyls. : (O) 16″ × 24″.
Dr. Wheels : 5′ 0″.   T.E. : 17,410 lb.
Walschaerts Valve Gear, P.V.
46400-46527
N.B. Locos. of this class are still being delivered.

2-4-0   1P
(Former L.M.S. number in brackets)
Introduced 1876. Johnson Midland "1" Class, rebuilt with Belpaire boiler, 1926.
Weight : 40 tons 10 cwt.

Right : Class 1F 0-4-4T No 41777 (with round-topped boiler).

Below : Class 1F 0-4-4T No. 41885 (with Belpaire boiler).
[A. F. Cook, J. Cupit.

Above : Class 2P 0-4-4T No. 41909.

Right : Class 3P 4-4-2T No. 41950.
H.C. Casserley, A. F. Cook

Facing Page.

Top to bottom : Class 3MT (Fowler) 2-6-2T No. 40048 ; Class 3MT (Stanier) 2-6-2T No. 40117 ; Class 2MT 2-6-2T No. 41247 ; Class 4MT 2-6-4T No. 42390.

[*F. F. Moss (No. 40117), P. Ransome-Wallis.*

This Page.

Top to bottom : Class 2P 4-4-0 No. 40439 (7ft. 0½in. drivers) ; Class 2P 4-4-0 No. 40634 (ex-S.D.J., 6ft. 9in. drivers) ; Class 4P 4-4-0 No. 41009.

[*E. D. Bruton, G. Wheeler, H. C. Casserley.*

103

This Page.

Top to bottom: 0-10-0 No. 58100 ; Class 7F (ex-L.N.W.) 0-8-0 No. 49407 ; Class 7F (ex-L. & Y.) 0-0-8 No. 52916 ; Class 6F (ex-L. & Y.) 0-8-0 No. 52727.
[*H. C. Casserley (2). A. F. Cook, N. Fields*

Facing Page.

Top to bottom : Class 5MT 2-6-0 No. 42931 ; Class 4MT 2-6-0 No. 43050 ; Class 2MT 2-6-0 No. 46444 ; Class 7F 0-9-0 No. 49586.
[*F. W. Day, T. C. Greaves, F. F. Moss, H. C. Casserley.*

Top left: Class 3F 0-6-0 No. 43305. Top right: Class 4F 0-6-0 No. 43977. Bottom left: Class 7F 2-8-0 No. 53801. Bottom right: 2-6-0 + 0-6-2 No. 47998 (with fixed coal bunker).
[C. R. L. Coles, P. H. Wells, I. Sansom, I. P. Wilson]

106

Class 5MT 4-6-0.

Right : No. 45164, with dome-shaped top feed.

Below : No. 45213, with top feed and dome combined and fitted with snow plough and tablet-exchange apparatus on cab.
[*P. Ransome-Wallis,*
E. M. Patterson.

Above : No. 44743, fitted with Caprotti valve gear and self-weighing tender.

Right : No. 44767, fitted with Stephenson link motion, double chimney and electric lighting.
[*P. Ransome-Wallis.*

Class 5XP " Jubilee " 4-6-0 No. 45690 *Leander*.   [*P. Ransome-Wallis*

Above : Class 5XP " Patriot " 4-6-0 No. 45508.   [*H. C. Casserley.*

Below : Class 6P " Royal Scot " 4-6-0 No. 46164 *The Artists' Rifleman*.   [*J. Wyndham.*

Top to bottom : Class 6P
"Rebuilt Scot" 4-6-0
No. 46112 Sherwood Forester ; Class 7P 4-6-2
No. 46200 The Princess
Royal ; Class 7P 4-6-2
No. 46231 Duchess of
Bristol!.

Photos : W. Earley (Right),
Eric Treacy.

109

Class 2F 0-6-0.
Top left : No. 58110.   Top right : No. 58283 (5ft. 3in. drivers).   Bottom left :
No. 58119 (4ft. 11in. drivers).   Bottom right : No. 58271 (with smaller cab).
[V. K. Pullin, C. R. L. Coles, P. Ransome-Wallis, J. N. Westwood.

112

Top left: Class 2F (ex-L. & Y.) 0-6-0 No. 52022. Top right: Class 2F (ex-N.L.R.) 0-6-0T No. 58851. Bottom left: Class 1P 0-4-4T No. 58046. Bottom right: Class 1F 0-6-0T No. 51536.
[J. Metcalfe, L. Reeves, J. Mills, H. Casserley.

113

Above left : Ex-L.N.W. 0-6-0ST No. CD7.   Above right : Class 3F
0-6-0T No. 56262.   Bottom left : Class 2P 0-4-4T No. 15122 (new No.
55122).   Bottom right : Class 2P 0-4-4T No. 55144 (with larger tanks
and bunker).

[S. Reid, C. Herbert, P. Ransome-Wallis, E. Patterson.

Above left : Class OF 0-4-0ST No. 41523.　　Above right : Class OF 0-4-0T No. 41532.　Bottom left : Ex-S.D.J. "Sentinel" 0-4-0T No. 47190.　　Bottom right : Class OF 0-4-0ST No. 51246.

T/. N. Westwood, W. Boot. A. F. Cook.

Top left : Class 7F 0-8-4T No. 47937.   Top right : Class 6F 0-8-2T No.
47877.   Bottom left : Class 2F 0-6-0 No. 58323 (ex-L.N.W. "Coal Engine").
Bottom right :   Class   2F   0-6-0   No. 58412 (ex-L.N.W. "Cauliflower").
[H. C. Casserley (2), F. F. Moss, D. J. Sutton.

Pressure : 140 lb.
Cyls. : 18″ × 24″.
Dr. Wheels : 6′ 3″.   T.E. : 12,340 lb.

58020 (20155)   **Total 1**

0-10-0

Introduced 1919. Fowler Midland
   banker for Lickey incline.
Weight : Loco. 73 tons 13 cwt.
Pressure : 180 lb. Su.
Cyls. : (4) 16¾″ × 28″.
Dr. Wheels : 4′ 7½″.   T.E. : 43,315 lb.
Walschaerts Valve Gear.

58100   **Total 1**

0-8-0   6F & 7F

G1 Class 6F
*Introduced 1912. Bowen Cooke
   L.N.W. superheated design, developed from earlier saturated design
   (many rebuilt from earlier Webb,
   Whale and Bowen Cooke compound
   and simple designs introduced 1892
   onwards). Many later rebuilt with
   Belpaire boilers.

G2 Class 7F
†Introduced 1921. Development of
   G1 with higher pressure boiler.
   Many later rebuilt with Belpaire
   boilers.

G2a Class 7F
‡Introduced 1936. G1 locos. rebuilt
   with G2 Belpaire boilers.
Weights : Loco. { 60 tons 15 cwt. (G1)
                  { 62 tons 0 cwt. (G2)
                                  G2a).
Pressure : { 160 lb. Su. (G1).
            { 175 lb. Su. (G2, G2a).
Cyls. : 20½″ × 24″.
Dr. Wheels : 4′ 5½″.
T.E. : { 25,640 lb. (G1).
        { 28,045 lb. (G2, G2a).
Joy Valve Gear, P.V.

*48902, 49017/30/71/89/92/8,
49140/51/6/62/71/87/93, 49204/
8/13/22/41/61, 49326/34/46/59/
64/70/1

†49395-49454

‡48893/5/8/9,   48901/5/7/14/5/7/
20-2/6/7/30/2/3/6/40/2-5/50-3/
64, 49002/5-10/4/8/20-5/7/8/31/
3-5/7/44-51/7/61-4/6/8/70/3/4/7
-9/81/2/7/8/90/3/4/6/9,   49101
/4-6/8/9/12-7/9-22/5/6/9/30/2/4
/7-9/41-50/3-5/7/8/60/1/3/4/7/8
/72-4/7/8/80/1/6/9/9l/6/8/9,
49200/2/3/5/9/10/2/4/6/8/9/23/
4/6/8-30/4/9/40/3-7/9/52-4/7/8/

60/2/4-8/70/1/5-8/81/2/7-9/92/
3/6, 49300-2/4/6-8/10-6/8/9/21-
3/7/8/30/1/5/9-45/7/8/50/2/4/5/
7/8/61/6-8/73/5-8/81/2/5-94

        Totals : Class G1   27
                   Class G2   60
                   Class G2a 252

0-8-0   7F

Introduced 1929. Fowler L.M.S. design,
   developed from L.N.W. G2.
Weight : Loco. 60 tons 15 cwt.
Pressure : 200 lb. Su.
Cyls. : 19½″ × 26″.
Dr. Wheels : 4′ 8½″.   T.E. : 29,745 lb.
Walschaerts Valve Gear, P.V.

49502/3/5/6/8-11/5/23/4/31/2/5/6/
8/40/4/5/7/8/52/4/5/7/8/60/3/6/
8/70/1/8/80/2/5-7/9-95/8, 49600
/2/3/8-10/2/7/8/20/3-5/7/31/5/
7/8/40/1/8-51/7/9-64/6-8/71-4

                                   Total 84

0-8-0   6F

*Introduced 1900. Aspinall L. & Y.
   Class 30 (survivor built 1903).
†Introduced 1910. Hughes Class 30 with
   larger boiler (some rebuilt from
   Aspinall design).
Weight : Loco. { 53 tons 16 cwt.*
                { 63 tons.†
Pressure : 180 lb.
Cyls. : 20″ × 26″.
Dr. Wheels : 4′ 6″.   T.E. : 29,465 lb.
Joy Valve Gear.

*52727   †52822/31   **Total 13**

0-8-0   7F

Introduced 1912. L. & Y. Cl. 31. Super-
   heated development of Class 30.
Weight : Loco. 66 tons 4 cwt.
Pressure : 180 lb. Su.
Cyls. : 21½″ × 26″.
Dr. Wheels : 4′ 6″.   T.E. : 34,055 lb.
Joy Valve Gear, P.V.

52857/70, 52906/10/6/45

                                   Total 6

0-6-0   4F

Introduced 1911. Fowler superheated
   Midland design.
Weight : 48 tons 15 cwt.
Pressure : 175 lb. Su.
Cyls. : 20″ × 26″.
Dr. Wheels : 5′ 3″.   T.E. : 24,555 lb.
P.V.

43835-44026   **Total 192**

0-6-0   4F

*Introduced 1924. Post grouping development of Midland design with reduced boiler mountings.
†Introduced 1922. Locos. built for S.D. & J.R. to M.R. design (taken into L.M.S. stock, 1930).
Weight : Loco. 48 tons 15 cwt.
Pressure : 175 lb. Su.
Cyls. : 20″×26″.
Dr. Wheels : 5′ 3″.   T.E. : 24,555 lb.
P.V.

*44027-44556/62-44606
†44557-61   **Total 580**

0-6-0   3F

*Introduced 1885. Johnson Midland locos., rebuilt from 1916 by Fowler with Belpaire boilers.
†Introduced 1896. Locos. built for S. & D.J. (taken into L.M.S. stock, 1930).
Weight : Loco. 43 tons 17 cwt.
Pressure : 175 lb.
Cyls. : 18″×26″.
Dr. Wheels : 5′ 3″.   T.E. : 19,890 lb.

*43191-3, 43200/3/5/7/8/10/2-4/9/
22-6/31-5/7/9-47/9-54/6-9/61 /
3/6-8/71/3-5/7/8/81-4/6/7/90/
2-6/8/9, 43300/1/5-10/2-5/7-9/21/
3 - 7/9-37/9-42/4/51/5-7/9/61/4/
7-71/3/4/8/9/81/6-9/92/4-6/8/9/
43400-2/5/6/10/1/9/27-9/31/3/
5/6/40/1/3/4/6/8/9/53/4/6/7/9/
62-4/8/9/74/6/82/4/90/1/4/6/7/
9, 43502/6/7/9/10/4/5/20-4/9/31
/8/40/4/6/8/50/3/8/62/5/8/70/2/
4/5/8-87/93-6/8/9, 43600/4/5/7/
8/12/5/18-24/7/9-31/3/4/6-9/44/
5/50-3/6-8/60-2/4/5/7-9/73-6/8-
84/6/7/90/3/8, 63705/9/10-2/4/
5/7/21/3/4/7-9/31/4/5/7/42/5/7-
9/51/3-7/9/60/2/3/5-7/70/1/3
†43194, 43201/4/11/6/8/28/48
     Total 321

0-6-0   3F

Introduced 1885. Johnson Midland locos., rebuilt from 1920 by Fowler with Belpaire boilers.
Weight : Loco. 43 tons 17 cwt.
Pressure : 175 lb.
Cyls. : 18″×26″.
Dr. Wheels : 4′11″.   T.E. : 21,240 lb.

43137/74/8/80/1/3/5-9   **Total 11**

0-6-0   3F

Introduced 1906. Deeley Midland design, rebuilt by Fowler with Belpaire boiler.
Weight : Loco. 46 tons 3 cwt.
Pressure : 175 lb.
Cyls. : 18½″×26″.
Dr. Wheels : 5′ 3″.   T.E. : 21,010 lb

43775-9/81/2/4-7/9/90-3/5/7-9,
43800-4/6-12/4/5/7/19-29/32/3
     Total 48

0-6-0   3F

*Introduced 1889. Aspinall L. & Y. Class 27.
†Introduced 1911. Rebuilt with Belpaire boiler and extended smokebox.
Weight : Loco. { 42 tons 3 cwt.*
           { 43 tons 11 cwt.†
Pressure : 180 lb.
Cyl. : 18″×26″.
Dr. Wheels : 5′ 1″.
T.E. : 21,130 lb.
Joy Valve Gear.

*52089/92-5/8/9, 52100/2/4/5/7/8/
11/2/8-21/3-6/9/32/3/5-9/41/
3/50/6/7/9/60/2-7/9/71/2/4/
5-7/9/82/3/6/9/91/4/6/7, 52203/
7/8/12/5-20/5/30-3/5-40/3-6/8/
52/5/8/60/2/8-72/5/8-80/4/5/8-
90/3/6/9, 52300/4/5/9/11/7/21/
2/8/31/3/4/6/8/41/3/5/8-51/3/
5-8/60/2/3/5/6/8/9/76/8/81/2/
6-90/3/7/9, 52404/5/7/8/10-6/8/
27/9/30/2/3/5/7/40/1/3/5-7/9/50
/2/3/5/6/8-61/4-6, 52515/7/
21-7/9
†52088/91, 52140/54/61, 52201/
50/3/66/73, 52312/9/30/79,
52400/28/31/8/44/8 **Total 221**

0-6-0   3F

*Introduced 1912. Hughes L. & Y. Class 28, superheated development of Class 27.
†Introduced 1913. Rebuilds of Class 27.
Weight : Loco. 46 tons 10 cwt.
Pressure : 180 lb. Su.
Cyls. : 20½″×26″.
Dr. Wheels : 5′ 1″.   T.E. : 27,405 lb.
Joy Valve Gear, P.V.

*52549/51/4
†52557-9/61/9/72/5/6/9-83/7/8/
90/2/8, 52608/15/6/9
     Total 25

0-6-0   3F

Introduced 1913. Pettigrew Furness Rly. design.
Weight : Loco. 42 tons 13 cwt.
Pressure : 170 lb.
Cyls. : 18"×26".
Dr. Wheels : 4' 7⅞".   T.E. : 21,935 lb.
52414/9, 52501/8-10   **Total 6**

0-6-0   3F

Introduced 1899. McIntosh Caledonian "812" (Nos. 57550-57628) and "652" (remainder) classes.
Weight : Loco. 45 tons 14 cwt.
Pressure : 180 lb.
Cyls. : 18½"×26".
Dr. Wheels : 5' 0".   T.E. : 22,690 lb.
57550/2-60/2-6/8-73/5-7/9-83/
5-97/9, 57600-5/7-9/11-5/7-23/
5-8/30-5/7/8/40/2-5   **Total 81**

0-6-0   3F

Introduced 1918. Pickersgill Caledonian "294" class (superheated) and "670" classes.
Weight : Loco. 50 tons 13 cwt.
Pressure : 180 lb. Su.
Cyls. : 18½"×26".
Dr. Wheels : 5' 0".   T.E. : 22,690 lb. P.V.
57650-5/8/9/61/3/5-74/9/81/2/4/
6/8-91   **Total 29**

0-6-0   3F

Introduced 1900. Drummond Highland design, later rebuilt with Caledonian boilers.
Weight : Loco. 43 tons 10 cwt.
Pressure : 175 lb.
Cyls. : 18¼"×26".
Dr. Wheels : 5' 0".   T.E. : 21,470 lb.
57695/7/8   **Total 3**

0-6-0   2F

Introduced 1868. Kirtley Midland double-framed design with round top boiler (Survivor built 1870).
Weight : Loco. 37 tons 12 cwt.
Pressure : 160 lb.
Cyls. : 18"×24".
Dr. Wheels : 5' 3".   T.E. : 16,785 lb.
58110   **Total 1**

0-6-0   2F

*Introduced 1875. Johnson Midland 4' 11" design, with round top boiler.
†Introduced 1917. Rebuilt with Belpaire boiler.

‡Introduced 1878. Johnson Midland 5' 3" design, with round top boiler.
§Introduced 1917. Rebuilt with Belpaire boiler.
Weight : Loco. Various.
37 tons 12 cwt. to 40 tons 3 cwt.
Pressure : 160 lb.
Cyls. : 18"×26".

Dr. Wheels : { 4' 11"*
           4' 11"†
           5' 3"‡
           5' 3"§

T.E. : { 19,420 lb.*
       19,420 lb.†
       18,185 lb.‡
       18,185 lb.§

(See p. 55 for former L.M.S. numbers.)

*58229/36/40/6/7
†58114-33/5-40/2-9/51-4/6-87,
58230-5/7/8/41/2/4/5/8
‡58262/74
§58188-99, 58200/1/3/4/6/7/9/11-
21/4-6/8/49/52/4/7-61/4/5/8/
9/71-3/6-81/3/5-91/3/5/6/8/9,
58300/2-10   **Total 168**

0-6-0   2F

Introduced 1873. Webb L.N.W. "Coal Engines."
Weight : Loco. 32 tons 0 cwt.
Pressure : 150 lb.
Cyls. : 17"×24".
Dr. Wheels : 4' 5½".   T.E. : 16,530 lb.
(See p. 55 for former L.M.S. numbers.)
58321-3/6-8/30/2/3/5/6/40/3/6/
7/9/50/2/4/60   **Total 20**

0-6-0   2F

Introduced 1887. Webb L.N.W. "18" Goods ("Cauliflowers") many later rebuilt with Belpaire boilers.
Weight : Loco. 36 tons 10 cwt.
Pressure : 150 lb.
Cyls. : 18"×24".
Dr. Wheels : 5' 2½".   T.E. : 15,865 lb.
Joy Valve Gear.
(See pp. 55-6 for former L.M.S. numbers.)
58362-5/8/75-8/81-3/8/9/92-4/6/8,
58400/9/10/2/3/5/8-21/6/7/9/30
    Total 33

0-6-0   2F

Introduced 1887. Barton Wright L. & Y. Class 25.
Weight : Loco. 39 tons 1 cwt.

Pressure : 140 lb.
Cyls : 17½"×26".
Dr. Wheels : 4' 6". T.E. : 17,545 lb

52016/21/2/4/30/1/4/7/41/3-5/51
3/6/9/64 **Total 17**

0-6-0 2F

Introduced 1883. Drummond Cale-
donian "Standard Goods"; later
additions by Lambie and McIntosh.
*Rebuilt with L.M.S. boilers.
Weight : Loco. { 41 tons 6 cwt.
{ 42 tons 4 cwt.*
Pressure : 180 lb.
Cyls. : 18"×26".
Dr. Wheels : 5' 0". T.E. : 21,480 lb.

57230/2-47/9-80/2-5/7-9/91/2/5/
6/9, 57300/2/3/6/7/9/11/2/4/5/
7-26/8/9/31/2/4-41/4-50/2-70/
2/3/5/7-9/83-9/91/2/4-8, 57404/
5/7/10-4/6-9/23-6/9-39/41/3-8
/50/1/3-65/8/70/2/3 **Total 191**

4-6-2T 4P

Introduced 1917. Pickersgill Cale-
donian "944" Class.
Weight : 91 tons 13 cwt.
Pressure : 180 lb. Su.
Cyls : (O) 19½"×26".
Dr. Wheels : 5' 9". T.E. : 21,920 lb.
P.V.

55350/2/3/9-61 **Total 6**

4-4-2T 3P

*Introduced 1905. Rebuild of White-
legg L.T. & S. "37" Class (originally
introduced 1897).
†Introduced 1909. L.T. & S. Whitelegg
"79" Class.
‡Introduced 1923. Midland and L.M.S.
development of L.T. & S. "79" Class.
{ 71 tons 10 cwt.†
Weight : { 71 tons 10 cwt.‡
{ 70 tons 15 cwt.*
Pressure : 170 lb.
Cyls. : (O) 19"×26".
Dr. Wheels : 6' 6". T.E. : 17,390 lb
*41953-64 †41965-8
‡41928-52/69-78 **Total 51**

4-4-2T 2P

Introduced 1900. Whitelegg L.T. & S.
"51" Class.
Weight : 67 tons 15 cwt.
Pressure : 170 lb.
Cyls. : (O) 19"×26".
Dr. Wheels : 6' 6". T.E. : 17,390 lb
41911/5-7/9/21/2/5/6 **Total 9**

2-6-4T 4MT

*Introduced 1927. Fowler L.M.S. parallel
boiler design.
†Introduced 1933. As earlier engines,
but with side-window cabs and doors.
‡Introduced 1934. Stanier taper-
boiler 3-cylinder design for L.T. & S.
section.
§Introduced 1935. Stanier taper
boiler 2-cylinder design.
‖Introduced 1945. Fairburn development of Stanier design with shorter
wheelbase and detail alterations.
{ 86 tons 5 cwt.*†
Weights: { 92 tons 5 cwt.‡
{ 87 tons 17 cwt.
{ 85 tons 5 cwt. ‖
Pressure (all types) : 200 lb. Su.
{ (O) 19"×26"*†
Cyls. : { (3) 16"×26"‡
{ (O) 19⅞"×26"§‖
Dr. Wheels (all types) : 5' 9".
{ 23,125 lb.*†
T.E. : { 24,600 lb.‡
{ 24,670 lb.§‖
Walschaerts Valve Gear, P.V.
*42300-94
†42395-42424
‡42425-36
§42425-504, 42537-42672
‖42050-42299, 42673-99
**N.B. Locomotives of this class are
still being delivered in the
42050-42106 series.**

2-6-2T 3MT

*Introduced 1930. Fowler L.M.S. design
with parallel boiler.
†Introduced 1930. Condensing locos.
for working to Moorgate, London.
Weight : { 70 tons 10 cwt.*
{ 71 tons 16 cwt.†
Pressure : 200 lb. Su.
Cyls. : (O) 17½"×26".
Dr. Wheels : 5' 3". T.E. : 21,485 lb.
Walschaerts Valve Gear, P.V.
*40001-20/41-70
†40021-40 **Total 70**

2-6-2T 3MT

*Introduced 1935. Stanier L.M.S. taper
boiler development of Fowler design
(above).
†Introduced 1941. Rebuilt with larger
boiler.
Weight : { 71 tons 5 cwt.*
{ 72 tons 10 cwt.†
Pressure : 200 lb. Su.
Cyls. : (O) 17½"×26".
Dr. Wheels : 5' 3". T.E. : 21,485 lb
Walschaerts Valve Gear, P.V.

2-6-2T   2MT

Introduced 1946. Ivatt L.M.S. taper boiler design.
Weight : 63 tons 5 cwt.
Pressure : 200 lb. Su.
Cyls. : (O) 16″ × 24″.
Dr. Wheels : 5′ 0″.   T.E. : 17,410 lb.
Walschaerts Valve Gear, P.V.
41200-99

N.B. Locomotives of this class are still being delivered.

2-4-2T   2P & 3P

*2P. Introduced 1889. Aspinall L. & Y. Class 5 with 2 tons coal capacity.
†Introduced 1892. Locos. built or rebuilt with smaller cylinders.
‡Introduced 1898. Locos. with longer tanks and 4 tons coal capacity.
‖ Introduced 1905. Hughes locos. built with Belpaire boiler and extended smokebox.
*Introduced 1910. Locos. rebuilt with Belpaire boiler.
(46762 was sold to the Wirral Rly. in 1921, and numbered by the L.M.S. in the ex-L.N.W.R. series with other Wirral locos., but the number 10638 (now 50638) was allotted to the loco. in its correct order in the ex-L. & Y. series).
Weight : { 55 tons 19 cwt.*
           { 59 tons 3 cwt.‡ ‖
Pressure : 180 lb.
Cyls. : { 17½″ × 26″.†
      { 18″ × 26″ (remainder).
Dr. Wheels : 5′ 8″.
T.E. : { 18,360 lb.*
     { 18,955 lb. (remainder).
Joy Valve Gear
3P. §Introduced 1911. Hughes L. & Y. Class 6 (superheated development of Class 5).
**Loco. as § but with reduced cylinder diameters.
Weight : 66 tons 9 cwt.
Pressure : 180 lb. Su.
Cyls. : { 19¼″ × 26″.**
      { 20½″ × 26″ (remainder).
T.E. : { 22,445 lb.**
    { 24,585 lb. (remainder).
Dr. Wheels : 5′ 8″.
Joy Valve Gear, P.V.
*50621 - 3/5/30/3/6/9/40/2/4/6 - 8/
54/5/60/71 /81 /6/7 /9 /95 /7,
50703 /5/12/20/1 /5/31 /5/46/9/
57/62/4/5/77/8/81/8. 50802/6/
12/8

*†46762, 50634/43/53/6/78, 50714
/5/52/66/95/9, 50807
*°50650/1, 50736
*°†50652, 50815
‡50831/40/2/50/2/9/69
‡‡50855/65
‡°50829
‖ 50872/3/86/7/92/8
§50909   **Total : 2P 79**
50925   **3P 2

2-4-2T   1P

Introduced 1890. Webb L.N.W. design.
Weight : 50 tons 10 cwt.
Pressure : 150 lb.
Cyls. : 17″ × 24″.
Dr. Wheels : 5′ 8½″.   T.E. : 12,910 lb.
Allan Straight Link Gear.

46601 /3/4/16/20/8/43/54/6/8/66/
80/3/8, 46701/12/27/49/57
                       Total 19

2-4-0T   1P

Introduced 1877. Webb L.N.W. design.
Weight : 38 tons 4 cwt.
Pressure : 150 lb.
Cyls. : 17″ × 20″.
Dr. Wheels : 4′ 8½″.   T.E. : 13,045 lb.
Allan Straight Link Gear.
58092   **Total 1**

2-6-6-2T   Beyer-Garratt

*Introduced 1927. Fowler & Beyer-Peacock, L.M.S. design with fixed coal bunker.
†Introduced 1930. Development with detail alterations, later fitted with revolving coal bunkers.
No. 47997 built 1927 to original design.
Weight : { 148 tons 15 cwt.*
          { 155 tons 10 cwt.†
Pressure : 190 lb. Su.
Cyls. : (4) 18½″ × 26″.
Dr. Wheels : 5′ 3″.   T.E. : 45,620 lb.
Walschaerts Valve Gear, P.V.
*47998/9   †47967-97 **Total 33**

0-8-4T   7F

Introduced 1923. Beames L.N.W. design, built after grouping (tank version of G2 0-8-0).
Weight : 88 tons 0 cwt.
Pressure : 185 lb. Su.
Cyls. : 20½″ × 24″.

Dr. Wheels : 4′ 5½″.   T.E. : 29,815 lb.
Joy Valve Gear, P.V.

47931/7/9   **Total 3**

0-8-2T   6F

Introduced 1911. Bowen Cooke
L.N.W. design (tank version of " G "
0-8-0).
Weight : 72 tons 10 cwt.
Pressure : 170 lb.
Cyls. . 20½″×24″.
Dr. Wheels : 4′ 5½″.   T.E. : 27,240 lb.
Joy Valve Gear.

47877/81/4/96   **Total 4**

0-6-2T   3F

Introduced 1903. Whitelegg L.T. &. S.
" 69 " Class (Nos. 41990-3 built 1912,
taken directly into M.R. stock).
Weight : 64 tons 13 cwt.
Pressure : 170 lb.
Cyls. : 18″×26″.
Dr. Wheels : 5′ 3″.   T.E. : 19,320 lb.

41980-93   **Total 14**

0-6-2T   2F

Introduced 1882. Webb L.N.W. " Coal
Tanks."
Weight : 43 tons 15 cwt.
Pressure : 150 lb.
Cyls. : 17″×24″.
Dr. Wheels : 4′ 5½″.   T.E. : 16,530 lb
**(See p. 56 for former L.M.S.
numbers.)**
58880/1/7-9/91/2/5/7/9, 58900/2-
4/8/10/1-3/5/6/9/21/4-6/8/32/
3/5   **Total 30**

0-6-2T   2MT

Introduced 1898. Webb L.N.W. "18″
Passenger Tank."
Weight : 52 tons 6 cwt.
Pressure : 150 lb.
Cyls. : 18″×24″.
Dr. Wheels : 5′ 2½″.   T.E. : 15,865 lb.
Joy Valve Gear.

46899, 46900/6/12/22   **Total 5**

0-6-0T   3F

*Introduced 1899. Johnson large Mid-
land design, rebuilt with Belpaire
boiler from 1919 ; fitted with con-
densers for London area.
†Introduced 1899.   Non-condensing
locos.
Weight : 48 tons 15 cwt.
Pressure : 160 lb.
Cyls. : 18″×26″.
Dr. Wheels : 4′ 7″.   T.E. : 20,835 lb.

*47200-29/40-5/7/9/51
†47230-9/46/8/50/2-9   **Total 60**

0-6-0T   3F

*Introduced 1924. Post-grouping devel-
opment of Midland design with detail
alterations.
†Introduced 1929. Locos. built for
S. & D.J. (taken into L.M.S. stock
1930).
Weight : 49 tons 10 cwt.
Pressure : 160 lb.
Cyls. : 18″×26″.
Dr. Wheels : 4′ 7″.   T.E. : 20,835 lb.
*47260-99, 47300-9/17-99, 47400-
55/7-99, 47500-52/4-99, 47600-
12/4-6/8-62/4-81
†47310-6   **Total 417**

0-6-0T   3F

Introduced 1895. McIntosh Cale-
donian " 29 " and " 782 " Classes
(56231-9 originally condensing).
Weight : 47 tons 15 cwt.
Pressure : 160 lb.
Cyls. : 18″×26″.
Dr. Wheels : 4′ 6″.   T.E. : 21,215 lb.
56230-69/71-99, 56300-50/2-76
   Total 145

0-6-0T   2F

Introduced 1928. Fowler L.M.S. short-
wheel-base dock tanks.
Weight : 43 tons 12 cwt.
Pressure : 160 lb.
Cyls. : (O) 17″×22″.
Dr. Wheels : 3′ 11″.   T.E. : 18,400 lb.
Walschaerts Valve Gear.

47160-9   **Total 10**

0-6-0T   2F

Introduced 1911. McIntosh Cale-
donian dock shunters, "498" Class.
Weight : 47 tons 15 cwt.
Pressure : 160 lb.
Cyls. : (O) 17″×22″.
Dr. Wheels : 4′ 0″.   T.E. : 18,015 lb
56151-73   **Total 23**

0-6-0T   2F

Introduced 1879. Park North London
design (oldest survivor built 1881).
Weight : 45 tons 10 cwt.
Pressure : 160 lb.
Cyls. : (O) 17″×24″.
Dr. Wheels : 4′ 4″.   T.E. : 18,140 lb.
**(See p. 56 for former L.M.S.
numbers.)**
58850-63   **Total 14**

0-6-0T   1F

*Introduced 1878. Johnson Midland design.
†Rebuilt with Belpaire boiler.
Weight : 39 tons 11 cwt.
Pressure : $\begin{cases} 150 \text{ lb.} \ddagger \\ 140 \text{ lb.} \S \end{cases}$
Cyls. : 17"×24".
Dr. Wheels : 4' 7".
T.E. : $\begin{cases} 16,080 \text{ lb.} \ddagger \\ 15,005 \text{ lb.} \S \end{cases}$

*41666/71/86, 41713/26/48/63/7/
77/9/81/93/5, 41805/35/53/7/65
/85

†41660/1/4/72/82/90/5/9, 41702/
6/8/10-2/20/4/5/7/34/9/45/7/9/
52-4/69/70/3/80/94/7, 41803/4/
11/3/4/20/6/9/33/8/9/44/6/7/
52/4-6/9/60/9/74/5/8/9/89/90

Total 79

0-6-0T   1F

Introduced 1897. Aspinall L. & Y.
Class 24 dock tanks.
Weight : 50 tons 0 cwt.
Pressure : 140 lb.
Cyls. : (O) 17"×24".
Dr. Wheels : 4' 0".   T.E. : 15,285 lb.
Allan Straight Link Gear.

51535-7/44/6   **Total 5**

0-6-0ST   2F

Introduced 1870.   Webb version of
Ramsbottom " Special Tank " (oldest
survivor built 1875).
Weight : 34 tons 10 cwt.
Pressure : 140 lb.
Cyls. : 17"×24".
Dr. Wheels : 4' 5½".   T.E. : 17,005 lb.
Departmental locomotives.

3323 (L.N.W. No) Crewe Loco.
Works

C.D.3 Wolverton Carriage
Works

C.D.6   ,,   ,,   ,,
C.D.7   ,,   ,,   ,,
C.D.8 "Earlestown" Wolverton
Carriage Works

Total 5

0-6-0ST   2F

Introduced 1891. Aspinall rebuild of
L. & Y. Barton Wright class 23
0-6-0 tender loco. (introduced 1876).
Weight : 43 tons 17 cwt.
Pressure : 140 lb.   Cyls. : 17½"×26".
Dr. Wheels : 4' 6".   T.E. : 17,545 lb.

51307/13/6/9/21/3/36/8/43/5/8/
53/8/61/71/5/6/9/81/90/6/7,
51404/8/10/2/3/5/9/23-5/9/32/
6/9/41-4-7/53/7/8/60/2/4/70-
2/4/7/9/81/4/6/8-91/6-9, 51500/
3/4/6/10-4/6/9/21/4/6/30

Departmental Locomotives :
51304/5/24/68/94   **Total 84**

0-4-4T   2P

Introduced 1932. Stanier L.M.S. design.
Weight : 58 tons 1 cwt.
Pressure : 160 lb.
Cyls. : 18"×26".   T.E. : 17,100 lb.
Dr. Wheels : 5' 7".   **Total 10**
41900-9

0-4-4T   2P

*Introduced 1895. McIntosh Cale-
donian " 19 " class, with railed coal
bunkers.
†Introduced 1897. McIntosh " 92 "
class, developed from " 29 " class
with larger tanks and high-sided coal
bunkers (both classes originally fitted
for condensing on Glasgow under-
ground system).
Weight : $\begin{cases} 53 \text{ tons } 16 \text{ cwt.} * \\ 53 \text{ tons } 19 \text{ cwt.} \dagger \end{cases}$
Pressure : 180 lb.
Cyls. : 18"×26".
Dr. Wheels : 5' 9".   T.E. : 18,680 lb.
*55119/21/2/4
†55125/6/32/2/4-6/8-46   **Total 19**

0-4-4T   2P

*Introduced 1900. McIntosh Cale-
donian " 439 " or " Standard Passenger " class.
†Introduced 1915. Pickersgill locos.
with detail alterations.
Weight : $\begin{cases} 53 \text{ tons } 19 \text{ cwt.} * \\ 57 \text{ tons } 12 \text{ cwt.} \dagger \end{cases}$
Pressure : 180 lb.
Cyls. : 18"×26".
Dr. Wheels : 5' 9".   T.E. : 18,680 lb.
*55160-2/4-79/81/2/5-9/91-9,
55200-4/6-26
†55227-36   **Total 71**

0-4-4T   2P

Introduced 1922. Pickersgill Caledonian " 431 " class (developed from
" 439 " class) with cast-iron front
buffer beam for banking.
Weight : 57 tons 17 cwt.
Pressure : 180 lb.
Cyls. : 18½"×26".
Dr. Wheels : 5' 9".   T.E. : 19,200 lb.
55237-40   **Total 4**

0-4-4T 2P

Introduced 1925. Post-Grouping development of Caledonian "439" class.
Weight : 59 tons 12 cwt.
Pressure : 180 lb.
Cyls. : 18½" × 26".
Dr. Wheels : 5' 9".   T.E. : 19 200 lb.

55260-9 **Total 10**

0-4-4T 1P

*Introduced 1875. Johnson Midland design.
†Rebuilt with Belpaire boiler.
Weight : 53 tons 4 cwt.
Pressure : 140 lb.
Cyls. : 18" × 24".
Dr. Wheels : 5' 7".   T.E. : 13,810 lb.

(See p. 53 for former L.M.S. numbers.)

*58034
†58038   **Total 2**

0-4-4T 1P

*Introduced 1881. Johnson Midland design, many later rebuilt with Belpaire boiler.
†Rebuilt with Belpaire boiler.
‡Locos. with increased boiler pressure
Weight : 53 tons 4 cwt.
Pressure : $\begin{cases} 140 \text{ lb.} \\ 150 \text{ lb.}‡ \end{cases}$
Cyls. : 18" × 24".   T.E. : $\begin{cases} 14,460 \text{ lb.} \\ 15,490 \text{ lb.}‡ \end{cases}$
Dr. Wheels : 5' 4".

(See pp. 53-4 for former L.M.S. numbers.)

*58040/2/7/51
†58043/5/6/50/2-4/6/8
*‡58071/2/89
†‡58059-63/5-70/3/5-7/80/3-8/
90/1   **Total 39**

0-4-4T 1P

Introduced 1905. Drummond Highland design.
Weight : 35 tons 15 cwt.
Pressure : 150 lb.
Cyls : 14" × 20".
D.. Wheels : 4' 6".   T.E. : 9,255 lb.

55051/3   **Total 2**

0-4-2ST 1F

Introduced 1896. Webb L.N.W. Bissel truck design (oldest survivor built 1901).
Weight : 34 tons 17 cwt.
Pressure : 150 lb.
Cyls : 17" × 24".
Dr. Wheels : 4' 5¼".   T.E. : 16,530 lb.

47862/5   **Total 2**

0-4-2ST   Crane Engine

Introduced 1872. Rebuild with crane of North London Sharp-Stewart 0-4-0T of 1858.
Weight : 32 tons 6 cwt.
Pressure : 120 lb.   Cyls. : 13" × 17".
Dr. Wheels : 3' 10".   T.E. : 6,370 lb.
Allan Straight Link Gear.

58865   **Total 1**

0-4-0ST 0F

Introduced 1932. Kitson design prepared to Stanier's requirements for L.M.S.
Weight : 33 tons 0 cwt.
Pressure : 160 lb.
Cyls. : (O) 15½" × 30".
Dr. Wheels : 3' 10".   T.E. : 14,205 lb.

47000-4

N.B. Further locomotives of this class are on order.

0-4-0ST 0F

*Introduced 1883. Johnson Midland design.
Weight : 23 tons 3 cwt.
Pressure : 140 lb.   Cyls. : 13" × 20".
Dr Wheels : 3' 10".   T.E. : 8,745 lb.

41516

Departmental Loco. : 41509

Total 2

0-4-0ST 0F

Introduced 1897. Larger Johnson Midland design.
Weight : 32 tons 3 cwt.
Pressure : $\begin{cases} 140 \text{ lb.}* \\ 150 \text{ lb.}† \end{cases}$
Cyls. : 15" × 20".
T.E. : $\begin{cases} 11,640 \text{ lb.}* \\ 12,475 \text{ lb.}† \end{cases}$

*41518   †4152   **Total 23**

0-4-0T 0F

Introduced 1907. Deeley Midland design.
Weight : 32 tons 16 cwt.
Pressure : 160 lb.
Cyls. : (O) 15" × 22".
Dr. Wheels : 3' 9¾".   T.E. : 14,635 lb.
Walschaerts Valve Gear.

41528-37   **Total 10**

0-4-0ST 0F

Introduced 1891. Aspinall L. & Y. Class 21.
Weight : 21 tons 5 cwt.
Pressure : 160 lb.
Cyls. : (O) 13" × 18".
Dr Wheels : 3' 0⅜".   T.E. : 11,335 lb.

51202/4/6/7/12/6-8/21/2/7/9-32/
4/5/7/40/1/4/6/53   **Total 23**

0-4-0ST   0F

Introduced 1885. Drummond and
  McIntosh Caledonian "Pugs."
Weight : 27 tons 7 cwt.
Pressure : 160 lb.
Cyls. : (O) 14"×20".
Dr. Wheels : 3' 8".   T.E. : 12,115 lb.

56011/20/5/7-32/5/8/9   **Total 12**

0-4-0ST   18" Gauge

Introduced 1887. Beyer Peacock design,
  purchased by L. & Y.
Weight : 3 tons 15 cwt.
Pressure : 180 lb.
Cyls. : (O) 5"×6".
Dr. Wheels : 1' 4½".   T.E. : 1,410 lb.
Allan Straight Link Gear.
Departmental locomotive :—
Wren

0-4-0T   Sentinel

Geared Sentinel locos.
*Introduced 1929. Single-speed locos.
  for S.D. & J. (taken into L.M.S. stock
  1930).
†Introduced 1930. Two-speed locos.
  for L.M.S.
‡Introduced 1932. Single-speed loco.
  for L.M.S.
Weight : { 27 tons 15 cwt.*
          { 20 tons 17 cwt.†
          { 18 tons 18 cwt.‡
Pressure : 275 lb. Su.
Cyls. : { (4) 6¾"×9".*
        { 6¼"×9"†‡

Dr. Wheels : { 3' 1½".*
             { 2' 6".†‡
T.E. : { 15,500 lb.*
       { 11,800 lb.†‡
Poppet Valves.
*47190/1   †47180-3   ‡47184
                        Total 7

0-4-0   Diesel

Introduced 1936. Fowler diesel.
Weight : 21 tons 5 cwt.
Departmental Locomotives :
  E.D.1-E.D.6   **Total 6**
  (E.D.1. renumbered from E.D.2.)

0-4-0 Diesel   18" Gauge

Introduced 1930. Hudswell Clarke
  47½ h.p. design for Crewe works
  transferred to Horwich in 1935.
Departmental locomotive :—
ZM9

0-4-0   Battery

Introduced 1914.
Weight : 18 tons.
Midland design, for West India Docks.
41550   **Total 1**

Unnumbered
Introduced 1917. North Staffordshire
  design, now used at Oakamoor
  (Electrical Engineer's dept.).
Weight : 17 tons.
                        Total 1

HISTORIC LOCOMOTIVES PRESERVED IN STORE

Type	Originating Company	Pre-Grouping No.	L.M.S. No.	Name	Place of Preservation
2-4-0	M.R.	158A	(20002)	—	Derby
4-2-2	M.R.	118	(673)	—	Derby
2-2-2	L.N.W.	(49)	—	Columbine	York Museum
2-2-2	L.N.W.	3020	—	Cornwall	Crewe
2-4-0	L.N.W.	790	(5031)	Hardwicke	Crewe
*0-4-0T	L.N.W.	—	—	Pet	Crewe
0-4-0	F.R.	3	—	Coppernob	Horwich
0-4-2	Liverpool & Manchester	—	—	Lion	Liverpool Lime St.
4-2-2	C.R.	123	(14010)	—	St. Rollox
4-6-0	H.R.	103	(17916)	—	St. Rollox

The un-bracketed numbers are the ones at present carried by the locos.
*18in. gauge works shunter.

NAMED LOCOMOTIVES

CLASS "5MT" 4-6-0

45154 Lancashire Yeomanry
45156 Ayrshire Yeomanry
45157 The Glasgow Highlander
45158 Glasgow Yeomanry

CLASS "5XP" "PATRIOT" 4-6-0

45500 Patriot
45501 St. Dunstan's
45502 Royal Naval Division
45503 The Royal Leicestershire
    Regiment
45504 Royal Signals
45505 The Royal Army Ordnance
    Corps
45506 The Royal Pioneer Corps
45507 Royal Tank Corps
45511 Isle of Man
45512 Bunsen
45514 Holyhead
45515 Caernarvon
45516 The Bedfordshire and
    Hertfordshire Regiment
45518 Bradshaw
45519 Lady Godiva
45520 Llandudno
45521 Rhyl
45522 Prestatyn
45523 Bangor

45524 Blackpool
45525 Colwyn Bay
45526 Morecambe and Heysham
45527 Southport
45529 Stephenson
45530 Sir Frank Ree
45531 Sir Frederick Harrison
45532 Illustrious
45533 Lord Rathmore
45534 E. Tootal Broadhurst
45535 Sir Herbert Walker, K.C.B.
45536 Private W. Wood, V.C.
45537 Private E. Sykes, V.C.
45538 Giggleswick
45539 E. C. Trench
45540 Sir Robert Turnbull
45541 Duke of Sutherland
45543 Home Guard
45545 Planet
45546 Fleetwood
45548 Lytham St. Annes

CLASS "5XP" and "6P" "JUBILEE" 4-6-0

45552 Silver Jubilee
45553 Canada
45554 Ontario
45555 Quebec
45556 Nova Scotia
45557 New Brunswick
45558 Manitoba
45559 British Columbia
45560 Prince Edward Island
45561 Saskatchewan
45562 Alberta
45563 Australia
45564 New South Wales

45565 Victoria
45566 Queensland
45567 South Australia
45568 Western Australia
45569 Tasmania
45570 New Zealand
45571 South Africa
45572 Eire
45573 Newfoundland
45574 India
45575 Madras
45576 Bombay
45577 Bengal

NAMED LOCOMOTIVES

45578	United Provinces	45624	St. Helena
45579	Punjab	45625	Sarawak
45580	Burma	45626	Seychelles
45581	Bihar and Orissa	45627	Sierra Leone
45582	Central Provinces	45628	Somaliland
45583	Assam	45629	Straits Settlements
45584	North West Frontier	45630	Swaziland
45585	Hyderabad	45631	Tanganyika
45586	Mysore	45632	Tonga
45587	Baroda	45633	Aden
45588	Kashmir	45634	Trinidad
45589	Gwalior	45635	Tobago
45590	Travancore	45636	Uganda
45591	Udaipur	45637	Windward Islands
45592	Indore	45638	Zanzibar
45593	Kolhapur	45639	Raleigh
45594	Bhopal	45640	Frobisher
45595	Southern Rhodesia	45641	Sandwich
45596	Bahamas	45642	Boscawen
45597	Barbados	45643	Rodney
45598	Basutoland	45644	Howe
45599	Bechuanaland	45645	Collingwood
45600	Bermuda	45646	Napier
45601	British Guiana	45647	Sturdee
45602	British Honduras	45648	Wemyss
45603	Solomon Islands	45649	Hawkins
45604	Ceylon	45650	Blake
45605	Cyprus	45651	Shovell
45606	Falkland Islands	45652	Hawke
45607	Fiji	45653	Barham
45608	Gibraltar	45654	Hood
45609	Gilbert and Ellice Islands	45655	Keith
45610	Gold Coast	45656	Cochrane
45611	Hong Kong	45657	Tyrwhitt
45612	Jamaica	45658	Keys
45613	Kenya	45659	Drake
45614	Leeward Islands	45660	Rooke
45615	Malay States	45661	Vernon
45616	Malta G.C.	45662	Kempenfelt
45617	Mauritius	45663	Jervis
45618	New Hebrides	45664	Nelson
45619	Nigeria	45665	Lord Rutherford of Nelson
45620	North Borneo	45666	Cornwallis
45621	Northern Rhodesia	45667	Jellicoe
45622	Nyasaland	45668	Madden
45623	Palestine	45669	Fisher

NAMED LOCOMOTIVES

45670 Howard of Effingham	45707 Valiant
45671 Prince Rupert	45708 Resolution
45672 Anson	45709 Implacable
45673 Keppel	45710 Irresistible
45674 Duncan	45711 Courageous
45675 Hardy	45712 Victory
45676 Codrington	45713 Renown
45677 Beatty	45714 Revenge
45678 De Robeck	45715 Invincible
45679 Armada	45716 Swiftsure
45680 Camperdown	45717 Dauntless
45681 Aboukir	45718 Dreadnought
45682 Trafalgar	45719 Glorious
45683 Hogue	45720 Indomitable
45684 Jutland	45721 Impregnable
45685 Barfleur	45722 Defence
45686 St. Vincent	45723 Fearless
45687 Neptune	45724 Warspite
45688 Polyphemus	45725 Repulse
45689 Ajax	45726 Vindictive
45690 Leander	45727 Inflexible
45691 Orion	45728 Defiance
45692 Cyclops	45729 Furious
45693 Agamemnon	45730 Ocean
45694 Bellerophon	45731 Perseverance
45695 Minotaur	45732 Sanspareil
45696 Arethusa	45733 Novelty
45697 Achilles	45734 Meteor
45698 Mars	45735 Comet
45699 Galatea	45736 Phoenix
45700 Britannia	45737 Atlas
45701 Conqueror	45738 Samson
45702 Colossus	45739 Ulster
45703 Thunderer	45740 Munster
45704 Leviathan	45741 Leinster
45705 Seahorse	45742 Connaught
45706 Express	

CLASS "6P" "ROYAL SCOT" 4-6-0

46100 Royal Scot	46106 Gordon Highlander
46101 Royal Scots Grey	46107 Argyll and Sutherland
46102 Black Watch	Highlander
46103 Royal Scots Fusilier	46108 Seaforth Highlander
46104 Scottish Borderer	46109 Royal Engineer
46105 Cameron Highlander	46110 Grenadier Guardsman

NAMED LOCOMOTIVES

46111	Royal Fusilier	46142	The York & Lancaster Regiment
46112	Sherwood Forester	46143	The South Staffordshire Regiment
46113	Cameronian		
46114	Coldstream Guardsman	46144	Honourable Artillery Company
46115	Scots Guardsman		
46116	Irish Guardsman	46145	The Duke of Wellington's Regt. (West Riding)
46117	Welsh Guardsman		
46118	Royal Welch Fusilier	46146	The Rifle Brigade
46119	Lancashire Fusilier	46147	The Northamptonshire Regiment
46120	Royal Inniskilling Fusilier		
46121	Highland Light Infantry, City of Glasgow Regiment	46148	The Manchester Regiment
		46149	The Middlesex Regiment
46122	Royal Ulster Rifleman	46150	The Life Guardsman
46123	Royal Irish Fusilier	46151	The Royal Horse Guardsman
46124	London Scottish		
46125	3rd Carabinier	46152	The King's Dragoon Guardsman
46126	Royal Army Service Corps		
46127	Old Contemptibles	46153	The Royal Dragoon
46128	The Lovat Scouts	46154	The Hussar
46129	The Scottish Horse	46155	The Lancer
46130	The West Yorkshire Regiment	46156	The South Wales Borderer
		46157	The Royal Artilleryman
46131	The Royal Warwickshire Regiment	46158	The Loyal Regiment
		46159	The Royal Air Force
46132	The King's Regiment Liverpool	46160	Queen Victoria's Rifleman
		46161	King's Own
46133	The Green Howards	46162	Queen's Westminster Rifleman
46134	The Cheshire Regiment		
46135	The East Lancashire Regiment	46163	Civil Service Rifleman
		46164	The Artists Rifleman
46136	The Border Regiment	46165	The Ranger (12th London Regt.)
46137	The Prince of Wales's Volunteers (South Lancashire)		
		46166	London Rifle Brigade
46138	The London Irish Rifleman	46167	The Hertfordshire Regiment
46139	The Welch Regiment		
46140	The King's Royal Rifle Corps	46168	The Girl Guide
		46169	The Boy Scout
46141	The North Staffordshire Regiment	46170	British Legion

CLASS "7P" "PRINCESS ROYAL" 4–6–2

46200	The Princess Royal	46204	Princess Louise
46201	Princess Elizabeth	46205	Princess Victoria
46203	Princess Margaret Rose	46206	Princess Marie Louise

NAMED LOCOMOTIVES

46207 Princess Arthur of
                Connaught
46208 Princess Helena Victoria
46209 Princess Beatrice

46210 Lady Patricia
46211 Queen Maud
46212 Duchess of Kent

CLASS "7P" "PRINCESS CORONATION" 4–6–2

46220 Coronation
46221 Queen Elizabeth
46222 Queen Mary
46223 Princess Alice
46224 Princess Alexandra
46225 Duchess of Gloucester
46226 Duchess of Norfolk
46227 Duchess of Devonshire
46228 Duchess of Rutland
46229 Duchess of Hamilton
46230 Duchess of Buccleuch
46231 Duchess of Atholl
46232 Duchess of Montrose
46233 Duchess of Sutherland
46234 Duchess of Abercorn
46235 City of Birmingham
46236 City of Bradford
46237 City of Bristol
46238 City of Carlisle
46239 City of Chester

46240 City of Coventry
46241 City of Edinburgh
46242 City of Glasgow
46243 City of Lancaster
46244 King George VI
46245 City of London
46246 City of Manchester
46247 City of Liverpool
46248 City of Leeds
46249 City of Sheffield
46250 City of Lichfield
46251 City of Nottingham
46252 City of Leicester
46253 City of St. Albans
46254 City of Stoke-on-Trent
46255 City of Hereford
46256 Sir William A. Stanier,
                        F.R.S.

46257 City of Salford

CLASS "2P" "BEN" CLASS 4–4–0

54398 Ben Alder
54399 Ben Wyvis

54404 Ben Clebrig

THE ABC OF BRITISH RAILWAYS LOCOMOTIVES

EDITED BY A. F. COOK

PART 4 - Nos. 60001-90774

EASTERN, NORTH EASTERN, SCOTTISH REGION & EX-W.D. STEAM LOCOMOTIVES

LONDON :

Ian Allan Ltd

FOREWORD

THIS booklet lists all British Railways locomotives numbered between 60000 and 90774. This series of numbers includes all Eastern, North Eastern and Scottish (ex-L.N.E.R.) Region steam locomotives, i.e. steam locomotives of the former L.N.E.R., and ex-Ministry of Supply locomotives. Under the general British Railways renumbering scheme, the numbers of L.N.E.R. steam locomotives were increased by 60000, with the exception of Classes W1 and L1. A later scheme involved the renumbering of all ex-M.o.S. locomotives in the 90000 series, and there have also been minor amendments to Classes B16 and D31 to make way for new locomotives.

Former L.N.E.R. electric, diesel electric and petrol locomotives have been renumbered in the 20000 and 15000 series, and details of them will be found in " ABC of British Railways Locomotives " Part 2 (Nos. 10000-39999).

NOTES ON THE USE OF THIS BOOK

1. This book is divided into two sections :

   SECTION ONE (pp. 1-12, 77-88). An alphabetical list of classes, with dimensions and subdivisions, and a summary of locomotives in the class.

   SECTION TWO (pp. 21-68). A list of locomotives in numerical order, under their appropriate class headings, and showing against each engine its shed allocation, followed by a list of named engines in numerical order.

The aim of the book is that SECTION ONE shall provide a ready reference to particulars of individual locomotives in a class, and that SECTION TWO shall be used for observation purposes.

2. The following notes are a guide to the system of reference marks and other details given in the lists of dimensions shown for each class in SECTION ONE :

(a) Many of the classes listed are sub-divided, the sub-divisions being denoted in some cases by " Parts " shown thus : D16/3. At the head of each class will be found a list of such subdivisions, if any, usually arranged in order of introduction. Each part is given there a reference mark by which its relevant dimensions, if differing from other parts, and the locomotives in the list which comprise it, may be identified. Any other differences between locomotives are also indicated, with reference marks, below the details of the class's introduction.

(b) " Su " indicates a superheated locomotive, and " SS " indicates that some locomotives of the class are superheated.

(c) Locomotives are fitted with two inside cylinders, slide valves and Stephenson link motion, except where otherwise stated, e.g. (O) indicates outside cylinders and " P.V." piston valves.

(d) The date on which a design of locomotive first appeared is indicated by " Introduced." If the oldest surviving locomotive was built at a later date, that also is indicated.

(e) The code in smaller bold type in the centre of the class description denotes power classification under the British Railways system.

3. In Section Two, the code numbers and letter shown against each locomotive are those of its home shed under the British Railways code, a key to which is provided on pp. 22-25. Any locomotive not given a shed code in the list was not in service or not allocated at the time of compilation. Where a letter or letters in brackets follows the shed code, this denotes that the locomotive is allocated to a sub-shed, of which the letter or letters form the initial(s). The name of this sub-shed is found below that of its parent shed in the key. Other points that should be noted are :

(a) Throughout named locomotives are indicated by an asterisk (*). Full lists of named locomotives in numerical order are found at the end of Section Two (pp. 60-67).

(b) A bold " S " (not borne by the locomotives concerned but used here for convenience) against a number denotes " Departmental locomotive ".

(c) Locomotives are listed under their appropriate class heading. For details of dimensions, class history, etc., the reader should consult Section One, where this information will be found under the appropriate class, in alphabetical order.

4. The information given in this booklet has been checked to August 31st, 1950. Supplementary information is published each month in the Ian Allan periodical *Trains Illustrated* (Price 1s. 6d.) to enable the reader to keep these lists up to date.

SUMMARY OF EX-L.N.E.R. AND W.D. STEAM LOCOMOTIVES

(In Alphabetical Order)

WITH HISTORICAL NOTES AND DIMENSIONS

4-6-2   **7P**   **Class A1**

A1/1* Introduced 1945. Thompson rebuild of A10.

A1† Peppercorn development of A1/1 for new construction.

A1‡ Fitted with roller bearings.

Weights : Loco. $\begin{cases} 101 \text{ tons.*} \\ 104 \text{ tons 2 cwt.†‡} \end{cases}$
Tender 60 tons 7 cwt.

Pressure : 250 lb. Su.
Cyls.: (3) 19″ × 26″
Driving Wheels : 6′ 8″ T.E.: 37,400 lb.
Walschaerts gear, P.V.

*60113
†60114-52/8-62
‡60153-7   **Total 50**

4-6-2   **7MT**   **Class A2**
(A2/1 are 6MT)

A2/2* Introduced 1943. Original Thompson Pacific, rebuilt from Gresley Class P2 2-8-2 (introduced 1934).
Weight : Loco. 101 tons 10 cwt.
Pressure : 225 lb. Su.
Cyls.: (3) 20″ × 26″
Driving Wheels : 6′ 2″ T.E.: 40,320 lb.

A2/1† Introduced 1944. Development of Class A2/2, incorporating Class V2 2-6-2 type boiler.
Weight : Loco. 98 tons.
Pressure : 225 lb. Su.
Cyls.: (3) 19″ × 26″
Driving Wheels : 6′ 2″ T.E.: 36,385 lb.

A2/3‡ Introduced 1946. Development of Class A2/2 for new construction
Weight : Loco. 101 tons 10 cwt.
Pressure : 250 lb. Su.
Cyls.: (3) 19″ × 26″
Driving Wheels : 6′ 2″ T.E.: 40,430 lb.

A2§ Introduced 1947. Peppercorn development of Class A2/3 with shorter wheelbase and single blast pipe (No. 60539 built with double blast pipe.)

A2** Rebuilt with double blast pipe and multiple valve regulator.
Weight : Loco. 101 tons.
Pressure : 250 lb. Su.
Cyls.: (3) 19″ × 26″
Driving Wheels : 6′ 2″ T.E.: 40,430 lb.
Tender weight (all parts): 60 tons 7 cwt. (except No. 60509, 52 tons).
Walschaerts gear, P.V.

*60501-6
†60507-10
‡60500/11-24
§60525/7/8/30/1/4-7/9
**60526/9/32/3/8

Totals : Class A2   15
Class A2/1   4
Class A2/2   6
Class A2/3   15

4-6-2   **7P**   **Class A3**

A3* Introduced 1927. Development of Gresley G.N. 180 lb. Pacific (introduced 1922, L.N.E.R. A1, later A10) with 220 lb. pressure (prototype and others rebuilt from A10). Some have G.N.-type tender† with coal rails, remainder L.N.E.R. pattern.

‡ Kylchap blast pipe and double chimney
Weights : Loco.   96 tons 5 cwt.
Tender $\begin{cases} 56 \text{ tons }6 \text{ cwt.†} \\ 57 \text{ tons 18 cwt.} \end{cases}$

Pressure : 220 lb. Su.
Driving Wheels : 6′ 8″ T.E.: 32,910 lb.
Walschaerts gear and derived motion, P.V.

*60035-96/8-60112
‡60097   **Total 78**

4-6-2   7P   **Class A4**

*Introduced 1935. Gresley streamlined design.

†‡ Inside cylinder reduced to 17″.

‡§ Non-corridor tender (remainder corridor).

** Kylchap blast pipe and double chimney.

Weights : Loco. 102 tons 19 cwt.

Tender $\begin{cases} 64 \text{ tons } 19 \text{ cwt.} \\ 60 \text{ tons } 7 \text{ cwt.}‡§ \end{cases}$

Pressure : 250 lb. Su.

Cyls. $\begin{cases} (3) \ 18\frac{1}{2}″ \times 26″. \\ (2) \ 18\frac{1}{2}″ \times 26″. \end{cases}$ (1) $17″ \times 26″$†

Driving Wheels : 6′ 8″

T.E. $\begin{cases} 35,455 \text{ lb} \\ 33,616 \text{ lb.}† \end{cases}$

Walschaerts gear and derived motion P.V.

*60006-11/3/5-7/24-9

†60003/12/4/31

‡600020

§60001/2/4/18/9/21/3/30/2

**60022/33/4

§**60005   **Total 34**

4-6-2T   4P   **Class A5**

A5/1* Introduced 1911. Robinson G.C. design.

A5/2† Introduced 1925. Post-grouping development of A5/1 with reduced boiler mountings and detail differences.

Weights : $\begin{cases} 85 \text{ tons } 18 \text{ cwt.}* \\ 90 \text{ tons } 11 \text{ cwt.}† \end{cases}$

Pressure : 180 lb. Su. Cyls.† $20″ \times 26″$

Driving Wheels : 5′ 7″ T.E.: 23,750 lb. P.V.

*69800-29

†69830-42

Totals : Class A5/1 30

Class A5/2 13

4-6-2T   4P   **Class A6**

*Introduced 1915. Raven N.E. design. (Rebuild of Worsdell Class "W" 4-6-0T, introduced 1907.) Later superheated.

† Saturated.

Weights : $\begin{cases} 79 \text{ tons.}* \\ 78 \text{ tons.}† \end{cases}$

Pressure : 175 lb. SS. Cyls.: $19″ \times 26″$

Driving Wheels : 5′ 1½″ T.E.: 23,830 lb. P.V.

*69791/3/6/7

†69794/8   **Total 6**

4-6-2T   5F   **Class A7**

*Introduced 1910. Raven N.E. design, later rebuilt with superheater and reduced pressure.

† Saturated.

Weight : 87 tons 10 cwt.

Pressure : $\begin{cases} 160 \text{ lb. Su. }* \\ 180 \text{ lb }† \end{cases}$

Cyls.: (3) $16\frac{1}{2}″ \times 26″$

Driving Wheels : 4′ 7¼″

T.E. $\begin{cases} 26,140 \text{ lb.} \\ 29,405 \text{ lb.}* \end{cases}$

P.V.

*69770-4/6/7/9-86/8/9

†69775/8/87   **Total 20**

4-6-2T   4P   **Class A8**

Introduced 1931. Gresley rebuild of Raven Class "D" 4-4-4T (introduced 1913.)

Weight : 86 tons 18 cwt.

Pressure : 175 lb. Su.

Cyls.: (3) $16\frac{1}{2}″ \times 26″$

Driving Wheels : 5′ 9″ T.E.: 22,940 lb. P.V.

69850-94   **Total 45**

4-6-0   5MT   **Class B1**

Introduced 1942. Thompson design

Weights : Loco. 71 tons 3 cwt.

Tender 52 tons.

Pressure : 225 lb. Su.

Cyls.: (O) $20″ \times 26″$

Driving Wheels : 6′ 2″ T.E.: 26,880 lb.

Walschaerts gear, P.V,

61000-56/8-61409   **Total 409**

4-6-0   4P   **Classes B2 & B17**

B17/1[1] Introduced 1928. Gresley design for G.E. section with G.E.-type tenders.

B17/6[3] Introduced 1947. B17/1 fitted with 100A (B1 type) boiler.

B17/4[3] Introduced 1936. Locos with L.N.E.R. 4200-gallon tenders.

B17/6[4] Introduced 1943. B17/4 fitted with 100A (B1 type) boiler.

B17/5[5] Introduced 1937. Rebuild of B17/4 with streamlined casing.

B17/5[6] B17/5 fitted with 100A boiler. (B17/2 and B17/3 were variants of B17/1 now included in that part.)

Weights : Loco.
$\begin{cases} 77 \text{ tons } 5 \text{ cwt.}^1 \\ 77 \text{ tons } 5 \text{ cwt.}^2 \\ 77 \text{ tons } 5 \text{ cwt.}^3 \\ 77 \text{ tons } 5 \text{ cwt.}^4 \\ 80 \text{ tons } 10 \text{ cwt.}^5 \\ 80 \text{ tons } 10 \text{ cwt.}^6 \end{cases}$

Tender
$\begin{cases} 39 \text{ tons } 6 \text{ cwt.}^1 \\ 39 \text{ tons } 6 \text{ cwt.}^3 \\ 52 \text{ tons }^3 \\ 52 \text{ tons }^4 \\ 52 \text{ tons } 13 \text{ cwt.}^5 \end{cases}$

Pressure :
$\begin{cases} 180 \text{ lb.}^1 \\ 225 \text{ lb.}^2 \\ 180 \text{ lb.}^3 \\ 225 \text{ lb.}^4 \\ 180 \text{ lb.}^5 \\ 225 \text{ lb.}^6 \end{cases}$ Su.

Cyls.: (3) $17\frac{1}{2}'' \times 26''$
Driving Wheels : 6' 8''

T.E. :
$\begin{cases} 22,485 \text{ lb.}^1 \\ 28,555 \text{ lb.}^2 \\ 22,485 \text{ lb.}^3 \\ 28,555 \text{ lb.}^4 \\ 22,485 \text{ lb.}^{5\,6} \end{cases}$

Walschaerts gear and derived motion, P.V.

B2⁷ Introduced 1945. Thompson 2-cyl. re-build of B17, with 100A boiler and ex-N.E. tender.

B2⁸ Introduced 1945, with L.N.E.R. tender.

Weights : Loco.   73 tons 10 cwt
Tender $\begin{cases} 46 \text{ tons } 12 \text{ cwt.}^7 \\ 52 \text{ tons }^8 \end{cases}$

Pressure : 225 lb. Su.
Cyls.: (O) $20'' \times 26''$
Driving Wheels : 6' 8'' T.E. : 24,865 lb.
Walschaerts gear and derived motion P.V.

1   61600-2/4/8-13/8-21/4-6/9/31/4/ 6/7/40/3/5/58
2   61605/6/22/3/7/8/30/3/5/8/41/2/6
3   61647-51/3/5-7/60 3/7/72
4   61652/42/64-6/8/9
5   61670
6   61659
7   61603/7/14/6/7/39/44
8   61615/32/71

Totals : Class **B2**   10
Class **B17/1** 26
Class **B17/4** 15
Class **B17/5**   2
Class **B17/6** 20

4-6-0   4P   **Class B4**

B4/4 Introduced 1906. Robinson G.C. design, later superheated.
Weights : Loco. 70 tons 14 cwt.
Tender 40 tons 6 cwt.
Pressure : 180 lb. Su.
Cyls.:(O) $19'' \times 26''$
Driving Wheels : 6' 7''
T.E. 18,180 lb.

61482   Total 1

4-6-0   4P   **Class B12**

B12/1* Introduced 1911. S. D. Holden G.E. design with small Belpaire boiler.

B12/3† Introduced 1932. Gresley re-build of B12/1 with large round-topped boiler and long-travel valves.

B12/1‡ Introduced 1943. Rebuild of B12/1 with small round-topped boiler, retaining original valves.
(B12/2 was a development of B12/1 with Lentz valves, since rebuilt to B12/3.)

Weights : Loco. $\begin{cases} 63 \text{ tons.}^*{}^‡ \\ 69 \text{ tons } 10 \text{ cwt.}† \end{cases}$
Tender 39 tons 6 cwt.
Pressure : 180 lb. Su. Cyls.: $20'' \times 28''$
Driving Wheels : 6' 6'' T.E.: 21,970 lb. P.V.

*61501-3/13/21/8/39/43/52/60/3
†61512/4-6/9/20/3/5/30/3/5/7/8/40-2/5-7/9/50/3-9/61/2/4-80
‡61505/7/8/11/24/6/32

Totals : Class B12/1 18
Class B12/3 47

4-6-0   **Class B13**

Introduced 1899 (Survivor built 1906). Worsdell N.E. design later rebuilt to counter-pressure loco for loco testing purposes. Now maintained at Rugby Testing Plant.
Pressure: 160 lb. Cyls.: (O) $20'' \times 26''$
Driving Wheels : 6' 1¼'' T.E.: 19,310 lb. P.V.

61699   Total 1

4-6-0　6MT　Class B16

B16/1* Introduced 1920. Raven N.E. design with inside Stephenson gear.
B16/2† Introduced 1937. Gresley rebuild of B16/1 with outside Walschaerts' gear and derived motion for inside cylinder.
B16/3‡ Introduced 1944. Thompson rebuild of B16/1 with three Walschaerts' gears.

Weights : Loco. $\begin{cases} 77 \text{ tons } 14 \text{ cwt.*} \\ 79 \text{ tons } 4 \text{ cwt.†} \\ 78 \text{ tons } 19 \text{ cwt.‡} \end{cases}$
Tender 46 tons 12 cwt.
Pressure : 180 lb. Su.
Cyls. : (3) $18\frac{1}{2}'' \times 26''$.
Driving Wheels : 5' 8"　T.E.: 30,030 lb.
P.V

*61410-6/9/22-33/6/40-3/5-7/50-2/6/8-60/2/5/6/9-71/3/4/7/8
†61421/35/7/8/55/7/75
‡61417/8/20/34/9/44/8/9/53/4/61/3/4/7/8/72/6

Totals : Class B16/1　45
Class B16/2　7
Class B16/3　17

4-6-0　Class B17

(See under Class B2)

4-4-2　2P　Class C1

Introduced 1902. (Survivor built 1905.)　G.N. Ivatt large Atlantic.
Weights : Loco. 69 tons 12 cwt.
Tender 43 tons 2 cwt.
Pressure : 170 lb. Su.
Cyls. : (O) $20'' \times 24''$
Driving Wheels : 6' 8"
T.E. : 17,340 lb.
P.V.

62822　　　　　　　Total 1

4-4-2　2P　Class C4

C4/2* Introduced 1902. Robinson G.C. design. Slide valves, originally saturated.
C4/4† Introduced 1911. Rebuilt with superheater and piston valves.
(C4/1 and C4/3 were locos of C4/2 and C4/4 before cutting down to L.N.E.R. loading gauge.)
Weights : Loco. $\begin{cases} 70 \text{ tons } 17 \text{ cwt.*} \\ 71 \text{ tons } 18 \text{ cwt.†} \end{cases}$
Tender 48 tons 6 cwt.
Pressure : 180 lb. Su.
Cyls. : (O) $\begin{cases} 19'' \times 26''* \\ 21'' \times 26''† \end{cases}$
Driving Wheels : 6' 9"
T.E. : $\begin{cases} 17,730 \text{ lb.*} \\ 21,660 \text{ lb.†} \end{cases}$
*62908/18
†62900/1/9/19

Totals : Class C4/2　2
Class C4/4　4

4-4-2T　2P　Class C12

*Introduced 1898. Ivatt G.N. design.
†‡Boiler pressure reduced to 170 lb.
‡§Push and pull fitted.
Weight : 62 tons 6 cwt.
Pressure : $\begin{cases} 175 \text{ lb. Su.} \\ 170 \text{ lb.†‡} \end{cases}$　Cyls. : $18'' \times 26''$
Driving Wheels : 5' 8"
T.E. : $\begin{cases} 18,425 \text{ lb.} \\ 17,900 \text{ lb.†‡} \end{cases}$
*67350/2/3/7/60-2/4-9/71-3/5/6/9-85/9-95/7
†67354/98
‡67363/74
§67356/86/7　　　　　Total 40

4-4-2T　2P　Class C13

*Introduced 1903. Robinson G.C. design, later rebuilt with superheater.
† Push-and-pull fitted.
Weight : 66 tons 13 cwt.
Pressure : 160 lb. Su.　Cyls. : $18'' \times 26''$
Driving Wheels : 5' 7"　T.E. : 17,100 lb.
*67400-15/9/22-32/4/5/7/9
†67416-8/20/1/33/6/8　　Total 40

4-4-2T　2P　Class C14

Introduced 1907. Robinson G.C. design later superheated, development of C13 with detail differences.
Weight : 71 tons.
Pressure : 160 lb. Su.　Cyls. : $18'' \times 26''$
Driving Wheels : 5' 7"　T.E. : 17,100 lb.
67440-51　　　　　　Total 12

4-4-2T　2P　Class C15

*Introduced 1911. Reid N.B. design.
† Push-and-pull fitted.
Weight : 68 tons 15 cwt.
Pressure : 175 lb.　Cyls. : $18'' \times 26''$
Driving Wheels : 5' 9"　T.E. : 18,160 lb.
*67452-9/61-81
†67460　　　　　　　Total 30

Classes C16-D16

4-4-2T 2P Class C16

*Introduced 1915. Reid N.B. design, superheated development of C15.
† Superheater removed.
Weight : 72 tons 10 cwt.
Pressure : 165 lb. SS. Cyls. : 19″ × 26″
Driving Wheels : 5′ 9″ T.E. : 19,080 lb.
P.V.

*67482/4-67502
†67483   **Total 21**

4-4-0 1P Class D1

Introduced 1911 Ivatt G.N. design
Weights : Loco.   53 tons 6 cwt.
     Tender 43 tons 2 cwt.
Pressure : 170 lb. Su. Cyls. : 18½″ × 26″
Driving Wheels : 6′ 8″ T.E. : 16,075 lb.
P.V.

62209   **Total 1**

4-4-0 1P Class D2

Introduced 1897. Ivatt G.N. design.
Weights : Loco.   47 tons 10 cwt.
     Tender 40 tons 18 cwt.
Pressure : 175 lb.
Cyls. : 17½″ × 26″
Driving Wheels : 6′ 8″
T.E. : 14,805 lb.

62154/72/81   **Total 3**

4-4-0 1P Class D3

*Introduced 1896. Ivatt G.N. design.
Rebuilt from 1912 with large boiler.
† Introduced 1944. Rebuilt with side-window cab for working officers' saloons.
Weights : Loco.   45 tons 14 cwt.
     Tender 38 tons 10 cwt.
Pressure : 175 lb. Cyls. : 17½″ × 26″
Driving Wheels : 6′ 8″ T.E. : 14,805 lb.

*62132/48
†62000   **Total 3**

4-4-0 3P Class D10

Introduced 1913. Robinson G.C. "Director" class.
Weights : Loco.   61 tons.
     Tender 48 tons 6 cwt.
Pressure : 180 lb. Su. Cyls. : 20″ × 26″
Driving Wheels : 6′ 9″ T.E. : 19,645 lb.
P.V.

62650-9   **Total 10**

4-4-0 3P Class D11

D11/1* Introduced 1920. Robinson G.C. "Large Director," development of D10.

D11/2† Introduced 1924. Post-grouping locos built to Scottish loading gauge. From 1938 the class has been rebuilt with long-travel valves.

Weights : Loco.   61 tons 3 cwt.
     Tender 48 tons 6 cwt.
Pressure : 180 lb. Su. Cyls. : 20″ × 26″
Driving Wheels : 6′ 9″ T.E. : 19,645 lb.
P.V.

*62660-70
†62671-94

     Totals : Class D11/1 11
             Class D11/2 24

4-4-0 2P Classes D15 & D16

D15[1] Introduced 1904. Belpaire boiler development of original J. Holden (G.E.) "Claud Hamilton" class, some rebuilt from D14.
D16/2[1] Introduced 1923. Hill "Super Claud"—D15 with larger boiler, some rebuilt from D15.
D16/3[3] Introduced 1933. Gresley rebuild of D15 with larger round-topped boiler and modified footplating.
D16/3[4] Introduced 1933. Rebuild of D15 with larger round-topped boiler, modified footplating and 8″ piston valves.
D16/3[6] Introduced 1936. Rebuild of D15 with larger round-topped boiler, modified footplating and 9½″ piston valves.
D16/3[6] Introduced 1938. Rebuild of D16/2 with round-topped boiler, but retaining original footplating and slide valves.
D16/3[7] Introduced 1939. Rebuild of D16/2 with round-topped boiler and modified footplating, retaining slide valves.
(At grouping the remaining locos of the "Claud Hamilton" class retaining small round-topped boilers were classified D14. Saturated locos of D15 were originally classified D15, superheated locos with short smokeboxes D15/1 and superheated locos with extended smokeboxes D15/2. All the remaining locos were converted to D15/2 and then known simply as D15. D16/1 were the original D16 locos with short smokeboxes.)

Weights : Loco. { 52 tons 4 cwt.[1]
54 tons 18 cwt.[2]
55 tons 18 cwt. (all D16/3)
Tender 39 tons 5 cwt.

Pressure : 180 lb. Su. Cyls.: 19″ × 26″
Driving Wheels : 7′ 0″ T.E.: 17,095 lb

[1] 62501-3/5-9/20/8/38
[2] 62547/77/90, 62603
[3] 62510/1/3-9/21-7/9-31/3/4/9-41/
5/8/9/51/5/9/61/6/7/71/2/4/5/
9/82/5/6/93/7/8, 62604/8/10
[4] 62546/68/87/8, 62609
[5] 62532/5/6/76/81/99
[6] 62542-4/52-4/6-8/62/4/5/9/70/3/
8/80/4/9/92/6, 62601/5-7/11-3/
5-20
[7] 62614

Totals : Class D15   11
Class D16/2   4
Class D16/3   93

4-4-0   2P   Class D20

D20/1*Introduced 1899. W. Worsdell
N.E. design. Since superheated.
D20/2† Introduced 1936. D20/1 rebuilt
with long-travel valves.
Weights : Loco. { 54 tons 2 cwt.*
55 tons 9 cwt.†
Tender { 41 tons 4 cwt.*
43 tons. †
Pressure : 175 lb. Cyls.: 19″ × 26″
Driving Wheels : 6′ 10″ T.E.: 17,025 lb.
P.V.

*62340-5/7/8/51-5/7-9/61-3/5/6/9/
70/2-4/6/8-84/6-9/91/2/5-7
†62349/60/71/5

Total : Class D20/1   43
Class D20/2   4

4-4-0   3P   Class D29

Introduced 1909. Reid N.B. " Scott "
class, later superheated.
Weights : Loco.   54 tons 4 cwt.
Tender 46 tons.
Pressure : 190 lb. Su. Cyls.: 19″ × 26″
Driving Wheels : 6′ 6″ T.E.: 19,435 lb.
P.V.

62405/10/1   Total 3

4-4-0   3P   Class D30

D30/1* Introduced 1912. Reid N.B.
" Scott " class.
D30/2† Introduced 1914. Development
of D30/1 with detail differences.
Weights : Loco. { 57 tons 6 cwt.*
57 tons 16 cwt.†
Tender { 46 tons.*
46 tons 13 cwt.†
Pressure : 165 lb. Su. Cyls.: 20″ × 26 ″
Driving Wheels : 6′ 6″ T.E.: 18,700 lb
P.V.

*62417
†62418-32/4-42

Totals : Class D30/1   1
Class D30/2   24

4-4-0   2P   Class D31

Introduced 1890. Holmes N.B. design.
(Rebuilt from 1918.)
Weights : Loco. 46 tons 8 cwt.
Tender 33 tons 9 cwt.
Pressure : 175 lb. Cyls.: 18½″ × 26′
Driving Wheels : 6′ 6″ T.E.: 16,515 lb.

62281/3   Total 2

4-4-0   3P   Class D32

Introduced 1906. Reid N.B. " Inter-
mediate " class. Since superheated.
Weights : Loco. 53 tons 14 cwt.
Tender 40 tons.
Pressure : 180 lb. Su. Cyls.: 19″ × 26″
Driving Wheels : 6′ 0″ T.E.: 19,945 lb
P.V.

62451   Total 1

4-4-0   3P   Class D33

Introduced 1909. Later Reid N.B.
" Intermediate " class. Since super-
heated.
Weights : Loco. 54 tons 3 cwt.
Tender 44 tons 11 cwt.
Pressure : 180 lb. Su. Cyls.: 19″ × 26″
Driving Wheels : 6′ 0″ T.E.: 19,945 lb.
P.V.

62457/9/60-2/4/6   Total 7

4-4-0   3P   Class D34

Introduced 1913. Reid N.B. "Glen" class
Weights : Loco. 57 tons 4 cwt.
Tender 46 tons 13 cwt.
Pressure : 165 lb. Su. Cyls.: 20″ × 26″
Driving Wheels : 6′ 0″ T.E.: 20,260 lb.
P.V.

62467-72/4/5/7-9/80/2-5/7-90/2-8
Total 27

4-4-0　2P　Class D40

*introduced 1899. Pickersgill G.NoS.
design.
† Introduced 1920. Heywood super-
heated locos.
Weights : Loco. {46 tons 7 cwt.*
{48 tons 13 cwt.†
Tender 37 tons 8 cwt.
Pressure.: 165 lb. SS. Cyls.: 18″×26″
Driving Wheels : 6′ 1″ T.E.: 16,185 lb.

*62260-2/4/5/7-72
†62273-9　　　　　　　Total 18

4-4-0　2P　Class D41

Introduced 1893. Pickersgill and
Johnson G.NoS. design.
Weights : Loco. 45 tons.
Tender 37 tons 8 cwt.
Pressure : 165 lb. Cyls.: 18″×26″
Driving Wheels : 6′ 1″ T.E.: 16,185 lb.

62225/7-32/41-3/6-9/51/2/5/6
　　　　　　　　　　　　Total 18

4-4-0　4P　Class D49

D49/1*† Introduced 1927. Gresley
design with piston valves, Walschaerts
gear and derived motion.
D49/2‡§ Introduced 1928. Development
of D49/1 with Lentz Rotary Cam
poppet valves.
D49/4ø Introduced 1942. Rebuild of
D49/2 with two inside cyls. of D11
pattern, Stephenson gear and piston
valves.
(D49/3 comprised locos 62720-4 as
built with Lentz Oscillating Cam
poppet valves. From 1938 these locos
were converted to D49/1. 62751-75
have larger valves than the earlier
D49/2, and were at first classified
D49/4.)
* Fitted with ex-G.C. tender.
†§ Fitted with ex-N.E. tender.
The remainder (†ø) have L.N.E.R.
tenders.
Weights : Loco. {66 tons.*†
{64 tons 10 cwt.‡§
{62 tons.ø
Tender {48 tons 6 cwt.*
{44 tons 2 cwt.†§
{52 tons. ‡ø
Pressure : 180 lb. Su.
Cyls. {(3) 17″×26″*†‡§
{20″×26″ø
Driving Wheels : 6′ 8″
T.E.: {21,555 lb.*†‡§
{19,890 lb.ø

*62700-2/4-19/25/8-35

†62703/20-4
‡62726/36-67/9-75
§62727
ø62768

Totals : Class D49/1　34
Class D49/2　41
Class D49/4　1

2-4-0　1MT　Class E4

*Introduced 1891. J. Holden G.E.
design.
† Fitted with side-window cab.
Weights : Loco. 40 tons 6 cwt.
Tender 30 tons 13 cwt.
Pressure : 160 lb. Cyls.: 17½″×24″
Driving Wheels : 5′ 8″ T.E.: 14,700 lb.

*62780/2/3/5-7/9-92/4/6
†62781/4/8/93/5/7　　Total 18

2-4-2T　1P　Class F2

Introduced 1898. Pollitt G.C. design,
push-and-pull fitted.
Weight : 62 tons 6 cwt.
Pressure : 160 lb. Cyls.: 18″×26″
Driving Wheels : 5′ 7″ T.E.: 17,100 lb.

67111　　　　　　　　　Total 1

2-4-2T　1P　Class F3

Introduced 1893. J. Holden G.E. design.
(Oldest survivor built 1895)
Weight : 58 tons 12 cwt.
Pressure : 160 lb. Cyls.: 17½″×24″
Driving Wheels : 5′ 8″ T.E.: 14,710 lb.

67127/8/39　　　　　　Total 3

2-4-2T　1P　Class F4

*Introduced 1884. Worsdell G.E. design,
modified by J Holden. (Oldest
survivor built 1906).
† Push-and-pull fitted.
Weight : 53 tons 19 cwt.
Pressure : 160 lb. Cyls.: 17½″×24″
Driving Wheels : 5′ 4″ T.E.: 15,620 lb.

*67152-8/62-7/71/4-8/82/4/6/7
†67151　　　　　　　　Total 24

2-4-2T   2P   **Class F5**

*Introduced 1911. S. D. Holden design
(Rebuilt from F4, oldest survivor
originally built 1903.)
†Introduced 1949. Push-and-pull fitted.
Weight : 53 tons 19 cwt.
Pressure : 180 lb.   Cyls.: 17½″×24″
Driving Wheels : 5′ 4″ T.E.: 17,570 lb.

*67188-92/4-9, 67201/4-19
†67193, 67200/2/3   **Total 32**

2-4-2T   2P   **Class F6**

Introduced 1911 S. D. Holden design,
development of F4 with higher
pressure and larger tanks.
Weight : 56 tons 9 cwt.
Pressure : 180 lb.   Cyls.: 17½″×24″
Driving Wheels : 5′ 4″ T.E.: 17,570 lb.

67220-39   **Total 20**

0-4-4T   2P   **Class G5**

*Introduced 1894. W. Worsdell N.E.
design.
† Push-and-pull fitted.
‡ Push-and-pull fitted and rebuilt with
larger tanks.
Weight : 54 tons 4 cwt.
Pressure : 160 lb.   Cyls.: 18″×24″
Driving Wheels : 5′ 1½″ T.E.: 17,265 lb.

*67240-9/51/2/4-60/2-72/4-8/83/4/
7-96/8,   67300-4/7-10/2-21/4-
36/8/41-9
†67250/3/61/73/9-82/6/97,   67305/
11/22/3/37/9
‡67340   **Total 107**

0-6-0   2MT   **Class J1**

Introduced 1908. Ivatt G.N. design
Weights : Loco.   46 tons 14 cwt.
         Tender 43 tons 2 cwt.
Pressure : 175 lb.   Cyls.: 18″×26″
Driving Wheels : 5′ 8″ T.E.: 18,430 lb.

65002-10/3/4   **Total 11**

0-6-0   2MT   **Class J2**

Introduced 1912. Ivatt/Gresley G.N.
design.
Weights : Loco.   50 tons 10 cwt.
         Tender 43 tons 2 cwt.
Pressure : 170 lb. Su. Cyls.: 19″×26″
Driving Wheels : 5′ 8″ T.E.: 19,945 lb.
P.V.

65015-23   **Total 9**

0-6-0   2F   **Classes J3 & J4**

J4* Introduced 1896. Ivatt G.N.
development of standard Stirling
0-6-0.
J3† Introduced 1912. Larger boilered
rebuild of J4 (some rebuilt from
Stirling domeless locos, oldest sur-
vivor built 1892)
Weights : Loco. $\begin{cases} 41 \text{ tons } 5 \text{ cwt.}^* \\ 42 \text{ tons } 12 \text{ cwt.}† \end{cases}$
       Tender $\begin{cases} 34 \text{ tons } 18 \text{ cwt.}^* \\ 38 \text{ tons } 10 \text{ cwt.}† \end{cases}$
Pressure : 175 lb.   Cyls.: 17½″×26″
Driving Wheels : 5′ 2″ T.E.: 19,105 lb.

*64105/14-9/22-5/8/9/31-3/5/7/40-
2/8/50/1/3/8/60
†64112/20/1/62
     Totals : Class J3   26
               Class J4   5

0-6-0   3F   **Class J5**

*Introduced 1909. Ivatt G.N. design.
† Rebuilt with superheater.
Weights : Loco.   47 tons 6 cwt.
         Tender 43 tons 2 cwt.
Pressure : $\begin{cases} 175 \text{ lb.}^* \\ 170 \text{ lb. Su.}† \end{cases}$ Cyls.: 18″×26″
Driving Wheels : 5′ 2″
T.E.: $\begin{cases} 20,210 \text{ lb. }^* \\ 19,630 \text{ lb.}† \end{cases}$

*65481-8/90-9
†65480/9   **Total 20**

0-6-0   3F   **Class J6**

Introduced 1911. Gresley G.N. design
Weights : Loco.   50 tons 10 cwt.
         Tender 43 tons 2 cwt.
Pressure : 170 lb. Su. Cyls.: 19″×26″
Driving Wheels : 5′ 2″ T.E.: 21,875 lb.
P.V.

64170-64279   **Total 110**

0-6-0   2F   **Class J10**

J10/2* Introduced 1892. Parker M.S. & L. design with small tenders.
J10/4† Introduced 1896. Pollitt development of J10/2 with larger bearings and larger tenders.
J10/6‡ Introduced 1901. Robinson locos with larger bearings and small tenders.

Weights : Loco.   41 tons 6 cwt.
Tender $\begin{cases} 37 \text{ tons } 6 \text{ cwt.}^{*‡} \\ 43 \text{ tons.}† \end{cases}$
Pressure : 160 lb.   Cyls. : 18″×26″
Driving Wheels : 5′ 1″   T.E. : 18,780 lb.

*65126/8/30
†65132-8/40-9/51/3-61/4-7/9-71/8
‡65131/9/62/3/8/72/3/5-7/9-94/6-99, 65200-5/8/9

Totals : Class J10/2   4
Class J10/4   35
Class J10/6   38

0-6-0   3F   **Class J11**

*Introduced 1901. Robinson G.C. design. Parts 1 and 4 have 3,250 gallon tenders ; Parts 2 and 5 4,000 gallon. Parts 1 and 2 have high boiler mountings ; Parts 4 and 5 low. All Parts 4 and 5 are superheated, and some of Parts 1 and 2. There are frequent changes between these parts
J11/3† Introduced 1942. Rebuilt with long-travel piston valves and boiler higher pitched.

Weights : Loco. $\begin{cases} 51 \text{ tons } 19 \text{ cwt. (Sat.)} \\ 52 \text{ tons } 2 \text{ cwt. (Su.)} \\ 53 \text{ tons } 6 \text{ cwt.}† \end{cases}$
Tender $\begin{cases} 44 \text{ tons } 3 \text{ cwt. (3,250 gall.)} \\ 48 \text{ tons } 6 \text{ cwt. (4,000 gall.)} \end{cases}$
Pressure : 180 lb. SS.   Cyls. : 18½″×26″
Driving Wheels : 5′ 2″   T.E. : 21,960 lb.

*64280-2/5-64303/5-13/5/9-23/5-31/4-45/7-51/3/5-8/60/1/3/5-72/4/6-8/80-5/7-64399, 64400/1/3-5/7-16/9/21-6/8-38/40/3-9/51-3
†64283/4, 64304/14/6-8/24/32/3/46/52/4/9/62/4/73/5/9/86, 64402/6/17/8/20/7/39/41/2/50

Totals : Class J11/3   30
Class J11
(other parts)   144

0-6-0   2F   **Class J15**

*Introduced 1883. Worsdell G E. design, modified by J. Holden. (Oldest survivor built 1886.)
† Fitted with side-window cab for Colne Valley line.

Weights : Loco.   37 tons 2 cwt.
Tender 30 tons 13 cwt.
Pressure : 160 lb.   Cyls. : 17⅛″×24″
Driving Wheels : 4′ 11″   T.E. : 16,940 lb.

*65350/4-6/9/61/2/6/9/70/3/4/7/8/82/4/8-90/6/8, 65401/2/4-6-8/13/7/20/2/3/5-7/9/30/1/3-5/7/9-79
†65391, 65405/24/32/8

Total 88

0-6-0   4F   **Class J17**

*Introduced 1901. J. Holden G. E. design. Many rebuilt from round-top boiler J16, introduced 1900.
†Fitted with small tender.

Weights : Loco.   45 tons 8 cwt.*
Tender $\begin{cases} 30 \text{ tons } 12 \text{ cwt.}† \\ 38 \text{ tons } 5 \text{ cwt.} \end{cases}$
Pressure : 180 lb. Su.   Cyls. : 19″×26″
Driving Wheels : 4′ 11″   T.E. : 24,340 lb.

*65509/20-7/9-49/51-70/2-89
†65500-8/10-9/28/71   Total 89

0-6-0   4F   **Class J19**

*Introduced 1912. S. Holden G.E. design rebuilt with round-topped boiler from 1934.
† Rebuilt with 19″ cyls. and 180 lb. pressure.
‡ Rebuilt with 19″ cyls. and 160 lb. pressure.

Weights : Loco.   50 tons 7 cwt.
Tender 38 tons 5 cwt.
Pressure : $\begin{cases} 170 \text{ lb. Su.} \\ 180 \text{ lb. Su.}† \\ 160 \text{ lb. Su.}‡ \end{cases}$
Cyls. : $\begin{cases} 20″×26″* \\ 19″×26″†‡ \end{cases}$
Driving Wheels : 4′ 11″
T.E. : $\begin{cases} 27,430 \text{ lb.}* \\ 26,215 \text{ lb.}† \\ 23,300 \text{ lb.}‡ \end{cases}$
P.V.

*64640-63/5-70/3/4
†64664/71
‡64672   Total 35

Class A1 4-6-2 No. 60159   [*P. Ransome-Wallis*

Class A3 4-6-2 No. 60076 *Galopin*   [*R. E. Vincent*

Class A4 4-6-2 No. 60012 *Commonwealth of Australia*   [*P. Ransome-Wallis*

This page
Top to Bottom : Class V4 2-6-2 No. 61701; Class B2 4-6-0 No. 61639 *Norwich City ;* Class B17/6 4-6-0 No. 61606 *Audley End* [*E. M. Patterson, P. Ransome - Wallis, C. C. B. Herbert*

Facing page
Top to Bottom : Class A2 4-6-2 No. 60528 *Tudor Minstrel ;* Class A2/3 4-6-2 No. 60518 *Tehran ;* Class A2/1 4 6-2 No.60510*Robert the Bruce;* Class A2/2 4-6-2 No. 60503 *Lord President* [¡.*P. Wilson, W. J. Anderson, C.C.B. Herbert, H. C. Casserley*

145

Above : Class B16/1
4-6-0 No. 61465
Left : Class B16/2
4-6-0 No. 61437
[J. F. Aylard, A. N.
Davenport

Above: Class D20/1
4-4-0 No. 62347
Left : Class D20/2
4-4-0 No. 62349
[P. H. Wells, J. F.
Aylard

From Top to Bottom :
Class D11/2 4-4-0 No.
62678 *Luckie Muckle-*
backit ; Class D49/1
4-4-0 No. 62733
Northumberland;Class
D3 4-4-0 No. 62000,
Class D2 4-4-0 No.
62172 /H. C. Casser-
ley, E. M. Patterson,
J. P. Wilson, H. C.
Casserley

This Page. *Above left :* Class D16/3 4-4-0 No. 62618. *Above right :* Class C4/2 4-4-2 No. 2918. *Below right :* Class K4 2-6-0 No. 61994 The Great Marquess.

[W. Dendy, P. Ransome-Wallis (2)]

Facing Page. *Above left :* Class D31 4-4-0 No. 62281. *Above right :* Class D40 4-4-0 No. 62265. *Below left :* Class D30/2 4-4-0 No. 62430 Jingling Geordie. *Below right :* Class D34 4-4-0 No. 62474 Glen Croe.

[S. Teasdale, E. M. Patterson, M. Maclean, P. Ransome-Wallis

148

(For captions see above)

149

Above left : Class O4/3 2-8-0 No. 63859.   Above right : Class O4/5 2-8-0 No. 63628.
Below left : Class O4/7 2-8-0 No. 63857.   Below right : Class O2/3 2-8-0 No. 63953.

[H. C. Casserley, T. C. Greaves, A. F. Cook, J. P. Wilson

From top to bottom :
Class J38 0-6-0 No.
65900 ; Class J39/1
0-6-0 No. 64766 ;
Class J21 0-6-0 No.
65119 (superheated);
Class J21 0-6-0 No.
65070 (24″ piston
stro' e, superheater
removed).

[E. M. Patterson, R. E.
Vincent, A. F. Cook,
B. W. Brooksbank

From top to bottom:
Class J2 0-6-0 No.
65017 ; Class J3
0-6-0 No. 64105 ;
Class J5 0-6-0 No.
65480 ; Class J1
0-6-0 No. 65007.

[P. H. Wells, R. E.
Vincent, J. P. Wilson,
P. H. Wells

Facing Page.

From top to bottom :
Class V1 2-6-2T No.
67617 ; Class J72
0-6-0T No. 69015 ;
Class G5 0-4-4T No.
67337 ; Class C12
4-4-2T No. 67368.

[*C. C. B. Herbert,
J. Davenport, P. Ran-
some-Wallis, P. H.
Wells*

This Page.

From top to bottom :
Class J26 0-6-0 No.
65765 ; Class Q7
0-8-0 No. 63471 ;
Class Q6 0-8-0 No.
63445.

[*J. F. Henton, J. F.
Aylard* (2)

*Above left : Class J63 0-6-0T No. 68209. Above right : Class
J83 0-6-0T No. 68481. Below left : Class J77 0-6-0T No. 68434.
Below right : Class Y4 0-4-0T No. 68125.
[J. N. Westwood, C. C. B. Herbert, H. C. Casserley, M. N. Clay*

Above left : Class N5/2 0-6-2T No. 69315 ; Above right : Class N5/3 No. 69311. Below left : Class L3 2-6-4T No. 69061. Below right : Class S1/1 0-8-4T No. 69900.

*From Top to Bottom :
Class A5/1 4-6-2T
No. 69808 ; Class A7
4-6-2T No. 69787 ;
Class A8 4 6 2T
No. 69884; Class A6
4-6-2T No. 69797
| C. C. B. Herbert, J. F.
Henton, L. A. Strud-
wick, P. Ransome
Wallis*

0-6-0 6F Class J20

J20* Introduced 1920. Hill G.E. design with Belpaire boiler.
J20/1† Introduced 1943. Rebuilt with B12/1 type round-topped boiler.
Weights : Loco. 54 tons 15 cwt.
Tender 38 tons 5 cwt.
Pressure : 180 lb. Su. Cyls. : 20″ × 28″
Driving Wheels : 4′ 11″ T.E. : 29,045 lb.
P.V.

*64675/6/83/7/9/96/8
†64677-82/4-6/8/90-5/7/9

Totals : Class J20   7
Class J20/1   18

0-6-0 2F Class J21

Introduced 1886. T. W. Worsdell N.E. design. Majority built as 2-cyl. compounds and later rebuilt as simple locos.
* Saturated with Joy's gear and slide valves.
† Rebuilt with superheater, Stephenson gear and piston valves.
‡ Rebuilt with piston valves, superheater removed, 24″ piston stroke.
§ Rebuilt with piston valves, superheater removed, 26″ piston stroke.
Weights : Loco. { 42 tons 1 cwt.*
{ 43 tons 15 cwt.†
{ 42 tons 9 cwt.‡§
Tender 36 tons 19 cwt.
Pressure : 160 lb. SS.
Cyls. : { 18″ × 24″*   T.E. : { 17,265 lb.*
{ 19″ × 24″†‡   { 19,240 lb.†‡
{ 19″ × 26″§   { 20,840 lb.§
Driving Wheels : 5′ 1¼″

*65041, 65122
†65028/33/8/40/7/57/61/2/4/8/75/
7/8/82/8-92/5/7/8, 65103/10/9
‡65025/30/5/9/42/67/70/6/80/99,
65100/2/5/11/7/8
§65043   **Total 44**

0-6-0 3F Class J24

Introduced 1894.
* W. Worsdell N.E. design, saturated with slide valves.
† Rebuilt with superheater and piston valves.
‡ Rebuilt with piston valves, superheater removed.
Weights : Loco. { 38 tons 10 cwt.*
{ 39 tons 11 cwt.†‡
Tender 36 tons 19 cwt.

Pressure : 160 lb. SS.
Cyls. : { 18″ × 24″*
{ 18½″ × 24″†‡
Driving Wheels : 4′ 7¼″
T.E. : { 19,140 lb.*
{ 20,220 lb. †‡

*65600/1/4/14/5/9/22/3/40/2
†65611/7/24/31/6
‡65621/7/8/44   **Total 19**

0-6-0 3F Class J25

Introduced 1898. W. Worsdell N.E. design.
*Original design, saturated with slide valves.
† Rebuilt with superheater and piston valves.
‡ Rebuilt with piston valves, superheater removed.
Weights : Loco. { 39 tons 11 cwt.*
{ 41 tons 14 cwt.†
{ 40 tons 17 cwt.‡
Tender 36 tons 19 cwt.
Pressure : 160 lb. SS. Cyls. : 18½″ × 26″
Driving Wheels : 4′ 7¼″ T.E. : 21,905 lb.

*65647/8/50/1/3/5-7/60/1/3/4/6/7/
70-2/5/6/9/80/5-91/3-65699,
65700/5/8/10/2-4/6/18/20/3/5-8
†65645/59/62, 65706/17
‡65654/73/7/83/92/, 65702

Total 61

0-6-0 4F Class J26

Introduced 1904. W. Worsdell N.E. design.
Weights : Loco. 46 tons 16 cwt.
Tender 36 tons 19 cwt.
Pressure : 180 lb. Cyls. : 18½″ × 26″
Driving Wheels : 4′ 7¼″ T.E. : 24,640 lb.
65730-79   **Total 50**

0-6-0 4F Class J27

*Introduced 1906. W. Worsdell N.E. design developed from J26.
† Introduced 1921. Raven locos superheated with piston valves.
‡ Introduced 1943. Piston valves, superheater removed.
Weights : Loco. { 47 tons Sat.
{ 49 tons 10 cwt. Su.
Tender 36 tons 19 cwt.
Pressure : 180 lb. SS. Cyls. : 18½″ × 26″
Driving Wheels : 4′ 7¼″ T.E. : 24,640 lb.

*65780-65859
†65863/6/9/71/2/4/8/80/1/3/5-7/9/
90/2-4
‡65860-2/4/5/7/8/70/3/5-7/9/82/4/8
91   **Total 115**

Classes J35-J50

0-6-0 3F Class J35

J35/5* Introduced 1906. Reid N.B. design with piston valves.
J35/4† Introduced 1908. Slide valves. (Parts 1, 2 and 3 were variations of Parts 4 and 5 before superheating.)
Weights : Loco. {51 tons.*
{50 tons 15 cwt.†
Tender {38 tons 1 cwt.*
{37 tons 15 cwt.†
Pressure : 180 lb. Su. Cyls.: 18½″ × 26″
Driving Wheels : 5′ 0″ T.E.: 22,080 lb.

*64464-6/6/8/70-7
†64478-80/2·64499, 64500-2/4-7/9-35

Totals: Class J35/4 55
Class J35/5 15

0-6-0 2F Class J36

Introduced 1888. Holmes N.B. design.
Weights : Loco. 41 tons 19 cwt.
Tender 33 tons 9 cwt.
Pressure : 165 lb. Cyls.: 18½″ × 26″
Driving Wheels : 5′ 0″ T.E.: 19,690 lb.

65210/1/3/4/6-8/21/2/4-55/7-61/4-8/70/1/3-83/5-8/90-3/5-8, 65300/3-25/7/9-31/3-5/8-46
Total 116

0-6-0 4F Class J37

Introduced 1914. Reid N.B. design. Superheated development of J35.
Weights : Loco. 54 tons 14 cwt.
Tender 40 tons 19 cwt.
Pressure : 180 lb. Su. Cyls.: 19¼″ × 26″
Driving Wheels : 5′ 0″ T.E.: 25,210 lb. P.V.

64536-64639 Total 104

0-6-0 6F Class J38

*Introduced 1926. Grasley design. Predecessor of J39, with 4′ 8″ wheels, boiler 6″ longer than J39 and smokebox 6″ shorter.
† Rebuilt with J39 boiler.
Weights : Loco. 58 tons 19 cwt.
Tender 44 tons 4 cwt.
Pressure : 180 lb. Su. Cyls.: 20″ × 26″
Driving Wheels : 4′ 8″ T.E.: 28,415 lb. P.V.

*65900-2/4/5/7/9-16/9-25/8-34
†65903/6/8/17/8/26/7 Total 35

0-6-0 4F Class J39

Introduced 1926. Grasley design.
J39/1* Standard 3,500 gallon tender.
J39/2† Standard 4,200 gallon tender
J39/3‡ Various ex-N.E. tenders (3,940 gallon on 64843-5, 4,125 gallon on 64855-9)
Weights : Loco. 57 tons 17 cwt.
Tender {44 tons 4 cwt.} and others
{52 tons 13 cwt.†}
Pressure : 180 lb. Su. Cyls.: 20″ × 26″
Driving Wheels : 5′ 2″ T.E.: 25,665 lb. P.V.

*64700-83/96-9, 64800-19/23-37/46-54/60-71, 64933-44
†64784-95, 64820-2/38-41/72-99, 64900-32/45-70
‡64842-5/55-9, 64971-88

Totals : Class J39/1 156
Class J39/2 106
Class J39/3 27

0-6-0T 4F Class J50

J50/2* Introduced 1922. Gresley G.N. design (68900-19 rebuilt from smaller J51, built 1915-22).
J50/3† Introduced 1926. Post-grouping development with detail differences.
J50/1‡ Introduced 1929. Rebuilt from smaller J51, built 1913-4.
J50/4§ Introduced 1937. Development of J50/3 with larger bunker.
Weights :{56 tons 6 cwt.‡
{58 tons 3 cwt.†§
{57 tons.*
Pressure : 175 lb. Cyls.: 18½″ × 26″
Driving Wheels : 4′ 8″ T.E.: 23,635 lb.

*68900-39
†68940-77
‡68890-9
§68978-91

Totals : Class J50/1 10
Class J50/2 40
Class J50/3 38
Class J50/4 14

0-6-0ST 3F Class J52

J52/2* Introduced 1897. Ivatt standard G.N. saddletank with domed boiler.
J52/1† Introduced 1922. Rebuild of Stirling domeless saddletank (introduced 1892)—non-condensing.
J52/1‡ Introduced 1922. Condensing rebuild of Stirling locos.
§ J52/2 with boiler pressure raised to 175 lb. Weight : 51 tons 14 cwt.
Pressure : $\begin{cases} 170 \text{ lb.} \\ 175 \text{ lb.§} \end{cases}$ Cyls.: $18'' \times 26''$
Driving Wheels: 4′ 8″ T.E. $\begin{cases} 21,735 \text{ lb.} \\ 22,370 \text{ lb. §} \end{cases}$

*68805-15/7-39/41-4/6-59/61-75/
7-89 Departmental locos. :
68816/45

†68762-72/5/9/80/6/9/90/2/7-9,
68800-4 Departmental loco. :
68782

‡68757-61/73/4/6-8/81/3-5/7/8/91/
3-6

§68840/60/76

Totals : Class J52/1 48
Class J52/2 83

0-6-0ST 0F Class J62

Introduced 1897. Pollitt M.S. & L. design.
Weight : 30 tons 17 cwt.
Pressure : 150 lb. Cyls.: (O) $13'' \times 20''$
Driving Wheels : 3′ 6″ T.E. 10,260 lb.

68200 Total 1

0-6-0T 0F Class J63

Introduced 1906. Robinson G.C. design.
Weight : 37 tons 9 cwt.
Pressure : 150 lb. Cyls.: (O) $13'' \times 20''$
Driving Wheels : 3′ 6″ T.E. 10,260 lb.

68204-10 Total 7

0-6-0T 0F Class J65

Introduced 1889. J. Holden G.C. design.
Weight : 36 tons 11 cwt.
Pressure : 160 lb. Cyls.: $14'' \times 20''$
Driving Wheels : 4′ 0″ T.E. 11,105 lb.

68211/4 Total 2

0-6-0T 2F Class J66

Introduced 1886. J. Holden G.E. design.
Weight : 40 tons 6 cwt.
Pressure : 160 lb. Cyls.: $16\frac{1}{2}'' \times 22''$
Driving Wheels : 4′ 0″ T.E. 16,970 lb.

68371-83/5/7/8
Departmental loco. : 68370
Total 17

0-6-0T Classes
2F J67
3F J69

J67/1* Introduced 1890. J. Holden G.E. design with 160 lb. pressure.
J69/1† Introduced 1902. Development of J67 with 180 lb. pressure, larger tanks and larger firebox. (some rebuilt from J67.)
J67/2‡ Introduced 1937. Rebuild of J69 with 160 lb. boiler and small firebox.
J69/2§ Introduced 1950. J67/1 rebuilt with 180 lb. boiler and large firebox.
Weights : $\begin{cases} 40 \text{ tons.*‡} \\ 40 \text{ tons 9 cwt.†§} \end{cases}$
Pressure : $\begin{cases} 160 \text{ lb.*‡} \\ 180 \text{ lb.†§} \end{cases}$ Cyls.: $16\frac{1}{2}'' \times 22''$
Driving Wheels : 4′ 0″
T.E. $\begin{cases} 16,970 \text{ lb.*‡} \\ 19,090 \text{ lb. †§} \end{cases}$

*68492/3/6/8, 68509/11-8/21/3/83/
4/6-8-90/2-5, 68606/8/11/6
†68491/4/5/7/9, 68500-5/7/8/24-8/
30/2-5/7/8/41-6/8-63/5-71/3-9/
81/5/7/91/6/8/9, 68600-3/5/7/12/
3/7-9/21/3/5/6/9-33/5/6
‡68529/31/6/40/7/72/97, 68609/10/
28
§68490, 68510/19/20/2

Totals : Class J67/1 29
Class J67/2 10
Class J69/1 90
Class J69/2 5

0-6-0T   3F   Class J68

Introduced 1912. Hill G.E. development of J69 with side-window cab
Weight : 42 tons 9 cwt.
Pressure : 180 lb.   Cyls.: $16\frac{1}{2}'' \times 22''$
Driving Wheels : 4' 0'' T.E.: 19,090 lb

68638-66	**Total 29**

0-6-0T   Class J69

(See under Class J67)

0-6-0T (Tram Locos)
0F   Class J70

Introduced 1903. J. Holden G.E. design.
Weight : 27 tons 1 cwt.
Pressure : 180 lb. Cyls.: (O) $12'' \times 15''$
Driving Wheels : 3' 1'' T.E.: 8,930 lb.
Walschaerts gear.

68216/7/9-26	**Total 10**

0-6-0T   0F   Class J71

*Introduced 1886. T. W. Worsdell N.E design.
†‡ Altered cylinder dimensions.
Weight : 37 tons 12 cwt.
Pressure : 140 lb. Dr. Wheels : 4' 7$\frac{1}{4}$''
Cyls.:$\begin{cases} 16'' \times 22''* \\ 16\frac{1}{2}'' \times 22''† \\ 18'' \times 22''‡ \end{cases}$ T.E.:$\begin{cases} 12,130 \text{ lb.*} \\ 13,300 \text{ lb.†} \\ 15,355 \text{ lb.‡} \end{cases}$

*68231-3/5/6/8-40/2/4/5/7-9/51/4-6/60/2-73/5-9/81-4/8/90-2/4-9 68300/1
†68230/4/46/50/2/3/8/9/80/6/7/9/93, 68302-11/3/6
‡68312

	Total 79

0-6-0T   2F   Class J72

*Introduced 1898. W. Worsdell N.E. design.
† Altered cylinder dimensions.
Weight : 38 tons 12 cwt.
Pressure : 140 lb.   Cyls.$\begin{cases} 17'' \times 24''* \\ 18'' \times 24''† \end{cases}$
Driving Wheels : 4' 1$\frac{1}{4}$''
T.E.:$\begin{cases} 16,760 \text{ lb.*} \\ 18,790 \text{ lb.†} \end{cases}$

*68670-84/6-99, 68700-54, 69001-20
†68685

	Total 96

0-6-0T   3F   Class J73

*Introduced 1891. W. Worsdell N.E. design.
Weight : 46 tons 15 cwt.
Pressure : 160 lb.   Cyls.: $19'' \times 24''$
Driving Wheels : 4' 7$\frac{1}{4}$'' T.E.: 21,320 lb.

68355-64	**Total 10**

0-6-0T   2F   Class J77

*Introduced 1899. W. Worsdell N.E. rebuild of Fletcher 0-4-4T originally built 1874-84.
† Darlington rebuilds with square-cornered cab roof (remainder York rebuilds with rounded cab).
Weight : 43 tons.
Pressure : 160 lb.   Cyls.: $17'' \times 22''$
Driving Wheels : 4' 1$\frac{1}{4}$'' T.E.: 17,560 lb.

*68391/8/9, 68401/2/6-10/3/4/7/21-31/3-8
†68392/3/5/7, 68404/5/12/20/32/40

	Total 40

0-6-0T   2F   Class J83

Introduced 1900. Holmes N.B. design.
Weight : 45 tons 5 cwt.
Pressure : 150 lb.   Cyls.: $17'' \times 26''$
Driving Wheels : 4' 6'' T.E.: 17,745 lb.

68442-61/3-81	**Total 39**

0-6-0T   0F   Class J88

Introduced 1904. Reid N.B. design with short wheelbase.
Weight : 38 tons 14 cwt.
Pressure : 130 lb.   Cyls.: (O) $15'' \times 22''$
Driving Wheels : 3' 9'' T.E.: 12,155 lb.

68320-54	**Total 35**

0-6-0 Crane Tank
0F   Class J92

Introduced 1891. J. Holden G.E. rebuild of Ruston & Proctor 0-6-0T (originally built 1868.)
Weight : 40 tons 8 cwt.
Pressure : 140 lb.   Cyls.: $16'' \times 22''$
Driving Wheels : 4' 0'' T.E.: 13,960 lb.

Departmental locos. :	68667-9
	Total 3

0-6-0ST   4F   Class J94

Introduced 1943. Riddles M.o.S. design. (Bought from M.o.S. 1946.)
Weight : 48 tons 5 cwt.
Pressure : 170 lb.   Cyls.: $18'' \times 26''$
Driving Wheels : 4' 3'' T.E.: 23,870 lb.

68006-80	**Total 75**

2-6-0 6MT K1 & K4

K4* Introduced 1937. Gresley loco for West Highland line.

Weights : Loco. 68 tons 8 cwt.
Tender 44 tons 4 cwt.

Pressure : 200 lb. Su.

Cyls.: (3) $18\frac{1}{2}'' \times 26''$

Driving Wheels : 5' 2" T.E.: 36,600 lb.

Walschaerts gear and derived motion, P.V.

K1/1† Introduced 1945. Thompson 2-cyl. loco. Rebuilt from K4.

K1‡ Introduced 1949. Peppercorn development of Thompson K1/1 for new construction, with increased length.

Weights : Loco. 66 tons 17 cwt.
Tender 44 tons 4 cwt.

Pressure : 225 lb. Su.

Cyls.: (O) $20'' \times 26''$

Driving Wheels : 5'2" T.E.: 32,080 lb.

Walschaerts gear, P.V.

*61993-6/8
†61997
‡62001-70

Total : Class K1 70
Class K1/1 1
Class K4 5

2-6-0 4MT Class K2

K2/2* Introduced 1914. Gresley G.N. design.

K2/1† Introduced 1931. Rebuilt from small-boilered K1 (introduced 1912).

‡ K2/2 fitted with side-window cab in Scottish Region.

§ K2/1 with side-window cab.

Weights : Loco. 64 tons 8 cwt.
Tender 43 tons 2 cwt.

Pressure : 180 lb. Su.

Cyls.: (O) $20'' \times 26''$

Driving Wheels : 5' 8" T.E.: 23,400 lb.

Walschaerts gear, P.V.

*61730-63/5-71/3/7/8/80
†61720-8
‡61764/72/4-6/9/81-94
§61729

Totals : Class K2/1 10
Class K2/2 65

2-6-0 6MT Classes K3 & K5

K3/2* Introduced 1924. Development of Gresley G.N. design, built to L.N.E.R. loading gauge.

K3/3† Introduced 1929. Differ in details only, such as springs, from K3/2.

‡ K3/2 fitted with ex-G.N. tender. (K3/1 were ex-G.N. locos (introduced 1920), with G.N. cabs, and K3/4, K3/5 and K3/6 were variations of K3/2, differing in weight and details. These locos have now been modified to K3/2.)

Weights : Loco. 72 tons 12 cwt.
Tender { 52 tons.
43 tons 2 cwt.‡

Pressure : 180 lb. Su.

Cyls.: (3) $18\frac{1}{2}'' \times 26''$

Driving Wheels : 5' 8" T.E.: 30,030 lb.

Walschaerts gear and derived motion, P.V.

K5§ Introduced 1945. Thompson 2-cyl. rebuild of K3.

Weights : Loco. 71 tons 5 cwt.
Tender 52 tons.

Pressure : 225 lb. Su.

Cyls.: (O) $20'' \times 26''$

Driving Wheels : 5' 8" T.E.. 29,250 lb.

Walschaerts gear, P.V.

*61800-11/3-40/2-53/60-2/4-9/90-9, 61900-92
†61870-89
‡61812/41/54-9
§61863

Totals : Class K3/2 172
Class K3/3 20
Class K5 1

2-6-0 Class K4

(See under Class K1)

2-6-4T 4MT Class L1

Introduced 1945. Thompson design.
Weight : 89 tons 9 cwt.
Pressure : 225 lb. Cyls.: (O) $20'' \times 26''$
Driving Wheels : 5' 2" T.E.: 32,080 lb.
Walschaerts gear, P.V.

67701-67800 Total 100

2-6-4T 5F Class L3

*Introduced 1914. Robinson G.C. design.
†Altered cylinder dimensions.
Weight : 97 tons 9 cwt.
Pressure : 180 lb. Su. Cyls. $\begin{cases} 21'' \times 26'' \\ 20'' \times 26''* \end{cases}$
Driving Wheels: 5' 1'' T.E. $\begin{cases} 28,760 \text{ lb.} \\ 26,085 \text{ lb.}* \end{cases}$

*69050-2/5/6/60/2/4/5/7/9
†69061 **Total 12**

0-6-2T 2MT Class N1

* Introduced 1907. Ivatt G.N. design, prototype of class.
†‡§¶ Introduced 1907. Standard design with shorter tanks and detail differences.
§¶ Rebuilt with superheater and reduced pressure.
‡¶ Fitted with condensing gear.
Weights : $\begin{cases} 64 \text{ tons 14 cwt.}* \\ 65 \text{ tons 17 cwt.} \end{cases}$
Pressure : $\begin{cases} 175 \text{ lb.} \quad \text{Cyls. : } 18'' \times 26'' \\ 170 \text{ lb. Su. §¶} \end{cases}$
Driving Wheels: 5' 8'' T.E. $\begin{cases} 18,430 \text{ lb.} \\ 17,900 \text{ lb.§¶} \end{cases}$

*69430
†69440/3/4/6-9/54/9/73/4
‡69431-4/41/2/5/50/1/3/5-8/60-3/5-71/5-7/80/1/4/5
§69436/52/72/83
¶69435/7/9/64/78/9/82 **Total 55**

0-6-2T 3MT Class N2

N2/2* Introduced 1925. Post-grouping development of Gresley ex-G.N. N2/1, introduced 1920, which class is now included in N2/2. Condensing gear and small chimney.

N2/2† Condensing gear removed.

N2/3‡ Introduced 1925. Locos built non-condensing, orginally fitted with large chimney. Some now with small chimney.

N2/4§ Introduced 1928. Development of N2/2, slightly heavier. Condensing gear and small chimney.
(The small chimneys are to suit the Metropolitan loading gauge, for working to Moorgate St. Condensing gear has been removed from or added to certain locos transferred from or to the London area.)

Weights : $\begin{cases} 70 \text{ tons 5 cwt.}* † \\ 70 \text{ tons 8 cwt.}‡ \\ 71 \text{ tons 9 cwt.§} \end{cases}$
Pressure : 170 lb. Su. Cyls.: 19'' × 26''
Driving Wheels : 5' 8'' T.E. : 19,945 lb. P.V.

*69490-9, 69504/6/12/3/7/20-49
†69500-3/5/7-11/4-6/8/9/50-5/7-61
‡69562-7/94-6
§69556/68-93

Totals : Class N2/2 70
Class N2/3 9
Class N2/4 28

0-6-2T 2MT Class N4

N4/2* Introduced 1889. Parker M.S. & L. design.
N4/4† Introduced 1892. Development of N4/2 with larger bunker. N4/1 and N4/3 were N4/2 and N4/4 with longer chimney.
Weights : $\begin{cases} 61 \text{ tons 14 cwt.}* \\ 61 \text{ tons 19 cwt.}† \end{cases}$
Pressure : 160 lb. Cyls.: 18'' × 26''
Driving Wheels : 5' 1'' T.E.: 18,780 lb. Joy gear.

*69225/7-36/9/40
†69242/4-6

Totals : Class N4/2 13
Class N4/4 4

0-6-2T 2MT Class N5

N5/2* Introduced 1891. Parker M.S. & L. design developed from N4.
N5/3† Introduced 1915. N5/2 rebuilt with larger tanks, bunker and cyls. (N5/1 was N5/2 with longer chimney).
Weights : $\begin{cases} 62 \text{ tons 7 cwt.}* \\ 64 \text{ tons 13 cwt.}† \end{cases}$
Pressure : 160 lb. Cyls.: $\begin{cases} 18'' \times 26''* \\ 18\frac{1}{2}'' \times 26''† \end{cases}$
Driving Wheels: 5' 1'' T.E. $\begin{cases} 18,780 \text{ lb.}* \\ 19,840 \text{ lb.}† \end{cases}$

*69250/2-99, 69300-10/2-70
†69311

Totals : Class N5/2 119
Class N5/3 1

0-6-2T 3MT Class N7

N7/1[1] Introduced 1925. Post-grouping development of Hill G.E. design with detail differences.

N7/2[2] Introduced 1926. Development of N7/1 with long-travel valves.

N7/3[3] Introduced 1927. Doncaster-built version of N7/2 with round-topped boiler.

N7/4[4] Introduced 1940. Pre-grouping N7 (G.E.) rebuilt with round-topped boiler, retaining short-travel valves.

N7/1[5] Introduced 1943. N7/1 rebuilt with round-topped boiler, retaining short-travel valves.

N7/3[6] Introduced 1943. N7/2 rebuilt with round-topped boiler.

Weights : $\begin{cases} \text{63 tons 13 cwt.}[1] \\ \text{64 tons 17 cwt.}[2] \\ \text{64 tons}[3] \\ \text{61 tons 16 cwt.}[4] \\ \text{64 tons}[5] \\ \text{64 tons}[6] \end{cases}$

Pressure : 180 lb. Su. Cyls.: 18″ × 24″
Driving Wheels : 4′ 10″ T.E.: 20,515 lb.
Walschaerts gear, P.V.

[1] 69623/4/6-31/4/7/8/40-3/5/6/53-5/7-9/61/5/8/70

[2] 69672/4/81/3/8-90/4/5/8, 69700

[3] 69702-33

[4] 69600-21

[5] 69622/5/32/3/5/6/9/44/7-52/6/60/2-4/6/7/9/71

[6] 69673/5-80/2/4-7/91-3/6/7/9, 69701

Totals : Class N7/1 27
Class N7/2 11
Class N7/3 74
Class N7/4 22

0-6-2T 3MT Class N8

* Introduced 1886. T. W. Worsdell N.E. design, saturated with Joy's gear and slide valves (majority rebuilt from compounds).

† Rebuilt with superheater, Stephenson gear and piston valves, 24″ piston stroke.

‡ As † but with 26″ stroke.

§ Rebuilt with Stephenson gear and piston valves, superheater removed, 24″ stroke.

¶ As § but with 26″ piston stroke.

Weights : $\begin{cases} \text{56 tons 5 cwt.* §¶} \\ \text{58 tons 14 cwt.† ‡} \end{cases}$

Pressure : 160 lb. SS.

Cyls.: $\begin{cases} 18″ \times 24″\text{*} \\ 19″ \times 24″\text{†§} \\ 19″ \times 26″‡¶ \end{cases}$

Driving Wheels : 5′ 1¼″.*

T.E.: $\begin{cases} \text{17,265 lb.*} \\ \text{19,235 lb.†§} \\ \text{20,840 lb.‡¶} \end{cases}$

*69389/92

†69371/7/9/80/5/90/1/3-5/8

‡69386, 69401

§69372/8/87

¶69381/2, 69400   Total 21

0-6-2T 3MT Class N9

Introduced 1893. T. W. Worsdell N.E. design.
Weight : 56 tons 10 cwt.
Pressure : 160 lb. Cyls.: 19″ × 26″
Driving Wheels : 5′ 1¼″ T.E.: 20,840 lb.

69410/3/8/23-7/9   Total 9

0-6-2T 3F Class N10

Introduced 1902. W. Worsdell N.E. design.
Weight : 57 tons 14 cwt.
Pressure : 160 lb. Cyls.: 18½″ × 26″
Driving Wheels : 4′ 7¼″ T.E.: 21,905 lb.

69090-69102/4-9   Total 19

0-6-2T 4F Class N13

Introduced 1913. Stirling H. & B. design.
Pressure : 175 lb. Cyls.: 18″ × 26″
Driving Wheels : 4′ 6″ T.E.: 23,205 lb.

69111-9   Total 9

0-6-2T 4MT Class N14

Introduced 1909. Reid N.B. design.
Pressure : 175 lb. Cyls.: 18″ × 26″
Driving Wheels : 4′ 6″ T.E.: 23,205 lb.

69120/4/5   Total 3

0-6-2T 4MT Class N15

N15/2* Introduced 1910. Reid N.B. design developed from N14. Cowlairs incline banking locos.

N15/1† Introduced 1910. Development of N15/2 with smaller bunker for normal duties.

Weight : $\begin{cases} \text{62 tons 1 cwt.*} \\ \text{60 tons 18 cwt.†} \end{cases}$

Pressure : 175 lb. Cyls.: 18″ × 26″
Driving Wheels : 4′ 6″ T.E.: 23,205 lb.

*69126-31

†69132-69224

Total : Class N15/1 93
Class N15/2 6

Classes O1 & O4

2-8-0 F8 (O1)
F7 (O4)

O4/1[1] Introduced 1911. Robinson G.C. design with small Belpaire boiler, steam and vacuum brakes and water scoop.

O4/3[3] Introduced 1917. Ex-R.O.D. locos with steam brake only and no scoop. Taken into L.N.E.R. stock from 1924.

O4/2[2] Introduced 1925. O4/3 with cab and boiler mountings reduced to Scottish loading gauge.

O4/5[4] Introduced 1932. Rebuilt with shortened O2-type boiler and separate smokebox saddle.

O4/6[5] Introduced 1924. Rebuilt from O5, retaining higher cab (63912-20 with side-windows).

O4/7[6] Introduced 1939. Rebuilt with shortened O2-type boiler, retaining G C. smokebox.

O4/8[7] Introduced 1944. Rebuilt with 100A(B1) boiler, retaining original cylinders.
(O4/4 were rebuilds with O2 boilers, since rebuilt again ; O5 was a G.C. development of O4 with larger Belpaire boiler.)

Weights: Loco. { 73 tons 4 cwt.[1]
73 tons 4 cwt.[3]
73 tons 4 cwt.[2]
74 tons 13 cwt.[4]
73 tons 4 cwt.[5]
73 tons 17 cwt.[6]
72 tons 10 cwt.[7]

Tender { 48 tons 6 cwt. (with scoop)
47 tons 6 cwt. (without scoop)
Pressure : 180 Ib. Su.
Cyls.: (O) 21" × 26"
Driving Wheels : 4' 8" T.E.: 31,325 Ib.
P.V.

O1[8] Introduced 1944. Thompson rebuild with 100A boiler, Walschaerts valve gear and new cylinders.
Weights : Loco. 73 tons 6 cwt.
Tender as O4.
Pressure : 225 Ib. Su.
Cyls.: (O) 20" × 26"
Driving Wheels : 4' 8" T.E.: 35,520 Ib.
Walschaerts gear, P.V.

1 63572-4/6/7/80/1/3-7/93/7-9,
63601/2/4-9/11/2/4/7/8/20-7/
31/2/5/40/54/8/60/4/71/7/83/4/
92/3/8, 63700/7/10/9/22/3/7/
36/43/57/62/78/97/9, 63805/9

3 63629/36-9/41/2/5/9/56/7/9/
65-8/72/9/81/5/6/8/91/4-7,
63701-3/13-8/20/1/4/8/9/31-5/

7/9/41/2/4/50/1/3/4/6/9/63-7/9/
71/4/6/9/81-3/7/90/1/3/8,
63800/1/4/7/12/3/21-3/9/32/3/
5/7/40-2/5/6/9/50/2/5/8/9/61/
2/4/70/3/7/8/81/3/5/8/9/95/
7-63899, 63900

3 63644/7/8/74/80/2/90, 63704/9/
30/47

4 63628, 63726/45/88, 63816/51

5 63902/4-8/11-5/7/20

6 63570/82/8/95,63660/3/15/6/34/
43/55/61/2/9/73/5/99, 63705/6/
8/47-9/58/61/70/2/5/94, 63824/
39/43/8/57/60/76/80/4/91/4

7 63575, 63613/33/51/3, 63738/
85, 63802/18/9/27/8/36/53/82/
93

8 63571/8/9/89-92/4/6, 63610/9/
30/46/50/2/63/70/6/8/87/9,
63711/2/25/40/6/52/5/60/8/
73/7/80/4/6/9/92/5/6, 63803/6/
8/17/38/54/6/63/5-9/72/4/9/86/
7/90, 63901

Totals : Class O1   58
Class O4/1   68
Class O4/2   11
Class O4/3   117
Class O4/5   6
Class O4/6   13
Class O4/7   40
Class O4/8   16

2-8-0 8F **Class O2**

O2/1[*] Introduced 1921. Development of experimental Gresley G.N. 3-cyl. loco (L.N.E.R. 3921). Subsequently rebuilt with side-window cab, and reduced boiler mountings.

O2/2[†] Introduced 1924. Development of O2/1 with detail differences.

O2/3[‡] Introduced 1932. Development of O2/2 with side-window cab and reduced boiler mountings.

O2/4[§] Introduced 1943. Rebuilt with 100A (B1 type) boiler and smokebox extended backwards (3924 retaining G.N. tender).

Weights : Loco. { 75 tons 16 cwt.[*][†]
78 tons 13 cwt.[‡]
74 tons 2 cwt.[§]
Tender { 43 tons 2 cwt. (63922-46)
52 tons (63947-87)

Pressure : 180 lb. Su.

Cyls.: (3) $18\frac{1}{2}'' \times 26''$

Driving Wheels : 4' 8'' T.E. : 36,470 lb.
Walschaerts gear and derived motion,
P.V.

*63922/3/5-31
†63933-46
‡63947-9/51-61/3-87
§63924/32/50/62

Totals : Class O2/1 9
Class O2/2 14
Class O2/3 39
Class O2/4 4

2-8-0   8F   Class O3

Introduced 1913. Gresley G.N. design.
Weights : Loco. 7o tons 4 cwt.
Tender 43 tons 2 cwt.
Pressure : 180 lb. Su.
Cyls.: (O) $21'' \times 28''$
Driving Wheels : 4' 8'' T.E. : 33,735 lb.
Walschaerts gear, P.V.

63475-86/8/91/3   Total 15

2-8-0   Class O4

(See under Class O1)

0-8-0T   5F   Class Q1

Thompson rebuild of Q4 0-8-0, intro-
duced 1902.
Q1/1* Introduced 1942. 1,500 gallon
tanks.
Q1/2† Introduced 1943. 2,000 gallon
tanks.
Weights : $\begin{cases} 69 \text{ tons 18 cwt.*} \\ 73 \text{ tons 18 cwt †} \end{cases}$
Pressure: 180 lb. Cyls.: (O) $19'' \times 26''$
Driving Wheels : 4' 8'' T.E. : 25,645 lb.

*69925-8
†69929-37

Totals : Class Q1/1 4
Class Q1/2 9

0-8-0   5F   Class Q4

Q4/1* Introduced 1902. Robinson
G.C. design. Saturated locos with
slide valves.
Q4/2† Introduced 1914. Superheated
rebuild, retaining slide valves.
Q4/2‡ Introduced 1914. Rebuilt with
superheater and piston valves.
Weights : Loco. $\begin{cases} 62 \text{ tons 8 cwt.*} \\ 63 \text{ tons.†} \\ 64 \text{ tons 1 cwt.‡} \end{cases}$
Tender 48 tons 6 cwt.
Pressure : 180 lb. SS.
Cyls.: (O) $\begin{cases} 19'' \times 26''*† \\ 21'' \times 26''‡ \end{cases}$

Classes O3-S1

Driving Wheels : 4' 8''
T.E.: $\begin{cases} 25,645 \text{ lb.*†} \\ 31,325 \text{ lb.‡} \end{cases}$

*63202-5/26/7/34
†63201/17/23/9/35/6/40/3
‡63220/1/5

Totals : Class Q4/1 7
Class Q4/2 11

0-8-0   6F   Class Q5

Q5/1* (Slide valve) Introduced 1901.
Worsdell N.E. design.
Q5/1† (Piston valve) Introduced 1903.
Weights : Loco. 58 tons 8 cwt.
Tender 40 tons 8 cwt.
Pressure : 175 lb. Cyls.: (O) $20'' \times 26''$
Driving Wheels : 4' $7\frac{1}{4}''$ T.E.: 28,000 lb.

*63270/1/4/80/2-5/7
†63251/7/9/61/7, 63303/11/4/9/26/
8/33/6   Total 22

0-8-0   6F   Class Q6

Introduced 1913. Raven N.E. design.
* Some locos are fitted with tenders
from withdrawn B15 locos.
Weights : Loco. 65 tons 18 cwt.
Tender $\begin{cases} 44 \text{ tons 2 cwt.} \\ 44 \text{ tons.*} \end{cases}$
Pressure : 180 lb.
Cyls.: (O) $20'' \times 26''$
Driving Wheels : 4' $7\frac{1}{4}''$ T.E.: 28,800 lb.
P.V.

63340-63459   Total 120

0-8-0   7F   Class Q7

Introduced 1919. Raven N.E. design.
Weights : Loco. 71 tons 12 cwt.
Tender 44 tons 2 cwt.
Pressure : 180 lb. Su.
Cyls.: (3) $18\frac{1}{2}'' \times 26''$
Driving Wheels : 4' $7\frac{1}{2}''$ T.E.: 36,965 lb.
P.V.

63460-74   Total 15

0-8-4T   7F   Class S1

S1/1* Introduced 1907. Robinson
G.C. design, since rebuilt with superheater.
S1/2† Introduced 1932. S1/1 rebuilt
with booster and superheater,
booster since removed.
S1/3‡ Introduced 1932. New locos
built with booster, booster later
removed,

Classes TI-WD

Weights : $\begin{cases} 99 \text{ tons } 6 \text{ cwt.}^* \\ 99 \text{ tons } 2 \text{ cwt.}\dagger \\ 99 \text{ tons } 1 \text{ cwt.}\ddagger \end{cases}$

Pressure : 180 lb. Su.
Cyls.: (3) 18″×26″
Driving Wheels : 4′ 8″ T.E.: 34,525 lb.

*69900/2/3   †69901   ‡69904/5
Totals : Class SI/1 3
Class SI/2 1
Class SI/3 2

4-8-0T   7F   Class TI

*Introduced 1909. W. Worsdell N.E. design.
†Rebuilt with superheater.
Weight : 85 tons 8 cwt.
Pressure : 175 lb. SS.
Cyls.: (3) 18″×26″
Driving Wheels: 4′ 7¼″ T.E.: 34,080 lb. P.V.

*69910-3/5-22
†69914   Total 13

2-8-8-2T Unclass. Class U1 (Beyer-Garratt Loco)

Introduced 1925. Gresley/Beyer Peacock design.
Weight : 178 tons 1 cwt.
Pressure : 180 lb. Su.
Cyls.: (6) 18½″×26″
Driving Wheels : 4′ 8″ T.E.: 72,940 lb.
Walschaerts gear, derived motion, P.V.

69999   Total 1

2-6-2T   4MT   Classes VI & V3

VI* Introduced 1930. Gresley design
V3† Introduced 1939. Development of VI with higher pressure (locos numbered below 67682 rebuilt from VI).

Weights : $\begin{cases} 84 \text{ tons.}^* \\ 86 \text{ tons } 16 \text{ cwt.}\dagger \end{cases}$

Pressure : $\begin{cases} 180 \text{ lb. Su.}^* \\ 200 \text{ lb. Su.}\dagger \end{cases}$

Cyls.: (3) 16″×26″
Driving Wheels : 5′ 8″
T.E.: $\begin{cases} 22,465 \text{ lb.}^* \\ 24,960 \text{ lb.}\dagger \end{cases}$

Walschaerts gear, derived motion, P.V

*67600-33/5-68/70/1/3/4/6-81
†67634/69/72/5/82-91
Totals : Class VI 78
Class V3 14

2-6-2   6MT   Class V2

Introduced 1936. Gresley design.
Weights : Loco. 93 tons 2 cwt.
Tender 52 tons.
Pressure : 220 lb. Su.
Cyls.: (3) 18½″×26″
Driving Wheels : 6′ 2″ T.E.: 33,730 lb
Walschaerts gear and derived motion, P.V.

60800-60983   Total 184

2-6-2T   Class V3

(See under Class VI)

2-6-2   5MT   Class V4

Introduced 1941. Gresley design.
Weights : Loco. 70 tons 8 cwt.
Tender 42 tons 15 cwt.
Pressure : 250 lb. Su.
Cyls.: (3) 15″×26″
Driving Wheels : 5′ 8″ T.E. : 27,420 lb.
Walscharts gear and derived motion, P.V.

61700/1   Total 2

4-6-4   7P   Class W1

Introduced 1937. Rebuilt from Gresley experimental high-pressure 4-cyl. compound with water-tube boiler, introduced 1929.
Weights : Loco. 107 tons 17 cwt.
Tender 60 tons 7 cwt.
Pressure : 250 lb. Su.
Cyls.: (3) 20″×26″
Driving Wheels : 6′ 8″ T.E.: 41,435 lb
Walschaerts gear and derived motion P.V.

60700   Total 1

2-8-0   8F   Class WD

Ministry of Supply " Austerity " 2-8-0 locomotives purchased by British Railways, 1948.
Introduced 1943. Riddles M.o.S. design.
Weights : Loco. 70 tons 5 cwt.
Tender 55 tons 10 cwt.
Pressure: 225 lb. Cyls.: (O) 19″×28″.
Driving Wheels : 4′ 8½″ T.E. 34,215 lb.
Walschaerts gear, P.V.

90000-90732   Total 733

2-10-0   8F   Class WD

Ministry of Supply "Austerity" 2-10-0 locomotives purchased by British Railways, 1948.

Introduced 1943. Riddles M.O.S. design.
Weights : Loco.   78 tons 6 cwt.
            Tender 55 tons 10 cwt.
Pressure : 225 lb. Cyls. (O) 19'' × 28''.
Driving Wheels : 4' 8½'' T.E. 34,215 lb.
Walschaerts gear, P.V.

90750-74   **Total 25**

0-4-0T   Unclass.   Class Y1

Sentinel Wagon Works design. Single-speed Geared Sentinel Locomotives. The four parts of this class differ in details, including size of boiler and fuel capacity.

Y1/1*   Introduced 1925.
Y1/2†   Introduced 1927.
Y1/3** Introduced 1926.
Y1/4‡   Introduced 1927.
§ Sprocket gear ratio 9 : 25 (remainder 11 : 25).

Weights : { 20 tons 17 cwt.*
            19 tons 16 cwt.†
            14 tons.**
            19 tons 7 cwt.‡
Pressure : 275 lb. Su. Cyls.: 6¾'' × 9''
Driving Wheels : 2' 6''
T.E.: { 7,260 lb.
        8,870 lb.§
Poppet valves.

*Departmental locos. 68130-3/52

†68137/8/40-2,   Departmental loco. : 68153

†§68143-51

**68139

‡Departmental loco : 68136

Totals : Class Y1/1   5
          Class Y1/2   15
          Class Y1/3   1
          Class Y1/4   1

0-4-0T   Unclass.   Class Y3

Sentinel Wagon Works design. Two-speed Geared Sentinel Locos.
Introduced 1927.
*Sprocket gear ratio 19 : 19.
†Sprocket gear ratio 15 : 19
Weight : 20 tons 16 cwt.
Pressure : 275 lb. Su. Cyls.: 6¾'' × 9''
Driving Wheels : 2' 6''

Classes WD-Y9

T.E.: { Low Gear : 12,600 lb.*
        High Gear : 4,705 lb.*
        Low Gear : 15,960 lb.†
        High Gear : 5,960 lb.†
Poppet valves.

*68154-65/8/9/71/2/4-6/9/84/5, Departmental locos : 68166/73/7/8

†68180-3   **Total 30**

0-4-0T   0F   Class Y4

Introduced 1913. Hill G.E. design.
Weight : 38 tons 1 cwt.
Pressure : 180 lb. Cyls. : (O) 17'' × 20''
Driving Wheels : 3' 10'' T.E.:19,225 lb.
Walschaerts gear.

68125-8, Departmental loco. : 68129   **Total 5**

0-4-0T (Tram Locos)
0F   Class Y6

Introduced 1883. Worsdell G.E. design. (Oldest survivor built 1897.)
Weight : 21 tons 5 cwt.
Pressure : 140 lb. Cyls. : 11'' × 15''
Driving Wheels : 3' 1'' T.E.: 5,835 lb.
68082/3   **Total 2**

0-4-0T   0F   Class Y7

Introduced 1888. T. W. Worsdell N.E design. (Survivors built 1923.)
Weight : 22 tons 14 cwt.
Pressure : 140 lb. Cyls. : 14'' × 20''
Driving Wheels : 3' 6½'' T.E.:11,040 lb.

68089, Departmental loco. 68088   **Total 2**

0-4-0T   0F   Class Y8

Introduced 1890. T. W. Worsdell N.E.
Weight : 15 tons 10 cwt.   [design.
Pressure : 140 lb.   Cyls.: 11'' × 15''
Driving Wheels : 3' 0'' T.E.: 6,000 lb.

68091   **Total 1**

0-4-0ST   0F   Class Y9

*Introduced 1882. Holmes N.B. design.
† Locos. running permanently attached to wooden tenders.
Weights : Loco.   27 tons 16 cwt.
            Tender   6 tons.†
Pressure : 130 lb. Cyls. : (O) 14'' × 20''
Driving Wheels : 3' 8'' T.E.: 9,845 lb.

*68092/5-8, 68100-2/4/5/10/1/3/5/23/4

†68093/4/9, 68103/6-9/12/4/6-22   **Total 33**

0-4-0T Unclass. Class Y10

Sentinel Wagon Works design. Double-ended Two-speed Geared Sentinel Loco.
Introduced 1930.
Weight : 23 tons 19 cwt.
Pressure : 275 lb. Su. Cyls.: $6\frac{3}{4}'' \times 9$
Driving Wheels : 3' 2''
T.E.: $\begin{cases} \text{Low Gear : 11,435 lb.} \\ \text{High Gear : 7,965 lb.} \end{cases}$
Poppet valves.

68186 **Total 1**

0-4-2T OF Class Z4

Introduced 1915. Manning-Wardle design for G.N. of S.
Weight : 25 tons 17 cwt.
Pressure : 160 lb. Cyls.: (O) 13'' × 20''
Driving Wheels : 3' 6'' T.E.: 10.945 lb.
68190/1 **Total 2**

0-4-2T OF Class Z5

Introduced 1915. Manning-Wardle design for G.N. of S.
Weight : 30 tons 18 cwt.
Pressure : 160 lb. Cyls.: (O) 14'' × 20''
Driving Wheels : 4' 0'' T.E.: 11,105 lb.
68192/3 **Total 2**

ROUTE AVAILABILITY OF LOCOMOTIVES

Restrictions on the working of locomotives over the routes of the former L.N.E.R. are denoted by Route Availability numbers. In general a locomotive is not permitted to work over a line of lower R.A. number than itself. The scheme is as follows :

R.A.1 : J15, J62, J63, J65, J71, Y1, Y3, Y6, Y7, Y8, Y10, Y11, Z4.

R.A.2 : E4, J24, J67/1, J70, J72, J77, Y9, Z5.

R.A.3 : B12/1, D3, D41, F2 (modified for Eastern Section), F3, F4, F5, J3, J4, J10, J21, J25, J36, J66, J67/2, J68, J69, J88, J92, N9, N10.

R.A.4 : A6, B12/3, D2, D31, D40, F6, G5, J1, J5, J17, J26, J83, N4, N5/2, N8, N13, N14, Q5, V4.

R.A.5 : A5, A8, B1, B2, B4, B17/1, B17/4, C12, C13, C14, D1, D15, D16, F2, J2, J6, J11, J19, J20, J27, J52, J73, J94, K2, L2, M2, N1, N5/3, N7.

R.A.6 : C15, C16, D10, D11, D20, D29, D30, D32, D33, D34, J35, J39, J50, K1, K4, N2, N15, O1, O2, O3, O4, O7, Q6, V1, Y4.

R.A.7 : A7, B16/1, B17/5, C1, C4, L1, L3, Q7, U1, V3.

R.A.8 : B16/2, B16/3, D49, J37, J38, K3, K5, Q1, S1, T1.

R.A.9 : A1, A2, A3, A4, V2, W1.

NAMED LOCOMOTIVES

IN THE 60000-90774 SERIES

CLASS "A4" 4-6-2

60001	Sir Ronald Matthews	60018	Sparrow Hawk
60002	Sir Murrough Wilson	60019	Bittern
60003	Andrew K. McCosh	60020	Guillemot
60004	William Whitelaw	60021	Wild Swan
60005	Sir Charles Newton	60022	Mallard
60006	Sir Ralph Wedgwood	60023	Golden Eagle
60007	Sir Nigel Gresley	60024	Kingfisher
60008	Dwight D. Eisenhower	60025	Falcon
60009	Union of South Africa	60026	Miles Beevor
60010	Dominion of Canada	60027	Merlin
60011	Empire of India	60028	Walter K. Whigham
60012	Commonwealth of	60029	Woodcock
	Australia	60030	Golden Fleece
60013	Dominion of New Zealand	60031	Golden Plover
60014	Silver Link	60032	Gannet
60015	Quicksilver	60033	Seagull
60016	Silver King	60034	Lord Faringdon
60017	Silver Fox		

CLASS "A3" 4-6-2

60035	Windsor Lad	60056	Centenary
60036	Colombo	60057	Ormonde
60037	Hyperion	60058	Blair Athol
60038	Firdaussi	60059	Tracery
60039	Sandwich	60060	The Tetrarch
60040	Cameronian	60061	Pretty Polly
60041	Salmon Trout	60062	Minoru
60042	Singapore	60063	Isinglass
60043	Brown Jack	60064	Tagalie
60044	Melton	60065	Knight of Thistle
60045	Lemberg	60066	Merry Hampton
60046	Diamond Jubilee	60067	Ladas
60047	Donovan	60068	Sir Visto
60048	Doncaster	60069	Sceptre
60049	Galtee More	60070	Gladiateur
60050	Persimmon	60071	Tranquil
60051	Blink Bonny	60072	Sunstar
60052	Prince Palatine	60073	St. Gatien
60053	Sansovino	60074	Harvester
60054	Prince of Wales	60075	St. Frusquin
60055	Woolwinder	60076	Galopin

Named Locomotives

60077	The White Knight	60095	Flamingo
60078	Night Hawk	60096	Papyrus
60079	Bayardo	60097	Humorist
60080	Dick Turpin	60098	Spion Kop
60081	Shotover	60099	Call Boy
60082	Neil Gow	60100	Spearmint
60083	Sir Hugo	60101	Cicero
60084	Trigo	60102	Sir Frederick Banbury
60085	Manna	60103	Flying Scotsman
60086	Gainsborough	60104	Solario
60087	Blenheim	60105	Victor Wild
60088	Book Law	60106	Flying Fox
60089	Felstead	60107	Royal Lancer
60090	Grand Parade	60108	Gay Crusader
60091	Captain Cuttle	60109	Hermit
60092	Fairway	60110	Robert the Devil
60093	Coronach	60111	Enterprise
60094	Colorado	60112	St. Simon

CLASS "A1" 4-6-2

60113	Great Northern	60138	Boswell
60114	W. P. Allen	60139	Sea Eagle
60115	Meg Merrilies	60140	Balmoral
60116	Hal o' the Wynd	60141	Abbotsford
60117	Bois Roussel	60142	Edward Fletcher
60118	Archibald Sturrock	60143	Sir Walter Scott
60119	Patrick Stirling	60144	King's Courier
60120	Kittiwake	60145	Saint Mungo
60121	Silurian	60146	Peregrine
60122	Curlew	60147	North Eastern
60123	H. A. Ivatt	60148	Aboyeur
60124	Kenilworth	60149	Amadis
60125	Scottish Union	60150	Willbrook
60126	Sir Vincent Raven	60151	Midlothian
60127	Wilson Worsdell	60152	Holyrood
60128	Bongrace	60153	Flamboyant
60129	Guy Mannering	60154	Bon Accord
60130	Kestrel	60155	Borderer
60131	Osprey	60156	Great Central
60132	Marmion	60157	Great Eastern
60133	Pommern	60158	Aberdonian
60134	Foxhunter	60159	Bonnie Dundee
60135	Madge Wildfire	60160	Auld Reekie
60136	Alcazar	60161	North British
60137	Redgauntlet	60162	Saint Johnstoun

Named Locomotives
CLASS "A2" 4-6-2

60500	Edward Thompson	60520	Owen Tudor
60501	Cock o' the North	60521	Watling Street
60502	Earl Marischal	60522	Straight Deal
60503	Lord President	60523	Sun Castle
60504	Mons Meg	60524	Herringbone
60505	Thane of Fife	60525	A. H. Peppercorn
60506	Wolf of Badenoch	60526	Sugar Palm
60507	Highland Chieftain	60527	Sun Chariot
60508	Duke of Rothsay	60528	Tudor Minstrel
60509	Waverley	60529	Pearl Diver
60510	Robert the Bruce	60530	Sayajirao
60511	Airborne	60531	Bahram
60512	Steady Aim	60532	Blue Peter
60513	Dante	60533	Happy Knight
60514	Chamossaire	60534	Irish Elegance
60515	Sun Stream	60535	Hornets Beauty
60516	Hycilla	60536	Trimbush
60517	Ocean Swell	60537	Bachelors Button
60518	Tehran	60538	Velocity
60519	Honeyway	60539	Bronzino

CLASS "V2" 2-6-2

60800	Green Arrow	60847	St. Peter's School, York A.D. 627
60809	The Snapper, The East Yorkshire Regiment, The Duke of York's Own	60860	Durham School
60835	The Green Howard, Alexandra Princess of Wales's Own Yorkshire Regiment	60872	King's Own Yorkshire Light Infantry
		60873	Coldstreamer

CLASS "B1" 4-6-0

61000	Springbok	61013	Topi
61001	Eland	61014	Oribi
61002	Impala	61015	Duiker
61003	Gazelle	61016	Inyala
61004	Oryx	61017	Bushbuck
61005	Bongo	61018	Gnu
61006	Blackbuck	61019	Nilghai
61007	Klipspringer	61020	Gemsbok
61008	Kudu	61021	Reitbok
61009	Hartebeeste	61022	Sassaby
61010	Wildebeeste	61023	Hirola
61011	Waterbuck	61024	Addax
61012	Puku	61025	Pallah

Named Locomotives

61026 Ourebi	61215 William Henton Carver
61027 Madoqua	61221 Sir Alexander Erskine-Hill
61028 Umseke	61237 Geoffrey H. Kitson
61029 Chamois	61238 Leslie Runciman
61030 Nyala	61240 Harry Hinchliffe
61031 Reedbuck	61241 Viscount Ridley
61032 Stembok	61242 Alexander Reith Gray
61033 Dibatag	61243 Sir Harold Mitchell
61034 Chiru	61244 Strang Steel
61035 Pronghorn	61245 Murray of Elibank
61036 Ralph Assheton	61246 Lord Balfour of Burleigh
61037 Jairou	61247 Lord Burghley
61038 Blacktail	61248 Geoffrey Gibbs
61039 Steinbok	61249 FitzHerbert Wright
61040 Roedeer	61250 A. Harold Bibby
61189 Sir William Gray	61251 Oliver Bury

CLASS "B4" 4-6-0

61482 Immingham

CLASS "B2" AND "B17" 4-6-0

61600 Sandringham	61625 Raby Castle
61601 Holkham	61626 Brancepeth Castle
61602 Walsingham	61627 Aske Hall
61603 Framlingham	61628 Harewood House
61604 Elveden	61629 Naworth Castle
61605 Lincolnshire Regiment	61630 Tottenham Hotspur
61606 Audley End	61631 Serlby Hall
61607 Blickling	61632 Belvoir Castle
61608 Gunton	61633 Kimbolton Castle
61609 Quidenham	61634 Hinchingbrooke
61610 Honingham Hall	61635 Milton
61611 Raynham Hall	61636 Harlaxton Manor
61612 Houghton Hall	61637 Thorpe Hall
61613 Woodbastwick Hall	61638 Melton Hall
61614 Castle Hedingham	61639 Norwich City
61615 Culford Hall	61640 Somerleyton Hall
61616 Fallodon	61641 Gayton Hall
61617 Ford Castle	61642 Kilverstone Hall
61618 Wynyard Park	61643 Champion Lodge
61619 Welbeck Abbey	61644 Earlham Hall
61620 Clumber	61645 The Suffolk Regiment
61621 Hatfield House	61646 Gilwell Park
61622 Alnwick Castle	61647 Helmingham Hall
61623 Lambton Castle	61648 Arsenal
61624 Lumley Castle	61649 Sheffield United

Named Locomotives

61650 Grimsby Town	61662 Manchester United
61651 Derby County	61663 Everton
61652 Darlington	61664 Liverpool
61653 Huddersfield Town	61665 Leicester City
61654 Sunderland	61666 Nottingham Forest
61655 Middlesbrough	61667 Bradford
61656 Leeds United	61668 Bradford City
61657 Doncaster Rovers	61669 Barnsley
61658 The Essex Regiment	61670 City of London
61659 East Anglian	61671 Royal Sovereign
61660 Hull City	61672 West Ham United
61661 Sheffield Wednesday	

CLASS "V4" 2-6-2

61700 Bantam Cock

CLASS "K2" 2-6-0

61764 Loch Arkaig	61787 Loch Quoich
61772 Loch Lochy	61788 Loch Rannoch
61774 Loch Garry	61789 Loch Laidon
61775 Loch Treig	61790 Loch Lomond
61781 Loch Morar	61791 Loch Laggan
61782 Loch Eil	61794 Loch Oich
61783 Loch Sheil	

CLASS "K1" AND "K4" 2-6-0

61993 Loch Long	61996 Lord of the Isles
61994 The Great Marquess	61997 MacCailin Mor
61995 Cameron of Locheil	61998 MacLeod of Macleod

CLASS "D40" 4-4-0

62273 George Davidson	62277 Gordon Highlander
62274 Benachie	62278 Hatton Castle
62275 Sir David Stewart	62279 Glen Grant
62276 Andrew Bain	

CLASS "D29" 4-4-0

62405 The Fair Maid	62411 Lady of Avenel
62410 Ivanhoe	

Named Locomotives

CLASS "D30" 4-4-0

62417 Hal o' the Wynd	62430 Jingling Geordie
62418 The Pirate	62431 Kenilworth
62419 Meg Dods	62432 Quentin Durward
62420 Dominie Sampson	62434 Kettledrummle
62421 Laird o' Monkbarns	62435 Norna
62422 Caleb Balderstone	62436 Lord Glenvarloch
62423 Dugald Dalgetty	62437 Adam Woodcock
62424 Claverhouse	62438 Peter Poundtext
62425 Ellangowan	62439 Father Ambrose
62426 Cuddie Headrigg	62440 Wandering Willie
62427 Dumbiedykes	62441 Black Duncan
62428 The Talisman	62442 Simon Glover
62429 The Abbot	

CLASS "D34" 4-4-0

62467 Glenfinnan	62484 Glen Lyon
62468 Glen Orchy	62485 Glen Murran
62469 Glen Douglas	62487 Glen Arklet
62470 Glen Roy	62488 Glen Aladale
62471 Glen Falloch	62489 Glen Dessary
62472 Glen Nevis	62490 Glen Fintaig
62474 Glen Croe	62492 Glen Garvin
62475 Glen Beasdale	62493 Glen Gloy
62477 Glen Dochart	62494 Glen Gour
62478 Glen Quoich	62495 Glen Luss
62479 Glen Sheil	62496 Glen Loy
62480 Glen Fruin	62497 Glen Mallie
62482 Glen Mamie	62498 Glen Moidart
62483 Glen Garry	

CLASS "D16" 4-4-0

62546 Claud Hamilton

CLASS "D10" 4-4-0

62650 Prince Henry	62655 The Earl of Kerry
62651 Purdon Viccars	62656 Sir Clement Royds
62652 Edwin A. Beazley	62657 Sir Berkeley Sheffield
62653 Sir Edward Fraser	62658 Prince George
62654 Walter Burgh Gair	62659 Worsley-Taylor

CLASS "D11" 4-4-0

62660 Butler-Henderson	62663 Prince Albert
62661 Gerard Powys Dewhurst	62664 Princess Mary
62662 Prince of Wales	62665 Mons

Named Locomotives

62666	Zeebrugge	62681	Captain Craigengelt
62667	Somme	62682	Haystoun of Bucklaw
62668	Jutland	62683	Hobbie Elliott
62669	Ypres	62684	Wizard of the Moor
62670	Marne	62685	Malcolm Graeme
62671	Bailie MacWheebie	62686	The Fiery Cross
62672	Baron of Bradwardine	62687	Lord James of Douglas
62673	Evan Dhu	62688	Ellen Douglas
62674	Flora MacIvor	62689	Maid of Lorn
62675	Colonel Gardiner	62690	The Lady of the Lake
62676	Jonathan Oldbuck	62691	Laird of Balmawhapple
62677	Edie Ochiltree	62692	Allan-Bane
62678	Luckie Mucklebackit	62693	Roderick Dhu
62679	Lord Glenallan	62694	James Fitzjames
62680	Lucy Ashton		

CLASS "D49" 4-4-0

62700	Yorkshire	62729	Rutlandshire
62701	Derbyshire	62730	Berkshire
62702	Oxfordshire	62731	Selkirkshire
62703	Hertfordshire	62732	Dumfries-shire
62704	Stirlingshire	62733	Northumberland
62705	Lanarkshire	62734	Cumberland
62706	Forfarshire	62735	Westmorland
62707	Lancashire	62736	The Bramham Moor
62708	Argyllshire	62737	The York and Ainsty
62709	Berwickshire	62738	The Zetland
62710	Lincolnshire	62739	The Badsworth
62711	Dumbartonshire	62740	The Bedale
62712	Morayshire	62741	The Blankney
62713	Aberdeenshire	62742	The Braes of Derwent
62714	Perthshire	62743	The Cleveland
62715	Roxburghshire	62744	The Holderness
62716	Kincardineshire	62745	The Hurworth
62717	Banffshire	62746	The Middleton
62718	Kinross-shire	62747	The Percy
62719	Peebles-shire	62748	The Southwold
62720	Cambridgeshire	62749	The Cottesmore
62721	Warwickshire	62750	The Pytchley
62722	Huntingdonshire	62751	The Albrighton
62723	Nottinghamshire	62752	The Atherstone
62724	Bedfordshire	62753	The Belvoir
62725	Inverness-shire	62754	The Berkeley
62726	The Meynell	62755	The Bilsdale
62727	The Quorn	62756	The Brocklesby
62728	Cheshire	62757	The Burton

Named Locomotives

62758 The Cattistock	62767 The Grove
62759 The Craven	62768 The Morpeth
62760 The Cotswold	62769 The Oakley
62761 The Derwent	62770 The Puckeridge
62762 The Fernie	62771 The Rufford
62763 The Fitzwilliam	62772 The Sinnington
62764 The Garth	62773 The South Durham
62765 The Goathland	62774 The Staintondale
62766 The Grafton	62775 The Tynedale

CLASS "J36" 0-6-0

65216 Byng	65235 Gough
65217 French	65236 Horne
65222 Somme	65243 Maude
65224 Mons	65253 Joffre
65226 Haig	65268 Allenby
65233 Plumer	

CLASS "WD" 2-10-0

90774 North British

SECTION TWO

MOTIVE POWER DEPOTS AND CODES

LONDON MIDLAND REGION

1A	**Willesden**	12B	Carlisle (Canal)
1B	Camden	12C	Penrith
1C	Watford	12D	Workington
1D	Devons Road	12E	Moor Row
2A	**Rugby**	14A	**Cricklewood**
2B	Nuneaton	14B	Kentish Town
2C	Warwick	14C	St. Albans
2D	Coventry	15A	**Wellingboro'**
3A	**Bescot**	15B	Kettering
3B	Bushbury	15C	Leicester
3C	Walsall	15D	Bedford
3D	Aston	16A	**Nottingham**
3E	Monument Lane	16C	Kirkby
4A	**Bletchley**	16D	Mansfield
4B	Northampton	17A	**Derby**
5A	**Crewe North**	17B	Burton
5B	Crewe South	17C	Coalville
5C	Stafford	17D	Rowsley
5D	Stoke	18A	**Toton**
5E	Alsager	18B	Westhouses
5F	Uttoxeter	18C	Hasland
6A	**Chester**	18D	Staveley
6B	Mold Junction	19A	**Sheffield**
6C	Birkenhead	19B	Millhouses
6D	Chester (Northgate)	19C	Canklow
6E	Wrexham	20A	**Leeds** (Holbeck)
6F	Bidston	20B	Stourton
7A	**Llandudno Junction**	20C	Royston
7B	Bangor	20D	Normanton
7C	Holyhead	20E	Manningham
7D	Rhyl	21A	**Saltley**
8A	**Edge Hill**	21B	Bournville
8B	Warrington	21C	Bromsgrove
8C	Speke Junction	21D	Stratford-on-Avon
8D	Widnes	22A	**Bristol**
8E	Brunswick	22B	Gloucester
9A	**Longsight**	23A	**Skipton**
9B	Stockport	23B	Hellifield
9C	Macclesfield	23C	Lancaster
9D	Buxton	24A	**Accrington**
9E	Trafford Park	24B	Rose Grove
9F	Heaton Mersey	24C	Lostock Hall
9G	Northwich	24D	Lower Darwen
10A	**Springs Branch**	25A	**Wakefield**
10B	Preston	25B	Huddersfield
10C	Patricroft	25C	Goole
10D	Plodder Lane	25D	Mirfield
10E	Sutton Oak	25E	Sowerby Bridge
10F	Wigan (C.L.)	25F	Low Moor
11A	**Carnforth**	25G	Farnley Junction
11B	Barrow	26A	**Newton Heath**
11C	Oxenholme	26B	Agecroft
11D	Tebay	26C	Bolton
12A	**Carlisle** (Upperby)	26D	Bury

MOTIVE POWER DEPOTS AND CODES

26E	Bacup	27D	Wigan (Central)
26F	Lees	27E	Walton
26G	Belle Vue	27E	Southport
27A	**Bank Hall**	28A	**Blackpool**
27B	Aintree	28B	Fleetwood
27C	Southport		

EASTERN REGION

30A	**Stratford**	34E	Neasden
30B	Hertford East	35A	**New England**
30C	Bishops Stortford	35B	Grantham
30D	Southend (Victoria)	35C	Peterborough (ex L.M.S.)
30E	Colchester	36A	**Doncaster**
30F	Parkeston	36B	Mexborough
31A	**Cambridge**	36C	Frodingham
31B	March	36D	Barnsley
31C	Kings Lynn	36E	Retford
31D	South Lynn	37A	**Ardsley**
31E	Bury St. Edmunds	37B	Copley Hill
32A	**Norwich**	37C	Bradford
32B	Ipswich	38A	**Colwick**
32C	Lowestoft	38B	Annesley
32D	Yarmouth (South Town)	38C	Leicester
32E	Yarmouth (Vauxhall)	38D	Staveley
32F	Yarmouth (Beach)	38E	Woodford
32G	Melton Constable	39A	**Gorton**
33A	**Plaistow**	39B	Sheffield
33B	Tilbury	40A	**Lincoln**
33C	Shoeburyness	40B	Immingham
34A	**Kings Cross**	40C	Louth
34B	Hornsey	40D	Tuxford
34C	Hatfield	40E	Langwith
34D	Hitchin	40F	Boston

NORTH EASTERN REGION

50A	**York**	52A	**Gateshead**
	Normanton		Bowes Bridge
50B	Leeds (Neville Hill)	52B	Heaton
	Ilkley	52C	Blaydon
50C	Selby		Alston
50D	Starbeck		Hexham
	Pateley Bridge		Reedsmouth
50E	Scarborough	52D	Tweedmoutn
50F	Malton		Alnmouth
	Pickering	52E	Percy Main
50G	Whitby	52F	North Blyth
51A	**Darlington**		South Blyth
	Middleton-in-Teasdale		Rothbury
51B	Newport	53A	**Hull** (Dairycoates)
51C	West Hartlepool	53B	Hull (Botanic Gardens)
51D	Middlesborough	53C	Hull (Springhead)
	Guisborough		Alexandra Dock
51E	Stockton	53D	Bridlington
51F	West Auckland	53E	Cudworth
	Wearhead	54A	**Sunderland**
51G	Haverton Hill		Durham
51H	Kirkby Stephen	54B	Tyne Dock
51J	Northallerton		Pelton Level
	Leyburn	54C	Borough Gardens
51K	Saltburn	54D	Consett

MOTIVE POWER DEPOTS AND CODES

SCOTTISH REGION

60A	**Inverness**	64G	Hawick
60B	Aviemore	65A	**Eastfield**
60C	Helmsdale	65B	St. Rollox
60D	Wick	65C	Parkhead
60E	Forres	65D	Dawsholm
61A	**Kittybrewster**	65E	Kipps
61B	Ferryhill (Aberdeen)	65F	Grangemouth
61C	Keith	65G	Yoker
62A	**Thornton**	65H	Helensburgh
62B	Dundee (Tay Bridge)	65I	Balloch
62C	Dunfermline (Upper)	66A	**Polmadie**
63A	**Perth South**	66B	Motherwell
63B	Stirling	66C	Hamilton
63C	Forfar	66D	Greenock
63D	Fort William	67A	**Corkerhill**
63E	Oban	67B	Hurlford
64A	**St. Margaret's**	67C	Ayr
64B	Haymarket	67D	Ardrossan
64C	Dalry Road	68A	**Carlisle** (Kingmoor)
64D	Carstairs	68B	Dumfries
64E	Polmont	68C	Stranraer
64F	Bathgate	68D	Beattock

SOUTHERN REGION

70A	**Nine Elms**	72F	Wadebridge
70B	Feltham	73A	**Stewarts Lane**
70C	Guildford	73B	Bricklayer's Arms
70D	Basingstoke	73C	Hither Green
70E	Reading	73D	Gillingham
71A	**Eastleigh**	73E	Faversham
71B	Bournemouth	74A	**Ashford**
71C	Dorchester	74B	Ramsgate
71D	Fratton	74C	Dover
71E	Newport (I.O.W.)	74D	Tonbridge
71F	Ryde	74E	St. Leonards
71G	Bath (S. & D.)	75A	**Brighton**
71H	Templecombe	75B	Redhill
71I	Southampton	75C	Norwood Junction
72A	**Exmouth Junction**	75D	Horsham
72B	Salisbury	75E	Three Bridges
72C	Yeovil	75F	Tunbridge Wells
72D	Plymouth	75G	Eastbourne
72E	Barnstaple Junction		

WESTERN REGION

81A	**Old Oak Common**	82E	Yeovil
81B	Slough	82F	Weymouth
81C	Southall	83A	**Newton Abbot**
81D	Reading	83B	Taunton
81E	Didcot	83C	Exeter
81F	Oxford	83D	Plymouth (Laira)
82A	**Bristol** (Bath Road)	83E	St. Blazey
82B	Bristol (St. Philip's Marsh)	83F	Truro
82C	Swindon	83G	Penzance
82D	Westbury	84A	**Wolverhampton** (Stafford Road)

MOTIVE POWER DEPOTS AND CODES

84B	Wolverhampton (Oxley)	86J	Aberdare
84C	Banbury	86K	Abergavenny
84D	Leamington	87A	**Neath**
84E	Tyseley	87B	Duffryn Yard
84F	Stourbridge	87C	Danygraig
84G	Shrewsbury	87D	Swansea East Dock
84H	Wellington	87E	Landore
84J	Croes Newydd	87F	Llanelly
84K	Chester	87G	Carmarthen
85A	**Worcester**	87H	Neyland
85B	Gloucester	87J	Goodwick
85C	Hereford	87K	Swansea Victoria
85D	Kidderminster	88A	**Cardiff** (Cathays)
86A	**Newport** (Ebbw. Jcn.)	88B	Cardiff East Dock
86B	Newport (Pill.)	88C	Barry
86C	Cardiff (Canton)	88D	Merthyr
86D	Llantrisant	88E	Abercynon
86E	Severn Tunnel Junction	88F	Treherbert
86F	Tondu	89A	**Oswestry**
86G	Pontypool Road	89B	Brecon
86H	Aberbeeg	89C	Machynlleth

WITH SHED ALLOCATIONS

YTW
0-4-0T
1* 87C

WCP
0-6-0T
5* 82C

V.o.R.
2-6-2T
7 89C
8 89C
9 89C

CMDP
0-6-0T
28 85D
29 85D

RR
0-6-2T
31 88A
33 88B
35 88A
36 88B
37 88B
38 88A
39 88B
40 88A
41 88A
42 88A
43 88A
44 88A
55 88B
56 88A
57 88C
58 88C
59 88C
60 87C
63 88A
65 86J
66 88B
67 88B
68 88B
69 87B
70 87B
72 88B
73 88B
74 88B
75 87A
76 88D
77 88D
78 88D

79 88D
80 88D
81 88D
82 88D
83 88D

RR
0-6-0T
90 88B
91 88B
92 88B
93 88B
94 88B
95 88B
96 88B

Class 4073
4-6-0
111* 83D

Car. R.
0-6-2T
155 88B

TV
0-6-0T
193 88F
194 88F
195 88F

TV
0-6-2T
203 86C
204 86J
205 86C
207 88F
208 86C
209 86C
210 89F
211 88D
215 88F
216 88F
217 88D
218 88F
219 88E
220 86C
236 88E

BR
0-6-2T
240 88C
263 88C

267 88C
270 88C
271 88C
274 88C
276 88C

TV
0-6-2T
278 88F
279 88F
282 86J
284 86J
285 88F
286 88A
290 88F
292 88D
293 88A
295 88E
299 88F
303 88F
304 88E
305 88A
306 88C
307 88A
308 87D
309 87D
312 88C
316 88D
322 88C
335 86C
337 88E
343 88A
344 88A
345 88A
346 88A
347 88A
348 88A
349 86G
351 88E
352 88F
356 88E
357 86C

LMM
0-6-0T
359* 87C

TV
0-6-2T
360 88A
361 88C
362 86J

364 88A
365 88F
366 88F
367 88A
368 88F
370 88D
371 88A
372 88C
373 88C
374 86J
375 88D
376 88A
377 88A
378 88F
379 88C
380 88E
381 86C
382 88C
383 88A
384 88A
385 86G
386 88E
387 88C
388 88C
389 88C
390 88A
391 88A
393 88A
394 88C
397 88E
398 88D
399 88F

BM
0-6-2T
425 86C
431 86A
432 86A
433 88A
434 88A
435 86A
436 86A

AD
0-6-0T
666 86B
667 86B

Car. R.
0-6-0T
681 88B

682 88B
683 88B
684 88B

LMM
0–6–0T
803 87C

W. & L.
0–6–0T
822* 89A
823* 89A

Cam. R.
0–6–0
844 89A
849 89A
855 89A
864 89C
873 89A
887 89A
892 89C
893 89A
894 89C
895 89A
896 89A

Class 1854
0–6–0T
907 81E

Class 1901
0–6–0T
992 82C

Class 1000
4–6–0
1000* 81A
1001* 87H
1002* 82A
1003* 81A
1004* 83G
1005* 82A
1006* 83D
1007* 82A
1008* 81A
1009* 87H
1010* 81A
1011* 82A
1012* 81A
1013* 83F
1014* 82A
1015* 81A
1016* 84A
1017* 84A
1018* 83A
1019* 83A
1020* 87H
1021* 81A
1022* 83D

1023* 83D
1024* 84A
1025* 84A
1026* 81A
1027* 82D
1028* 82A
1029* 84A

Class 1101
0–4–0T
1101 87C
1102 87C
1103 87C
1104 87C
1105 87C
1106 87C

SHT
0–4–0T
1140 87D
1141 87C
1142 87C
1143 87C
1144 87D
1145 87C

SHT
0–6–0T
1146 87D
1147 87C

PM
0–4–0T
1150 87D
1151 87C
1152 87D
1153 87C

AD
2–6–2T
1205 86D
1206 85C

MSWJ
2–4–0
1334 81E
1335 81D
1336 81D
1338 83B

Class 1361
0–6–0T
1361 83D
1362 83A
1363 83D
1364 83D
1365 83D

Class 1366
0–6–0T
1366 82C
1367 82F
1368 82F
1369 82C
1370 82F
1371 82C

Class 1400
0–4–2T
1400 82C
1401 84C
1402 85B
1403 82C
1404 85B
1405 83C
1406 85B
1407 81D
1408 85A
1409 85B
1410 84A
1411 84C
1412 89A
1413 85B
1414 84F
1415 82A
1416 84J
1417 6C
1418 85A
1419 83E
1420 88A
1421 86D
1422 86G
1423 87J
1424 85B
1425 88A
1426 34E
1427 83A
1428 89A
1429 83C
1430 82A
1431 87J
1432 89A
1433 82C
1434 84K
1435 83C
1436 82C
1437 81B
1438 84F
1439 83A
1440 83C
1441 85B
1442 81B
1443 81C
1444 81D
1445 85C
1446 82C
1447 81D
1448 81F
1449 83C
1450 81F

1451 83C
1452 87J
1453 82F
1454 82F
1455 85C
1456 85B
1457 84J
1458 84C
1459 89A
1460 85C
1461 88A
1462 81C
1463 82A
1464 85B
1465 89C
1466 83A
1467 82F
1468 83C
1469 83C
1470 83A
1471 86D
1472 87G
1473 84J
1474 89C

Class 1500
0–6–0T
1500 81A
1501 81A
1502 81A
1503 81A
1504 81A
1505 81A
1506 86B
1507 86B
1508 86E
1509 86A

Class 1501
0–6–0T
1542 92C

Class 1600
0–6–0T
1600 88C
1601 87B
1602 87B
1603 89C
1604 89A
1605 81C
1606 87C
1607 87F
1608 83A
1609 87F
1610 88B
1611 87H
1612 85B
1613 87G
1614 87F
1615 86C
1616 85B
1617 81F

1618	87F		
1619	84H		
1620	88B		
1621	84F		
1622	87B		
1623	85B		
1624	84J		
1625	85B		
1626	83E		
1627			
1628			
1629			

Class 1854
0–6–0T

1705	88B
1709	86B

Class 1501
0–6–0T

1782	83F
1789	82F

Class 1854
0–6–0T

1855	87A
1858	87A
1861	81E
1862	86A
1870	86F

Class 1901
0–6–0T

1903	87G
1917	6C
1925	81C
1935	81F
1941	87F
1943	85B
1957	87F
1964	87H
1967	87F
1968	6C
1989	85B
1991	87F
1993	88C
1996	87H
2001	85A
2002	87F
2004	6C
2008	88E
2009	85B
2010	87H
2011	87H
2012	87F
2014	82C
2016	85A
2017	82C

Class 2021
0–6–0T

2021	86G
2023	82D
2025	85B
2026	85C
2027	87F
2030	84H
2031	82B
2032	89A
2033	86B
2034	85B
2035	86G
2038	83B
2040	85C
2042	87F
2043	85B
2044	85B
2048	88B
2050	83E
2051	85D
2053	82D
2054	89A
2055	87C
2056	87G
2060	82C
2061	84A
2063	86A
2066	88A
2067	6C
2068	89A
2069	87G
2070	82B
2072	82A
2073	86A
2075	89A
2076	81F
2079	87B
2080	85B
2081	87F
2082	87C
2083	87F
2085	87F
2086	88B
2088	83C
2089	6C
2090	84F
2092	6C
2093	85A
2094	86G
2095	84A
2097	83F
2098	87F
2099	85A
2100	85A
2101	85A
2104	6C
2106	6C
2107	84F
2108	6C
2109	84A
2111	87G
2112	81B

2115	85C
2117	86G
2121	85B
2122	86A
2123	88B
2126	85C
2127	83B
2129	6C
2131	85B
2134	87C
2135	82B
2136	86B
2138	85C
2140	88A
2141	88B
2144	85B
2146	85B
2147	88B
2148	83D
2150	87F
2151	87C
2152	6C
2153	85B
2154	86B
2155	85B
2156	6C
2159	86J
2160	85C

BPGV
0–6–0T

2162	87F
2165	87F
2166	87D
2167	87F
2168	87F
2176	87F

Class 2181
0–6–0T

2181	83A
2182	83E
2183	83A
2184	84J
2185	84F
2186	84F
2187	84F
2188	84J
2189	84F
2190	84J

BPGV
0–6–0T

2192*	87A
2193*	87F
2194*	83B
2195	82C
2196*	87F
2197*	87F
2198	87F

Class 2251
0–6–0

2200	89C
2201	89C
2202	81E
2203	84E
2204	89C
2205	85A
2206	89C
2207	85A
2208	81D
2209	84J
2210	89A
2211	83B
2212	83B
2213	83B
2214	83B
2215	82B
2216	87G
2217	87G
2218	86A
2219	89C
2220	82B
2221	81E
2222	81E
2223	89C
2224	82C
2225	82B
2226	81E
2227	86A
2228	84G
2229	84G
2230	83C
2231	84G
2232	84J
2233	84G
2234	84G
2235	84G
2236	87G
2237	85A
2238	84E
2239	86A
2240	81E
2241	85A
2242	85A
2243	85C
2244	89A
2245	81D
2246	84F
2247	85A
2248	85B
2249	81F
2250	82C
2251	82B
2252	81E
2253	82B
2254	85B
2255	89A
2256	84C
2257	84E
2258	83D
2259	84J
2260	89C

2261	83B	2444	82D	2817	86A	2881	83A
2262	84J	2445	82A	2818	82B	2882	84K
2263	85A	2449	89A	2819	86A	2883	84C
2264	81D	2452	89B	2820	86C	2884	86G
2265	82B	2458	85A	2821	86A	2885	84F
2266	83B	2460	86E	2822	84J	2886	84C
2267	83B	2462	82B	2823	85B	2887	86E
2268	83B	2468	89B	2824	87F	2888	86G
2269	82B	2474	87G	2825	84B	2889	86A
2270	84F	2482	89A	2826	81A	2890	84K
2271	87G	2483	89A	2827	81F	2891	86C
2272	87G	2484	89A	2828	86J	2892	86E
2273	87E	2513	84K	2829	86E	2893	86G
2274	85A	2515	85C	2830	84B	2894	86A
2275	83B	2516	89A	2831	86J	2895	81A
2276	81A	2532	81E	2832	84B	2896	86A
2277	85A	2534	82A	2833	84B	2897	84C
2278	85A	2537	86C	2834	86A	2898	84C
2279	84F	2538	89A	2835	81A	2899	84C
2280	86C	2541	85C	2836	86J		
2281	85C	2543	89A	2837	86C		
2282	81A	2551	85A	2838	86E	**Class 2900**	
2283	89C	2556	89A	2839	82B	**4-6-0**	
2284	87G	2568	82C	2840	84J		
2285	81C	2572	89A	2841	84G	2906*	86C
2286	85C	2573	81D	2842	86A	2908*	82C
2287	89B	2578	82B	2843	81C	2912*	82F
2288	87H	2579	81E	2844	82B	2915*	84K
2289	81E			2845	81F	2920*	85C
2290	85A			2846	82B	2926*	84K
2291	85B	**Class 1501**		2847	84C	2927*	82C
2292	89C	**0-6-0T**		2848	84E	2931*	82A
2293	82B			2849	84E	2932*	84E
2294	85A	2716	84J	2850	87F	2933*	84D
2295	84C	2719	84J	2851	86A	2934*	82C
2296	84E			2852	84F	2936*	86A
2297	84J			2853	84C	2937*	85C
2298	89C	**Class 2721**		2854	84B	2938*	85B
2299	81D	**0-6-0T**		2855	87F	2939*	82A
				2856	84F	2940*	86C
		2722	87A	2857	84F	2943*	86C
Class 2301		2743	85A	2858	81C	2944*	85C
0-6-0		2744	84G	2859	82B	2945*	82C
		2754	88B	2860	81F	2947*	82C
2322	82B	2760	88D	2861	86A	2948*	82A
2323	89C			2862	86G	2949*	82C
2327	89A			2863	84C	2950*	82A
2339	85B	**Class 2800**		2864	86G	2951*	85B
2340	82B	**2-8-0**		2865	86A	2952*	86E
2343	89B			2866	86A	2953*	84K
2349	85C	2800	86G	2867	84E	2954*	82C
2350	85B	2801	86G	2868	81A	2979*	86A
2351	89B	2802	86G	2869	84C	2981*	84C
2354	89A	2803	87F	2870	86J		
2385	86G	2804	86E	2871	84J		
2386	89A	2805	84C	2872	87F	**Class R.O.D.**	
2401	89B	2806	86J	2873	83C	**2-8-0**	
2407	86C	2807	85C	2874	84F		
2408	89A	2808	86J	2875	83D	3010	87G
2409	89A	2809	83A	2876	86A	3011	87G
2411	87A	2810	84K	2877	86C	3012	86G
2414	86E	2811	86G	2878	84J	3014	82B
2426	82D	2812	84K	2879	86A	3015	87G
2431	87G	2813	86G	2880	86J	3016	84E
		2814	83B			3017	81A
		2815	86A				
		2816	84C				

3018	86G
3020	84C
3022	85A
3023	86G
3024	81E
3025	81D
3026	84J
3028	84J
3029	85A
3031	84B
3032	82B
3033	84B
3034	82B
3036	86C
3038	86G
3040	86G
3041	82B
3042	86G
3043	84C
3044	86G
3047	81D
3048	85A

Class 3100
2-6-2T

3100	86F
3101	84E
3102	84A
3103	86A
3104	84A

Class 3150
2-6-2T

3150	86E
3151	84E
3153	85B
3154	86E
3157	86E
3160	84A
3161	86E
3163	85B
3164	85B
3167	86E
3168	86E
3170	86E
3171	85B
3172	86E
3174	86E
3176	86E
3177	86E
3178	83D
3180	84E
3183	86E
3185	86E
3186	83D
3187	83D
3188	86E
3190	86E

Class 2251
0-6-0

3200	89C
3201	89C
3202	89C
3203	84J
3204	85B
3205	85B
3206	84J
3207	89C
3208	89A
3209	85C
3210	81E
3211	81E
3212	81E
3213	85B
3214	85A
3215	82B
3216	84C
3217	84G
3218	84C
3219	85A

Class 3300
4-4-0

3377	85A
3406*	85C
3444*	82C
3447*	85A
3449*	82C
3451*	82C
3453*	82C
3454*	81D

Class 5700
0-6-0T

3600	83A
3601	85D
3602	84G
3603	83C
3604	82B
3605	86J
3606	83C
3607	85A
3608	81F
3609	85B
3610	86J
3611	87A
3612	86D
3613	84H
3614	82B
3615	84A

3616	86F
3617	86D
3618	81C
3619	84K
3620	81C
3621	87A
3622	81E
3623	82B
3624	84E
3625	84E
3626	6C
3627	86F
3628	86G
3629	83D
3630	84C
3631	84D
3632	82B
3633	87D
3634	86A
3635	83E
3636	86A
3637	87J
3638	89B
3639	83D
3640	86H
3641	87D
3642	87F
3643	82B
3644	86D
3645	82C
3646	84K
3647	86A
3648	81A
3649	84F
3650	84E
3651	86G
3652	86F
3653	84E
3654	87H
3655	86J
3656	86D
3657	84E
3658	84E
3659	83A
3660	84E
3661	87F
3662	86A
3663	86B
3664	84E
3665	84K
3666	82C
3667	84F
3668	86F
3669	83B
3670	86C
3671	82E
3672	88B
3673	84E
3674	86F
3675	83D
3676	82B
3677	83C
3678	87E
3679	87D

3680	86H
3681	88B
3682	82C
3683	86H
3684	82C
3685	81A
3686	83D
3687	84H
3688	81A
3689	84E
3690	86G
3691	86D
3692	86G
3693	84E
3694	84C
3695	86F
3696	82D
3697	81D
3698	87F
3699	86F
3700	86A
3701	87E
3702	84G
3703	86D
3704	81C
3705	83D
3706	89B
3707	88B
3708	86H
3709	81E
3710	81A
3711	86A
3712	86A
3713	87E
3714	86A
3715	81D
3716	86H
3717	86G
3718	87B
3719	87F
3720	82B
3721	81E
3722	81F
3723	81D
3724	82C
3725	85A
3726	86A
3727	81C
3728	85C
3729	86C
3730	86G
3731	82B
3732	84H
3733	82E
3734	88A
3735	82D
3736	81D
3737	82C
3738	81B
3739	82C
3740	84F
3741	87A
3742	6C
3743	84E

3744	84B
3745	84B
3746	82B
3747	86J
3748	82C
3749	84H
3750	81C
3751	84E
3752	87F
3753	86J
3754	81A
3755	86C
3756	84A
3757	87A
3758	82D
3759	82B
3760	84H
3761	87F
3762	84K
3763	82B
3764	82B
3765	82B
3766	87A
3767	89B
3768	87E
3769	84E
3770	89B
3771	87F
3772	86F
3773	82B
3774	87A
3775	84H
3776	86H
3777	87F
3778	84A
3779	86G
3780	82C
3781	87C
3782	84G
3783	88B
3784	82B
3785	87E
3786	84K
3787	83D
3788	84G
3789	85C
3790	83D
3791	87B
3792	84B
3793	84B
3794	83C
3795	82B
3796	86A
3797	87E
3798	86A
3799	81C

Class 2800
2-8-0

3800	86A
3801	86A
3802	84C

3803	81C
3804	86A
3805	86A
3806	86E
3807	86A
3808	86E
3809	86C
3810	86A
3811	87F
3812	86C
3813	81A
3814	86C
3815	86E
3816	86A
3817	86C
3818	86E
3819	84C
3820	84C
3821	84F
3822	86G
3823	86C
3824	86C
3825	84J
3826	86G
3827	84F
3828	86G
3829	84C
3830	86A
3831	84C
3832	83D
3833	86A
3834	83C
3835	81F
3836	86A
3837	84E
3838	86E
3839	85A
3840	81D
3841	81D
3842	82B
3843	86E
3844	86E
3845	81D
3846	81D
3847	81F
3848	85B
3849	84C
3850	86E
3851	87F
3852	81A
3853	81A
3854	81C
3855	81C
3856	81C
3857	81C
3858	84K
3859	84K
3860	84K
3861	84C
3862	86G
3863	84C
3864	83D
3865	84C
3866	81F

Class 4073
4-6-0

4000*	84A

Class 4000
4-6-0

4003*	87E
4007*	85A
4015*	82C

Class 4073
4-6-0

4016*	81A

Class 4000
4-6-0

4018*	84A
4020*	82A
4021*	81F
4022	82C
4023	87E
4028	82D
4031*	84A

Class 4073
4-6-0

4032*	83D

Class 4000
4-6-0

4033*	82A
4034*	82A
4035*	82A
4036*	82C

Class 4073
4-6-0

4037*	81A

Class 4000
4-6-0

4038*	82D
4039*	87E
4040*	84G
4041*	82A
4042*	82A
4043*	82A
4044*	84G
4045*	82D
4046*	84G
4047*	82A
4048*	87E
4049*	84A
4050*	87E
4051*	85A
4052*	84G
4053*	84A
4054*	83D
4055*	82C

4056*	82A
4057*	82C
4058*	84A
4059*	85B
4060*	84A
4061*	84G
4062*	82C

Class 4073
4-6-0

4073*	82A
4074*	87E
4075*	81A
4076*	84K
4077*	83A
4078*	87E
4079*	85B
4080*	82F
4081*	82C
4082*	85A
4083*	86C
4084*	82A
4085*	81D
4086*	85A
4087*	83D
4088*	83D
4089*	83D
4090*	83G
4091*	82A
4092*	85A
4093*	82A
4094*	86C
4095*	87E
4096*	82A
4097*	83D
4098*	83A
4099*	83A

Class 5100
2-6-2T

4100	85D
4101	84E
4102	84D
4103	84A
4104	84F
4105	84A
4106	84E
4107	84E
4108	84E
4109	83A
4110	84E
4111	84E
4112	84D
4113	83B
4114	85A
4115	84A
4116	84E
4117	83B
4118	84G
4119	86E
4120	6C
4121	86G

4122	6C	4203	86A	4280	86B	4515	87H
4123	6C	4206	86A	4281	87F	4516	83E
4124	6C	4207	87E	4282	86E	4517	83D
4125	6C	4208	86D	4283	87F	4518	83D
4126	6C	4211	86B	4284	87A	4519	87H
4127	6C	4212	87B	4285	86C	4520	82F
4128	6C	4213	87F	4286	86E	4521	82C
4129	6C	4214	86H	4287	86C	4522	86H
4130	86G	4215	83E	4288	87A	4523	83F
4131	86G	4217	86H	4289	86A	4524	83D
4132	87H	4218	86F	4290	86A	4525	83G
4133	83A	4221	87A	4291	86B	4526	83E
4134	87E	4222	86C	4292	87B	4527	82F
4135	86G	4223	86H	4293	87A	4528	83D
4136	83B	4224	86C	4294	86A	4529	83E
4137	86A	4225	86A	4295	87A	4530	89C
4138	86G	4226	86B	4296	87D	4532	83A
4139	85A	4227	86C	4297	86J	4533	86G
4140	85A	4228	86J	4298	83E	4534	85B
4141	85B	4229	86B	4299	87C	4535	82A
4142	82A	4230	86A			4536	82A
4143	82A	4231	86C	**Class 4300**		4537	83G
4144	86E	4232	87A	**2–6–0**		4538	82C
4145	86C	4233	86B	4303	86G	4539	82A
4146	84F	4235	86B	4318	81E	4540	83C
4147	84E	4236	86F	4326	81E	4541	86G
4148	86A	4237	86B	4337	84A	4542	83D
4149	84C	4238	86H	4358	87H	4544	82C
4150	84F	4241	86F	4375	84I	4545	83G
4151	82A	4242	86A	4377	82D	4546	85A
4152	82A	4243	86E	4381	82C	4547	83A
4153	85D	4246	86B			4548	83G
4154	84H	4247	86A	**Class 4400**		4549	89C
4155	82A	4248	86A	**2–6–2T**		4550	82C
4156	86A	4250	87E	4400	84H	4551	82C
4157	84E	4251	86F	4401	84H	4552	83E
4158	86G	4252	87A	4403	84H	4553	87H
4159	84E	4253	86B	4404	86F	4554	83F
4160	88C	4254	87F	4405	83A	4555	89C
4161	88C	4255	86C	4406	84H	4556	87H
4162	88F	4256	87B	4407	83D	4557	86F
4163	88C	4257	86J	4408	86F	4558	81F
4164	87B	4258	86B	4409	83D	4559	83E
4165	84E	4259	87A	4410	83C	4560	89C
4166	84E	4260	86F			4561	83F
4167	83F	4261	86D	**Class 4500**		4562	82F
4168	86A	4262	82B	**2–6–2T**		4563	82A
4169	87A	4263	86A	4500	83G	4564	85B
4170	84E	4264	86J	4501	89C	4565	83E
4171	84D	4265	87F	4502	82C	4566	83G
4172	84E	4266	86C	4503	83E	4567	85B
4173	84F	4267	86H	4504	83F	4568	83E
4174	85B	4268	86A	4505	83E	4569	83E
4175	85D	4269	86B	4506	87H	4570	83E
4176	83C	4270	86C	4507	82F	4571	89C
4177	88F	4271	86G	4508	82D	4572	82D
4178	87G	4272	87A	4509	83G	4573	82D
4179	83A	4273	86F	4510	82D	4574	83G
		4274	87A	4511	81F	4575	89C
Class 4200		4275	86C	4512	89C	4576	87H
2–8–0T		4276	86F	4513	81F	4577	82A
4200	86E	4277	86E	4514	86H	4578	85D
4201	86B	4278	87F			4579	87H
		4279	87A			4580	82A

4581	89C
4582	83A
4583	83D
4584	85D
4585	82C
4586	85D
4587	83A
4588	83F
4589	83F
4590	82C
4591	83D
4592	82C
4593	86G
4594	85D
4595	82A
4596	85A
4597	86H
4598	83E
4599	85D

Class 5700
0–6–0T

4600	85C
4601	88C
4602	84G
4603	82B
4604	83B
4605	84E
4606	81B
4607	82B
4608	81C
4609	81D
4610	81C
4611	86G
4612	82C
4613	85A
4614	85A
4615	81A
4616	88B
4617	84K
4618	88B
4619	82B
4620	86D
4621	87A
4622	86C
4623	84G
4624	82B
4625	85D
4626	82B
4627	85B
4628	85B
4629	85A
4630	88B
4631	84C
4632	88D
4633	86C
4634	86F
4635	88D
4636	82D
4637	86H
4638	84F
4639	86G
4640	87B
4641	85A
4642	86G
4643	86F
4644	81A
4645	81F
4646	84C
4647	82D
4648	84E
4649	81E
4650	81B
4651	82C
4652	86H
4653	83D
4654	87H
4655	82B
4656	83D
4657	85C
4658	83D
4659	85B
4660	82B
4661	81D
4662	86B
4663	83B
4664	85A
4665	81D
4666	81A
4667	88A
4668	86G
4669	86F
4670	81D
4671	86A
4672	84G
4673	81C
4674	86D
4675	86F
4676	81F
4677	86C
4678	85C
4679	83D
4680	81F
4681	87B
4682	86H
4683	84E
4684	87B
4685	86H
4686	86H
4687	84F
4688	82B
4689	82E
4690	88C
4691	81B
4692	88C
4693	83D
4694	87C
4695	81C
4696	84F
4697	82C
4698	81A
4699	81A

Class 4700
2–8–0

4700	81A
4701	81A
4702	81A
4703	83D
4704	6C
4705	81A
4706	82B
4707	81A
4708	84B

Class 4900
4–6–0

4900*	81A
4901*	86C
4902*	81F
4903*	81F
4904*	84G
4905*	84K
4906*	83F
4907*	82B
4908*	87H
4909*	82B
4910*	87G
4912*	86G
4913*	86C
4914*	82A
4915*	87G
4916*	82B
4917*	81C
4918*	84K
4919*	84G
4920*	81D
4921*	81F
4922*	87G
4923*	81A
4924*	84E
4925*	82C
4926*	82D
4927*	82D
4928*	81F
4929*	85B
4930*	82F
4931*	81D
4932*	86G
4933*	86G
4934*	82B
4935*	81E
4936*	83F
4937*	87G
4938*	81F
4939*	81D
4940*	83E
4941*	86A
4942*	82A
4943*	81D
4944*	81C
4945*	82C
4946*	83G
4947*	83G
4948*	82B
4949*	83B
4950*	83A
4951*	82A
4952*	86C
4953*	86C
4954*	82A
4955*	84B
4956*	82C
4957*	87H
4958*	81A
4959*	84E
4960*	84A
4961*	81A
4962*	81D
4963*	82D
4964*	84E
4965*	83G
4966*	83D
4967*	82B
4968*	83D
4969*	82B
4970*	83B
4971*	83B
4972*	83D
4973*	82C
4974*	86C
4975*	86C
4976*	84K
4977*	85B
4978*	81C
4979*	86C
4980*	84E
4981*	87G
4982*	87H
4983*	82C
4984*	87G
4985*	82A
4986*	82B
4987*	84K
4988*	82F
4989*	81D
4990*	82B
4991*	84B
4992*	83D
4993*	85A
4994*	81D
4995*	81D
4996*	85B
4997*	87H
4998*	81D
4999*	82B

Class 407
4–6–0

5000*	82A
5001*	86C
5002*	87E
5003*	83B
5004*	81A
5005*	86C
5006*	86C
5007*	86C
5008*	84A
5009*	82C
5010*	84A
5011*	83A
5012*	83D

5013*	87E	5077*	83B	5158	83A	5218	86A
5014*	81A	5078*	83A	5159	88F	5219	87E
5015*	84A	5079*	83A	5160	84F	5220	87B
5016*	87E	5080*	86C	5161	84D	5221	87D
5017*	85A	5081*	81A	5162	87E	5222	86A
5018*	82A	5082*	82A	5163	84D	5223	87F
5019*	82A	5083*	82C	5164	84E	5224	86A
5020*	86C	5084*	82C	5165	84F	5225	87A
5021*	83D	5085*	81A	5166	84E	5226	86C
5022*	84A	5086*	84G	5167	84F	5227	87D
5023*	83D	5087*	81A	5168	84G	5228	86E
5024*	83A	5088*	84A	5169	82A	5229	86A
5025*	82A	5089*	86C	5170	84F	5230	87F
5026*	83D	5090*	83D	5171	84E	5231	86B
5027*	81A	5091*	82C	5172	83B	5232	87D
5028*	83A	5092*	85A	5173	85A	5233	86A
5029*	81A	5093*	87E	5174	84K	5234	86A
5030*	86C	5094*	82A	5175	84E	5235	86B
5031*	84A	5095*	83D	5176	6C	5236	86H
5032*	84G	5096*	82A	5177	84E	5237	86J
5033*	84K	5097*	84G	5178	84H	5238	86A
5034*	83A	5098*	83D	5179	84K	5239	87A
5035*	81A	5099*	86C	5180	84F	5240	87F
5036*	81D			5181	84K	5241	86D
5037*	82A			5182	84E	5242	87A
5038*	81A	**Class 5100**		5183	88C	5243	86A
5039*	81A	**2–6–2T**		5184	84K	5244	86B
5040*	81A	5101	84F	5185	84D	5245	86J
5041*	81A	5102	84E	5186	84K	5246	87D
5042*	85B	5103	84K	5187	84E	5247	87F
5043*	81A	5104	84D	5188	84E	5248	87F
5044*	81A	5105	84F	5189	84F	5249	86C
5045*	81A	5106	84E	5190	84E	5250	86B
5046*	86C	5107	84F	5191	84F	5251	86A
5047*	83A	5108	83A	5192	84D	5252	86B
5048*	82A	5109	84H	5193	84F	5253	86E
5049*	86C	5110	85D	5194	84D	5254	87A
5050*	84G	5112	85B	5195	88C	5255	86A
5051*	87E	5113	83A	5196	84F	5256	86A
5052*	86C	5114	85B	5197	84F	5257	87B
5053*	84A	5122	84F	5198	84E	5258	86J
5054*	86C	5125	84H	5199	84F	5259	86A
5055*	81A	5129	84K			5260	86B
5056*	81A	5132	83A			5261	87F
5057*	83D	5134	84F	**Class 4200**		5262	86E
5058*	83D	5136	84F	**2–8–0T**		5263	86J
5059*	83C	5137	84H	5200	86B	5264	86A
5060*	83D	5138	84H	5201	86A		
5061*	84G	5139	84H	5202	86F		
5062*	83C	5140	83A	5203	87F	**Class 4300**	
5063*	85A	5141	84K	5204	87F	**2–6–0**	
5064*	84G	5142	83A	5205	86E	5300	84F
5065*	81A	5143	84A	5206	86A	5303	85A
5066*	81A	5144	84D	5207	86H	5305	82F
5067*	82A	5147	84F	5208	86A	5306	82D
5068*	82C	5148	83D	5209	87F	5307	86C
5069*	81A	5150	83A	5210	87D	5309	84B
5070*	84A	5151	84A	5211	87E	5310	87H
5071*	83A	5152	84E	5212	86A	5311	82A
5072*	87E	5153	83A	5213	87F	5312	85B
5073*	84G	5154	84G	5214	86E	5313	84B
5074*	82A	5155	84F	5215	87F	5314	82F
5075*	84K	5156	84E	5216	87B	5315	84J
5076*	82A	5157	83A	5217	86A	5316	6C

5317	84C	5396	82C	5527	82A	5612	87B
5318	83D	5397	81E	5528	82A	5613	88F
5319	84J	5398	85B	5529	82E	5614	88C
5321	83C	5399	84K	5530	85B	5615	88F
5322	82C			5531	83E	5616	87D
5323	81F			5532	86G	5617	88D
5324	84C	**Class 5400**		5533	83B	5618	88E
5325	82A	**0–6–0T**		5534	82C	5619	88E
5326	82D	5400	87E	5535	82A	5620	86E
5327	82A	5401	81C	5536	82A	5621	88C
5328	82F	5402	82D	5537	83F	5622	88D
5330	81E	5403	82D	5538	85B	5623	88A
5331	84K	5404	84C	5539	82A	5624	84B
5332	84C	5405	81C	5540	83D	5625	86E
5333	84E	5406	82D	5541	89C	5626	86E
5334	84J	5407	84C	5542	83B	5627	88C
5335	87F	5408	87E	5543	83B	5628	87D
5336	85B	5409	81B	5544	83A	5629	87B
5337	82F	5410	81C	5545	86A	5630	88E
5338	82F	5411	88A	5546	82A	5631	87E
5339	87G	5412	83B	5547	82A	5632	88C
5341	87E	5413	81F	5548	82A	5633	86F
5344	84K	5414	81C	5549	87H	5634	84D
5345	85B	5415	81C	5550	86A	5635	88D
5346	84E	5416	81C	5551	83A	5636	88A
5347	85B	5417	84C	5552	83A	5637	88E
5348	85C	5418	81C	5553	82A	5638	86B
5350	83A	5419	82D	5554	82D	5639	87B
5351	82B	5420	81C	5555	82A	5640	88A
5353	87H	5421	88E	5556	86F	5641	88E
5355	86G	5422	82D	5557	83A	5642	84G
5356	81C	5423	82D	5558	82A	5643	88E
5357	87H	5424	84C	5559	82A	5644	88E
5358	82B			5560	89C	5645	86E
5359	82F			5561	82A	5646	87B
5360	81C	**Class 4500**		5562	83F	5647	84K
5361	84C	**2–6–2T**		5563	82C	5648	88C
5362	86E	5500	83F	5564	82A	5649	86J
5364	86A	5501	83B	5565	82E	5650	88E
5365	84J	5502	83E	5566	82C	5651	84F
5367	82C	5503	83B	5567	83D	5652	88D
5368	87H	5504	83B	5568	87H	5653	88D
5369	84E	5505	83A	5569	83D	5654	88D
5370	84E	5506	82A	5570	89C	5655	88D
5371	84C	5507	89C	5571	83B	5656	87E
5372	87H	5508	82D	5572	82A	5657	84B
5375	81D	5509	82D	5573	85A	5658	84F
5376	83D	5510	82C	5574	85B	5659	88D
5377	85C	5511	82A			5660	88D
5378	87F	5512	82A			5661	87H
5379	84B	5513	87H	**Class 5600**		5662	88D
5380	81E	5514	82A	**0–6–2T**		5663	88F
5381	81E	5515	83F	5600	88F	5664	88C
5382	86C	5516	86G	5601	88A	5665	88C
5384	82F	5517	89C	5602	86A	5666	88D
5385	82D	5518	85B	5603	88D	5667	88C
5386	84B	5519	83E	5604	87E	5668	88F
5388	86C	5520	86H	5605	88D	5669	88A
5390	88H	5521	83B	5606	84B	5670	88A
5391	83A	5522	83B	5607	88F	5671	88D
5392	87H	5523	82A	5608	88F	5672	88A
5393	6C	5524	89C	5609	88C	5673	84G
5394	85B	5525	83C	5610	88F	5674	88D
5395	87J	5526	83F	5611	88F	5675	87F

192

5676	88F
5677	88D
5678	88A
5679	86C
5680	88F
5681	88A
5682	88E
5683	88D
5684	84B
5685	86C
5686	88E
5687	88A
5688	88F
5689	82D
5690	84K
5691	88F
5692	88D
5693	88F
5694	88D
5695	88F
5696	88D
5697	88A
5698	88D
5699	88C

Class 5700 0-6-0T

5700	84E
5701	84A
5702	87F
5703	87A
5704	87D
5705	87F
5706	86E
5707	86F
5708	86D
5709	86A
5710	88B
5711	88D
5712	84E
5713	87B
5714	86B
5715	81B
5716	87J
5717	81B
5718	82D
5719	84F
5720	87A
5721	88D
5722	87F
5723	84K
5724	84C
5725	84K
5726	84F
5727	81C
5728	86G
5729	86E
5730	87C
5731	87B
5732	86A
5733	86H
5734	87B
5735	81E
5736	84E
5737	81B
5738	84E
5739	84A
5740	86B
5741	86A
5742	84J
5743	87D
5744	81E
5745	84E
5746	87A
5747	86B
5748	84B
5749	86C
5750	86B
5751	81C
5752	81E
5753	81C
5754	84F
5755	81C
5756	86F
5757	82D
5758	84H
5759	87E
5760	83C
5761	87B
5762	81D
5763	81D
5764	81A
5765	85C
5766	81D
5767	82E
5768	86G
5769	88D
5770	86J
5771	82D
5772	81D
5773	87B
5774	84J
5775	87C
5776	86C
5777	86H
5778	87A
5779	83F
5780	84A
5781	82D
5782	87F
5783	81B
5784	82B
5785	82D
5786	86C
5787	86J
5788	86D
5789	86H
5790	84E
5791	84K
5792	86G
5793	88D
5794	84F
5795	84F
5796	86J
5797	86F
5798	83A
5799	81C

Class 1400 0-4-2T

5800	82C
5801	89B
5802	82C
5803	89A
5804	82C
5805	82C
5806	89A
5807	85C
5808	85C
5809	82A
5810	84J
5811	84J
5812	89A
5813	82A
5814	85C
5815	85A
5816	85A
5817	85C
5818	86G
5819	87G

Class 4900 4-6-0

5900*	82D
5901*	81D
5902*	83C
5903*	81E
5904*	81F
5905*	87J
5906*	86A
5907*	84E
5908*	87J
5909*	84E
5910*	86C
5911*	86A
5912*	84K
5913*	87E
5914*	85A
5915*	83G
5916*	84E
5917*	85A
5918*	81A
5919*	82B
5920*	83A
5921*	84B
5922*	82C
5923*	84K
5924*	82D
5925*	82D
5926*	83E
5927*	84E
5928*	87J
5929*	87E
5930*	84C
5931*	81A
5932*	81A
5933*	81D
5934*	82C
5935*	81E
5936*	81A
5937*	81A
5938*	81A
5939*	81A
5940*	81A
5941*	81A
5942*	84A
5943*	82C
5944*	84A
5945*	84B
5946*	86C
5947*	81A
5948*	81D
5949*	82B
5950*	84E
5951*	85B
5952*	81A
5953*	86C
5954*	84D
5955*	87F
5956*	81D
5957*	81D
5958*	86C
5959*	81D
5960*	81F
5961*	82D
5962*	81A
5963*	87G
5964*	83D
5965*	81F
5966*	84K
5967*	84C
5968*	82F
5969*	83G
5970*	86C
5971*	82D
5972*	87G
5973*	81D
5974*	82D
5975*	86G
5976*	83C
5977*	86C
5978*	82F
5979*	81D
5980*	85B
5981*	84G
5982*	82B
5983*	81C
5984*	87G
5985*	82D
5986*	81A
5987*	81A
5988*	85B
5989*	81C
5990*	85B
5991*	84B
5992*	82B
5993*	84E
5994*	84G
5995*	84A
5996*	81A
5997*	84E
5998*	83D
5999*	83B

Class 6000 4-6-0		Class 4300 2-6-0 (cont.)					

Class 6000
4-6-0

6000*	82A
6001*	81A
6002*	81A
6003*	81A
6004*	81A
6005*	84A
6006*	84A
6007*	84A
6008*	84A
6009*	81A
6010*	83D
6011*	84A
6012*	83D
6013*	81A
6014*	81A
6015*	81A
6016*	83D
6017*	81A
6018*	81A
6019*	81A
6020*	84A
6021*	81A
6022*	83D
6023*	83D
6024*	83D
6025*	83D
6026*	83D
6027*	83D
6028*	81A
6029*	83D

Class 6100
2-6-2T

6100	81D
6101	81D
6102	81C
6103	81D
6104	81B
6105	81D
6106	81B
6107	81B
6108	81B
6109	81F
6110	81C
6111	81F
6112	81E
6113	81B
6114	81B
6115	81B
6116	81B
6117	81A
6118	81E
6119	81B
6120	81A
6121	81F
6122	81F
6123	81B
6124	81B
6125	81C
6126	81C
6127	81B
6128	81C
6129	34E
6130	81D
6131	81B
6132	81E
6133	81B
6134	81E
6135	81A
6136	81B
6137	81A
6138	81F
6139	81C
6140	81B
6141	81A
6142	81A
6143	81B
6144	81A
6145	81D
6146	81B
6147	81C
6148	81C
6149	81A
6150	81B
6151	81B
6152	81B
6153	81D
6154	81B
6155	81A
6156	81C
6157	81B
6158	81A
6159	81A
6160	81B
6161	81B
6162	81D
6163	81D
6164	81B
6165	81C
6166	34E
6167	81E
6168	81A
6169	81C

Class 4300
2-6-0

6300	81F
6301	83C
6302	81D
6303	84J
6304	87G
6305	83B
6306	85A
6307	84G
6308	84K
6309	85B
6310	87G
6311	84J
6312	81D
6313	81F
6314	82D
6316	84J
6317	83B
6318	83G
6319	83D
6320	82C
6321	84A
6322	82C
6323	83B
6324	85A
6325	81C
6326	85C
6327	84J
6328	83B
6329	81E
6330	83E
6331	87G
6332	84F
6333	86G
6334	81D
6335	84B
6336	84E
6337	84K
6338	84G
6339	84K
6340	81E
6341	85B
6342	84C
6343	83B
6344	87G
6345	83A
6346	6C
6347	87H
6348	84G
6349	85C
6350	6C
6351	82A
6352	85C
6353	86C
6354	83G
6355	87H
6356	83E
6357	82C
6358	82C
6359	81E
6360	82C
6261	84B
6362	84B
6363	81D
6364	83B
6365	82D
6366	81D
6367	87G
6368	82D
6369	82D
6370	86G
6371	87H
6372	83B
6373	83F
6374	82C
6375	82D
6376	6C
6377	83B
6378	85A
6379	81D
6380	84K
6381	85B
6382	85D
6383	81D
6384	82C
6385	85B
6386	86E
6387	82C
6388	81C
6389	87H
6390	84C
6391	84A
6392	84K
6393	81D
6394	83B
6395	85C
6396	85A
6397	83C
6398	83B
6399	82D

Class 6400
0-6-0T

6400	86G
6401	88E
6402	88A
6403	86G
6404	84J
6405	84J
6406	83D
6407	83D
6408	88D
6409	86A
6410	86J
6411	88E
6412	87E
6413	86J
6414	83D
6415	86A
6416	88A
6417	83D
6418	84C
6419	83D
6420	83D
6421	83D
6422	84J
6423	88A
6424	86G
6425	87E
6426	86A
6427	88D
6428	86A
6429	86G
6430	86G
6431	87E
6432	86G
6433	88A
6434	88D
6435	88A
6436	88A
6437	86J
6438	88E
6439	86A

Class 5600
0–6–2T

6600	84B
6601	82B
6602	87H
6603	88A
6604	87E
6605	86J
6606	84G
6607	88A
6608	88A
6609	84B
6610	84B
6611	84E
6612	88A
6613	87D
6614	88C
6615	88C
6616	87B
6617	84F
6618	88A
6619	88C
6620	88C
6621	86F
6622	86J
6623	87B
6624	84K
6625	84D
6626	88A
6627	88A
6628	86J
6629	87B
6630	84E
6631	85B
6632	84D
6633	84G
6634	88A
6635	88A
6636	86G
6637	88C
6638	84B
6639	86E
6640	84B
6641	88C
6642	86F
6643	88C
6644	87B
6645	84B
6646	84F
6647	88A
6648	88F
6649	86F
6650	87B
6651	86J
6652	86J
6653	88C
6654	86A
6655	88F
6656	82B
6657	84D
6658	88C
6659	88A
6660	88A

6661	88E
6662	87D
6663	86G
6664	88A
6665	88A
6666	86E
6667	84F
6668	88C
6669	88C
6670	82B
6671	82B
6672	86A
6673	86E
6674	84F
6675	86F
6676	86E
6677	84F
6678	84F
6679	87E
6680	87E
6681	85C
6682	88A
6683	84G
6684	88A
6685	86H
6686	87B
6687	86G
6688	87F
6689	86E
6690	82D
6691	87B
6692	86J
6693	86J
6694	84J
6695	87E
6696	84C
6697	84D
6698	84J
6699	82D

Class 5700
0–6–0T

6700	88B
6701	88B
6702	88B
6703	88B
6704	88B
6705	88B
6706	88B
6707	88B
6708	88B
6709	88B
6710	86B
6711	86B
6712	88C
6713	87C
6714	87D
6715	87B
6716	82C
6717	87B
6718	87B
6719	87B
6720	87B

6721	88B
6722	88C
6723	88C
6724	88C
6725	86B
6726	86B
6727	86B
6728	86B
6729	86B
6730	86B
6731	86B
6732	86B
6733	88C
6734	87C
6735	86B
6736	88C
6737	82C
6738	84F
6739	82C
6740	88C
6741	82C
6742	86G
6743	88B
6744	88B
6745	88C
6746	88C
6747	88C
6748	88C
6749	87B
6750	88C
6751	88B
6752	88C
6753	88C
6754	88C
6755	86B
6756	86B
6757	86B
6758	86B
6759	86B
6760	86B
6761	87B
6762	87C
6763	87C
6764	86B
6765	86B
6766	87C
6767	88B
6768	87B
6769	88C

Class 6800
4–6–0

6800*	83G
6801*	83G
6802*	81D
6803*	84C
6804*	82D
6805*	82B
6806*	83G
6807*	85A
6808*	83G
6809*	83G
6810*	87F

6811*	82B
6812*	84A
6813*	83A
6814*	83A
6815*	83B
6816*	84C
6817*	83G
6818*	87G
6819*	84C
6820*	86A
6821*	86A
6822*	83A
6823*	87J
6824*	87F
6825*	83G
6826*	83G
6827*	82B
6828*	84F
6829*	83A
6830*	82B
6831*	6C
6832*	82B
6833*	84D
6834*	86A
6835*	84C
6836*	82B
6837*	82B
6838*	83G
6839*	84C
6840*	82B
6841*	6C
6842*	82B
6843*	84E
6844*	6C
6845*	82D
6846*	82B
6847*	84E
6848*	84A
6849*	82B
6850*	82B
6851*	85A
6852*	82B
6853*	84E
6854*	84C
6855*	83D
6856*	84B
6857*	84F
6858*	84C
6859*	6C
6860*	6C
6861*	82B
6862*	84B
6863*	82B
6864*	81D
6865*	81D
6866*	84E
6867*	82B
6868*	83B
6869*	83G
6870*	86A
6871*	86E
6872*	82B
6873*	83D
6874*	86A

6875* 83B	6955* 82D	7011* 82A	7233 86G
6876* 82B	6956* 84B	7012* 87E	7234 86G
6877* 85A	6957* 82B	7013* 81A	7235 86G
6878* 6C	6958* 82A	7014* 82A	7236 85A
6879* 84B		7015* 82C	7237 84D
	Class 6959	7016* 86C	7238 84B
Class 4900	**4-6-0**	7017* 86C	7239 86E
4-6-0	6959* 81A	7018* 87E	7240 85A
6900* 81A	6960* 81A	7019* 82A	7241 86A
6901* 84A	6961* 81C	7020* 86C	7242 86J
6902* 82F	6962* 81A	7021* 87G	7243 84B
6903* 87E	6963* 84G	7022* 86C	7244 87E
6904* 84E	6964* 84A	7023* 86C	7245 86A
6905* 85C	6965* 82A	7024* 81A	7246 86E
6906* 84C	6966* 82D	7025* 81A	7247 86A
6907* 83D	6967* 84B	7026* 84A	7248 85A
6908* 82C	6968* 81D	7027* 83D	7249 86A
6909* 82B	6969* 86C	7028* 87E	7250 83A
6910* 81A	6970* 81F	7029* 83A	7251 86E
6911* 83G	6971* 84E	7030* 81A	7252 86A
6912* 82F	6972* 82A	7031* 83D	7253 86A
6913* 83D	6973* 81A	7032* 81A	
6914* 82C	6974* 81A	7033* 81A	
6915* 82C	6975* 84B	7034* 82A	**Class 4300**
6916* 85C	6976* 84G	7035* 84G	**2-6-0**
6917* 85B	6977* 82A	7036*	7300 82D
6918* 87E	6978* 82D	7037*	7301 85A
6919* 87G	6979* 84C		7302 82D
6920* 84B	6980* 84G		7303 85B
6921* 85B	6981* 82A	**Class 7200**	7304 83B
6922* 82B	6982* 82D	**2-8-2T**	7305 84J
6923* 81E	6983* 81A	7200 83A	7306 87H
6924* 84A	6984* 85C	7201 86C	7307 85C
6925* 81F	6985* 81A	7202 88A	7308 85C
6926* 81A	6986* 82B	7203 86A	7309 82D
6927* 86A	6987* 85B	7204 87F	7310 84J
6928* 86C	6988* 82F	7205 88A	7311 84B
6929* 82C	6989* 85C	7206 86G	7312 85B
6930* 85A	6990* 81A	7207 84B	7313 84J
6931* 83F	6991* 82D	7208 84D	7314 85C
6932* 81A	6992* 85B	7209 83A	7315 84A
6933* 81F	6993* 82F	7210 86E	7316 83C
6934* 83A	6994* 83C	7211 87E	7317 84E
6935* 82D	6995* 83B	7212 86E	7318 81D
6936* 85C	6996* 81D	7213 86J	7319 84G
6937* 81F	6997* 82A	7214 86A	7320 81D
6938* 85A	6998* 86C	7215 86A	7321 82C
6939* 86C	6999* 86C	7216 86E	
6940* 85B		7217 86A	
6941* 84K		7218 84D	**Class 7400**
6942* 84E	**Class 4073**	7219 86C	**0-6-0T**
6943* 86C	**4-6-0**	7220 83A	7400 87G
6944* 81A	7000* 83A	7221 86J	7401 87G
6945* 82F	7001* 81A	7222 85A	7402 84F
6946* 86C	7002* 87E	7223 86E	7403 84J
6947* 85A	7003* 87E	7224 86E	7404 81F
6948* 86C	7004* 81A	7225 87E	7405 89A
6949* 83D	7005* 85A	7226 84B	7406 89C
6950* 85A	7006* 85B	7227 84B	7407 87G
6951* 85C	7007* 85A	7228 87F	7408 82F
6952* 81E	7008* 81F	7229 86E	7409 84J
6953* 81A	7009* 87E	7230 86A	7410 89A
6954* 82A	7010* 81F	7231 86A	7411 81F
		7232 86E	7412 81F

7413 87H	7723 85B	7787 87E	7913* 84E
7414 84J	7724 86G	7788 81D	7914* 82C
7415 82C	7725 86F	7789 86B	7915* 84A
7416 85C	7726 82B	7790 82B	7916* 82C
7417 89C	7727 82D	7791 81A	7917* 82A
7418 82C	7728 82B	7792 82C	7918* 84E
7419 87G	7729 82B	7793 82B	7919* 81D
7420 85C	7730 81C	7794 82C	7920*
7421 83B	7731 81C	7795 82B	7921*
7422 83F	7732 81C	7796 84B	7922*
7423 86J	7733 87B	7797 84B	7923*
7424 82C	7734 81A	7798 86F	7924*
7425 87G	7735 84E	7799 87A	7925*
7426 86G	7736 86A		7926*
7427 83A	7737 87A		7927*
7428 84F	7738 88A		7928*
7429 84F	7739 87A	**Class 7800**	7929*
7430 84F	7740 86G	**4-6-0**	
7431 84J	7741 85B	7800 84E	
7432 84F	7742 87A	7801* 83D	**Class 8100**
7433 84J	7743 87A	7802* 89C	**2-6-2T**
7434 89A	7744 87B	7803* 89C	8100 84D
7435 84F	7745 87F	7804* 83D	8101 85D
7436 81F	7746 86F	7805* 84C	8102 87H
7437 85A	7747 87J	7806* 84C	8103 89A
7438 84E	7748 86J	7807* 89A	8104 87A
7439 87K	7749 82B	7808* 89A	8105 82B
7440 84J	7750 85A	7809* 83D	8106 85A
7441 81B	7751 88B	7810* 84D	8107 87H
7442 81B	7752 86F	7811* 84C	8108 84E
7443 84J	7753 86A	7812* 83A	8109 84D
7444 87G	7754 84H	7813* 83A	
7445 88A	7755 87F	7814* 83D	
7446 83E	7756 87D	7815* 85B	**Class 9400**
7447 84J	7757 87A	7816* 87H	**0-6-0T**
7448 84F	7758 84C	7817* 84J	8400 84C
7449 84F	7759 84B	7818* 85B	8401 86C
	7760 81F	7819* 89A	8402 86H
	7761 83C	7820*	8403 83A
Class 5700	7762 83D	7821*	8404 83D
0-6-0T	7763 84C	7822*	8405 84C
	7764 86E	7823*	8406 86A
7700 85D	7765 87F	7824*	8407 84C
7701 87A	7766 88D	7825*	8408 87C
7702 84D	7767 87A	7826*	8409 83G
7703 86H	7768 86A	7827*	8410 84E
7704 87D	7769 87A	7828*	8411 84A
7705 84F	7770 86F	7829*	8412 83F
7706 87B	7771 86A		8413 82B
7707 85C	7772 88D		8414 88B
7708 81D	7773 86J	**Class 6959**	8415 84E
7709 83E	7774 86B	**4-6-0**	8416 88B
7710 81E	7775 86H	7900* 82B	8417 84B
7711 82B	7776 87F	7901* 82A	8418 84F
7712 86B	7777 81D	7902* 81A	8419 84F
7713 84E	7778 86H	7903* 91A	8420 87A
7714 6C	7779 82B	7904* 81A	8421 83C
7715 83E	7780 82B	7905* 83D	8422
7716 83C	7781 86A	7906* 82B	8423
7717 88D	7782 82B	7907* 82B	8424
7718 82B	7783 82B	7908* 82B	8425
7719 82B	7784 82D	7909* 83D	8426
7720 86J	7785 87F	7910* 81C	8427
7721 86H	7786 87A	7911* 81A	8428
7722 88A		7912* 84E	

8429		8493		8753	81A	9015 81E
8430		8494		8754	81A	9016 89A
8431		8495		8755	86G	9017 89C
8432		8496		8756	81A	9018 82C
8433		8497		8757	81A	9020 89A
8434		8498		8758	81C	9021 89C
8435		8499		8759	81A	9022 89A
8436				8760	81A	9023 82C
8437		**Class 5700**		8761	81A	9024 89C
8438		**0–6–0T**		8762	81A	9025 89C
8439		8700 84E		8763	81A	9026 89A
8440		8701 85B		8764	81A	9027 89C
8441		8702 82B		8765	81A	9028 89A
8442		8703 82B		8766	82B	
8443		8704 84F		8767	81A	**Class 3252**
8444		8705 84A		8768	81A	**4–4–0**
8445		8706 87F		8769	81A	9083* 82C
8446		8707 81A		8770	81A	9084* 89A
8447		8708 87F		8771	81A	9089 82C
8448		8709 83D		8772	81A	
8449		8710 86A		8773	81A	**Class 4300**
8450	86A	8711 86A		8774	81C	**2–6–0**
8451	88C	8712 86F		8775	87A	9300 81C
8452	84E	8713 82B		8776	86H	9301 81C
8453	86A	8714 82B		8777	86F	9302 81A
8454	84D	8715 87A		8778	86A	9303 81D
8455	88B	8716 86G		8779	82C	9304 81A
8456	83C	8717 85B		8780	88A	9305 81A
8457	88B	8718 85D		8781	85B	9306 81A
8458	87C	8719 83D		8782	87A	9307 81D
8459	84C	8720 87C		8783	83E	9308 81A
8460	88C	8721 86F		8784	84E	9309 81A
8461	88C	8722 82B		8785	87F	9310 81C
8462	84A	8723 86C		8786	86J	9311 81C
8463		8724 86H		8787	84C	9312 84B
8464		8725 6C		8788	86G	9313 81D
8465		8726 84A		8789	87E	9314 84B
8466		8727 85D		8790	82B	9315 81A
8467		8728 86C		8791	84F	9316 81F
8468		8729 84C		8792	84F	9317 81F
8469		8730 82B		8793	82C	9318 81D
8470		8731 85B		8794	86H	9319 81D
8471		8732 87F		8795	82B	
8472		8733 82C		8796	86B	**Class 9400**
8473		8734 84A		8797	84F	**0–6–0T**
8474		8735 88C		8798	84B	9400 82C
8475		8736 88D		8799	86E	9401 81A
8476		8737 82B				9402 81A
8477		8738 87F				9403 81A
8478		8739 86D		**Class 9000**		9404 81A
8479		8740 86F		**4–4–0**		9405 81A
8480		8741 82B		9000 89C		9406 81A
8481		8742 84F		9001 89A		9407 81C
8482		8743 88B		9002 89C		9408 84B
8483		8744 82D		9003 89A		9409 81C
8484		8745 82E		9004 89C		9410 81D
8485		8746 82B		9005 89C		9411 81D
8486		8747 82B		9008 84E		9412 81D
8487		8748 86F		9009 89C		9413 81E
8488		8749 87F		9010 89C		9414 81B
8489		8750 81A		9011 82C		9415 81B
8490		8751 81A		9012 89C		9416 81F
8491		8752 81C		9013 89C		
8492				9014 89C		

9417	81E	9481		9641	81C	9722	81D
9418	81A	9482		9642	82F	9723	86C
9419	81A	9483		9643	88D	9724	84E
9420	81D	9484		9644	86A	9725	81A
9421	81B	9485		9645	87D	9726	81C
9422	81A	9486		9646	83B	9727	85B
9423	81D	9487		9647	83C	9728	84K
9424	81B	9488		9648	86C	9729	82B
9425		9489		9649	86F	9730	84B
9426		9490		9650	86G	9731	86A
9427		9491		9651	6C	9732	82E
9428		9492		9652	87H	9733	84E
9429		9493		9653	81B	9734	87A
9430		9494		9654	81F	9735	87B
9431		9495		9655	83E	9736	87B
9432		9496		9656	84G	9737	87B
9433		9497		9657	84G	9738	87E
9434		9498		9658	81A	9739	84B
9435		9499		9659	81A	9740	84D
9436				9660	86F	9741	84F
9437		**Class 5700**		9661	81A	9742	84B
9438		**0–6–0T**		9662	86A	9743	87F
9439		9600	82C	9663	83B	9744	87D
9440		9601	82E	9664	86A	9745	86E
9441		9602	87J	9665	82B	9746	86D
9442		9603	87J	9666	87A	9747	84B
9443		9604	82B	9667	86A	9748	84E
9444		9605	82B	9668	83A	9749	81D
9445		9606	82B	9669	84J	9750	87A
9446		9607	86J	9670	83B	9751	81A
9447		9608	84E	9671	83D	9752	84B
9448		9609	86J	9672	84G	9753	84E
9449		9610	84E	9673	83D	9754	81A
9450		9611	81F	9674	86F	9755	83E
9451		9612	82D	9675	88D	9756	87A
9452		9613	84F	9676	82C	9757	83B
9453		9614	84E	9677	88B	9758	81A
9454		9615	82D	9678	6C	9759	86C
9455		9616	86A	9679	88B	9760	87J
9456		9617	87B	9680	84E	9761	87E
9457		9618	88D	9681	86F	9762	82D
9458		9619	85C	9682	84E	9763	81D
9459		9620	82B	9700	81A	9764	82B
9460		9621	84A	9701	81A	9765	83D
9461		9622	88D	9702	81A	9766	87B
9462		9623	83A	9703	81A	9767	84F
9463		9624	84H	9704	81A	9768	84B
9464		9625	87D	9705	81A	9769	84B
9465		9626	82B	9706	81A	9770	83D
9466		9627	87A	9707	81A	9771	82E
9467		9628	82D	9708	81A	9772	82C
9468		9629	86C	9709	81A	9773	82C
9469		9630	84H	9710	81A	9774	84K
9470		9631	88C	9711	83D	9775	87E
9471		9632	86A	9712	86J	9776	88C
9472		9633	83A	9713	86C	9777	87E
9473		9634	87B	9714	84B	9778	83A
9474		9635	84E	9715	84B	9779	87A
9475		9636	84F	9716	83D	9780	86D
9476		9637	86A	9717	83G	9781	81B
9477		9638	88D	9718	83B	9782	84C
9478		9639	84H	9719	84G	9783	87A
9479		9640	81B	9720	82C	9784	81A
9480				9721	82C	9785	87B

		Diesel Railcars					
9786	87A		13	87E	27	85A
9787	87F		14	84F	28	85B
9788	87F	1	81D	15	87G	29	84D
9789	81B	2	87E	16	87G	30	86G
9790	82C	3	86A	17	81C	31	85A
9791	81D	4	87E	18	86D	32	85A
9792	87A	5	85A	19	81D	33	84F
9793	84E	6	85A	20	82F	34	81C
9794	84K	7	85A	21	82B	35	82B
9795	82C	8	84F	22	81D	36	82B
9796	86H	10	81F	23	86A	37	81D
9797	86G	11	87E	24	82B	38	81D
9798	84E	12	87E	25	85B		
9799	87B			26	84D		

LOCOMOTIVES ON ORDER

Class 1500 **0-6-0T**			
1510	1526	1641	6776
1511	1527	1642	6777
1512	1528	1643	6778
1513	1529	1644	6779
1514		1645	
1515	**Class 1600**	1646	
1516	**0-6-0T**	1647	**Class 9400**
1517		1648	**0-6-0T**
1518	1630	1649	3400
1519	1631		3401
1520	1632		3402
1521	1633	**Class 5700**	3403
1522	1634	**0-6-0T**	3404
1523	1635		3405
1524	1636	6770	3406
1525	1637	6771	3407
	1638	6772	3408
	1639	6773	3409
	1640	6774	
		6775	

BRITISH RAILWAYS
INTERNAL COMBUSTION LOCOMOTIVES
Nos. 10000-18000

WITH SHED ALLOCATIONS

**Diesel Electric
Co+Co
London Midland**

No.	Class	Shed
10000	1A	
10001	1A	

**Diesel Mech.
4-8-4
London Midland**

No.	Class	Shed
10100		

**Diesel Electric
1-Co+Co-1
Southern**

No.	Class	Shed
10201		
10202		

**Diesel Electric
Bo+Bo
London Midland**

No.	Class	Shed
10800	4A	

**Diesel Mech.
0-6-0
Southern**

No.	Class	Shed
11001	75C	

**Diesel Electric
0-6-0
London Midland**

No.	Class	Shed
12000	5B	
12001	5B	
12002	5B	
12003	8C	
12004	1A	
12005	1A	
12006	18A	
12007	8C	
12008	8C	
12009	1A	
12010	1A	
12011	8C	
12012	8C	
12013	8C	
12014	8C	
12015	8C	
12016	8C	
12017	8C	
12018	5B	
12019	1A	
12020	8C	
12021	1A	
12022	1A	
12023	1A	
12024	12A	
12025	12A	
12026	12A	
12027	12A	
12028	12A	
12029	1A	
12030	1A	
12031	1A	
12032	1A	
12033	5B	
12034	5B	
12035	5B	
12036	5B	
12037	5B	
12038	18A	
12039	21A	
12040	21A	
12041	21A	
12042	21A	
12043	21A	
12044	21A	
12045	18A	
12046	18A	
12047	18A	
12048	18A	
12049	5B	
12050	5B	
12051	5B	
12052	5B	
12053	5B	
12054	5B	
12055	5B	
12056	18A	
12057	18A	
12058	1A	
12059	21A	
12060	21A	
12061	21A	
12062	21A	
12063	14A	
12064	14A	
12065	14A	
12066	14A	
12067	14A	
12068	14A	
12069	18A	
12070	18A	
12071	18A	
12072	18A	
12073	18A	
12074	21A	
12075	21A	
12076	21A	
12077	21A	
12078	5B	
12079	8C	
12080	68A	
12081	68A	
12082	68A	

**Diesel Electric
0-6-0
Eastern**

No.	Class	Shed
15000	31B	
15001	31B	
15002	31B	
15003	31B	
15004	31B	

**Petrol Electric
0-4-0
Eastern**

No.	Class	Shed
15097	51C	
15098	30A	
15099	30A	

**Diesel Electric
0-6-0
Western**

No.	Class	Shed
15100	82B	
15101	81A	
15102	81A	
15103	81A	
15104	81A	
15105	81A	
15106	81A	
15107	82B	

**Diesel Electric
0-6-0
Southern**

No.	Class	Shed
15201	75C	
15202	75C	
15203	75C	
15211	75C	
15212	75C	
15213	75C	
15214	75C	
15215	75C	
15216	75C	
15217	75C	
15218	73C	
15219	73C	
15220	73C	
15221	73C	
15222	73C	
15223	73C	
15224	73C	
15225	73C	

**Gas Turbine
A-I-A-A-I-A
Western**

No.	Class	Shed
18000	81A	

BRITISH RAILWAYS ELECTRIC LOCOMOTIVES
Nos. 20001-26510
WITH SHED ALLOCATIONS

No.	Class	Shed	No.	Class	Shed	No.	Class	Shed	No.	Class	Shed
Class CC			26010			26031			26052		
Co–Co			26011			26032			26053		
Southern			26012			26033			26054		
20001	Durnsford Rd.		26013			26034			26055		
20002	Durnsford Rd.		26014			26035			26056		
20003	Durnsford Rd.		26015			26036			26057		
			26016			26037					
			26017			26038					
Class EM1			26018			26039			**Class ES1**		
Bo—Bo			26019			26040			**Bo—Bo**		
Eastern			26020			26041			**North Eastern**		
26000†			26021			26042			26500	52B	
26001			26022			26043			26501	52B	
26002			26023			26044					
26003			26024			26045			**Class EB1**		
26004			26025			26046			**Bo—Bo**		
26005			26026			26047			**Eastern**		
26006			26027			26048			26510	30A	
26007			26028			26049					
26008			26029			26050			†On loan to		
26009			26030			26051			Netherlands Rlys.		

BRITISH RAILWAYS LOCOMOTIVES
Nos. 30007-36005
WITH SHED ALLOCATIONS

No.	Class	Shed	No.	Class	Shed	No.	Class	Shed	No.	Class	Shed
30007	T1	72D	30032	M7	71A	30045	M7	71D	30058	M7	72C
30020	T1	71D	30033	M7	71A	30046	M7	72A	30059	M7	71B
30021	M7	70C	30034	M7	72A	30047	M7	75D	30060	M7	70C
30022	M7	70C	30035	M7	72D	30048	M7	71A	30061	U.S.A.	711
30023	M7	72B	30036	M7	72E	30049	M7	72A	30062	U.S.A.	711
30024	M7	72A	30037	M7	72D	30050	M7	71D	30063	U.S.A.	711
30025	M7	72A	30038	M7	70A	30051	M7	71B	30064	U.S.A.	711
30026	M7	70C	30039	M7	72A	30052	M7	71B	30065	U.S.A.	711
30027	M7	75D	30040	M7	71B	30053	M7	71A	30066	U.S.A.	711
30028	M7	71B	30041	M7	72B	30054	M7	71D	30067	U.S.A.	711
30029	M7	71A	30042	M7	72E	30055	M7	72A	30068	U.S.A.	711
30030	M7	72A	30043	M7	70B	30056	M7	70C	30069	U.S.A.	711
30031	M7	71A	30044	M7	72E	30057	M7	71B	30070	U.S.A.	711

No.	Class	Shed	No.	Class	Shed	No.	Class	Shed	No.	Class	Shed
30071	U.S.A.	711	30172	L11	71D	30285	T9	71D	30379	M7	71B
30072	U.S.A.	711	30173	L11	71A	30286	T9	71A	30384	K10	70C
30073	U.S.A.	711	30174	L11	70B	30287	T9	71A	30389	K10	72C
30074	U.S.A.	711	30175	L11	71A	30288	T9	72B	30395	S11	71D
30082	B4	71A	30177	O2	71C	30289	T9	72B	30396	S11	71D
30083	B4	74A	30179	O2	71C	30300	T9	71A	30397	S11	71D
30084	B4	72D	30182	O2	72D	30301	T9	72B	30398	S11	71B
30086*	B4	71B	30183	O2	72D	30302	T9	70D	30399	S11	71C
30087	B4	71B	30192	O2	72A	30303	T9	71D	30400	S11	71D
30088	B4	72D	30193	O2	72A	30304	T9	71A	30401	S11	71A
30089*	B4	71A	30197	O2	71C	30305	T9	71D	30402	S11	71D
30093*	B4	71A	30199	O2	72A	30306	700	71A	30403	S11	71B
30094	B4	72D	30200	O2	72F	30307	T9	71C	30404	S11	71B
30096*	B4	71A	30203	O2	72F	30308	700	70C	30405	L11	70A
30102*	B4	72D	30204	O2	71B	30309	700	70B	30406	L11	70A
30104	M7	71B	30207	O2	72D	30310	T9	71D	30408	L11	72A
30105	M7	71A	30212	O2	71B	30311	700	70C	30409	L11	72A
30106	M7	71B	30213	O2	71A	30312	700	70C	30411	L11	71A
30107	M7	72D	30216	O2	72D	30313	700	71A	30412	L11	72C
30108	M7	70C	30221	O2	70A	30314	T9	71D	30413	L11	70A
30109	M7	71A	30223	O2	71C	30315	700	72B	30414	L11	71A
30110	M7	70C	30224	O2	72A	30316	700	71A	30415	L12	71C
30111	M7	71B	30225	O2	71A	30317	700	72B	30416	L12	70C
30112	M7	71A	30229	O2	71C	30318	M7	71B	30417	L12	71D
30113	T9	71D	30230	O2	72A	30319	M7	70A	30418	L12	70D
30114	T9	71D	30231	O2	71C	30320	M7	72A	30419	L12	71D
30115	T9	71D	30232	O2	72A	30321	M7	72E	30420	L12	70C
30116	T9	71C	30233	O2	71A	30322	M7	70A	30421	L12	72B
30117	T9	72C	30236	O2	72D	30323	M7	72A	30422	L12	71A
30118	T9	71D	30238	G6	70C	30324	M7	70C	30423	L12	71A
30119	T9	70A	30241	M7	70A	30325	700	70C	30424	L12	70C
30120	T9	71D	30242	M7	71A	30326	700	70C	30425	L12	70C
30121	T9	72B	30243	M7	72B	30327	700	70C	30426	L12	71D
30122	T9	72B	30244	M7	70A	30328	M7	70C	30427	L12	71D
30123	M7	70A	30245	M7	72A	30330	H15	72B	30428	L12	70C
30124	M7	72A	30246	M7	70C	30331	H15	72B	30429	L12	71A
30125	M7	71A	30247	M7	72E	30332	H15	72B	30430	L12	71A
30127	M7	72B	30248	M7	70A	30333	H15	72B	30431	L12	71A
30128	M7	71A	30249	M7	70B	30334	H15	72B	30432	L12	71A
30129	M7	72C	30250	M7	72E	30335	H15	72B	30433	L12	71A
30130	M7	70A	30251	M7	71B	30336	T9	70C	30434	L12	71A
30131	M7	71B	30252	M7	72A	30337	T9	72C	30436	L11	70C
30132	M7	72A	30253	M7	72A	30338	T9	71C	30437	L11	71A
30133	M7	72A	30254	M7	70B	30339	700	70A	30438	L11	70B
30134	L11	72C	30255	M7	72A	30346	700	70B	30441	L11	71D
30148	L11	71A	30256	M7	72A	30349	G6	70C	30442	L11	71A
30154	L11	71A	30258	G6	70D	30350	700	71A	30446	T14	70A
30155	L11	71A	30259	G6	70A	30352	700	70B	30448*	N15	72B
30156	L11	71A	30260	G6	71B	30353	G6	70A	30449*	N15	72B
30157	L11	71A	30266	G6	70D	30355	700	72B	30450*	N15	72B
30158	L11	70C	30268	G6	70C	30356	M7	72D	30451*	N15	70A
30159	L11	71A	30270	G6	70C	30357	M7	71A	30452*	N15	72B
30160	G6	70A	30274	G6	71H	30367	T1	71A	30453*	N15	72B
30162	G6	71A	30277	G6	71H	30368	700	70D	30454*	N15	72B
30163	L11	70A	30280	T9	71D	30374	M7	72A	30455*	N15	72A
30164	L11	71B	30281	T9	70C	30375	M7	72D	30456*	N15	70D
30165	L11	70A	30282	T9	71A	30376	M7	72A	30457*	N15	72A
30170	L11	71D	30283	T9	72A	30377	M7	72A			
30171	L11	71A	30284	T9	71C	30378	M7	71A			

No.	Class	Shed	No.	Class	Shed	No.	Class	Shed	No.	Class	Shed	No.	Class	Shed
30458*	0458	70C	30520	H16	70B	30676	M7	70A	30748*	N15	72B			
30461	T14	70A	30521	H15	71A	30687	700	70B	30749*	N15	71A			
30463	D15	71A	30522	H15	71A	30688	700	70B	30750*	N15	71B			
30464	D15	71A	30523	H15	71A	30689	700	70B	30751*	N15	71B			
30465	D15	71A	30524	H15	71A	30690	700	72B	30752*	N15	71A			
30466	D15	71A	30530	Q	71A	30691	700	72B	30753*	N15	72B			
30467	D15	71A	30531	Q	71A	30692	700	70A	30754*	N15	71B			
30468	D15	71A	30532	Q	71A	30693	700	70D	30755*	N15	70A			
30469	D15	71A	30533	Q	75C	30694	700	70A	30756*	756	73A			
30470	D15	71A	30534	Q	75C	30695	700	71B	30757*	757	72D			
30471	D15	71A	30535	Q	71A	30696	700	70B	30758*	757	72D			
30472	D15	71A	30536	Q	71A	30697	700	70B	30763*	N15	73A			
30473	H15	71A	30537	Q	75C	30698	700	70B	30764*	N15	73A			
30474	H15	71A	30538	Q	75C	30699	700	70A	30765*	N15	72B			
30475	H15	71A	30539	Q	75C	30700	700	71A	30766*	N15	73A			
30476	H15	71A	30540	Q	75E	30701	700	70A	30767*	N15	74C			
30477	H15	71A	30541	Q	75E	30702	T9	72A	30768*	N15	74C			
30478	H15	71A	30542	Q	71A	30703	T9	72A	30769*	N15	74C			
30479	M7	71A	30543	Q	71A	30704	T9	72C	30770*	N15	74C			
30480	M7	71D	30544	Q	71A	30705	T9	71A	30771*	N15	74C			
30481	M7	70C	30545	Q	75D	30706	T9	72A	30772*	N15	71A			
30482	H15	70A	30546	Q	75D	30707	T9	72A	30773*	N15	72B			
30483	H15	71A	30547	Q	75C	30708	T9	71A	30774*	N15	73A			
30484	H15	70A	30548	Q	71B	30709	T9	72B	30775*	N15	73A			
30485	H15	70A	30549	Q	71B	30710	T9	70C	30776*	N15	73A			
30486	H15	70A	30564	0395	71A	30711	T9	71A	30777*	N15	71A			
30487	H15	70A	30565	0395	71A	30712	T9	70D	30778*	N15	71A			
30488	H15	70A	30566	0395	71A	30713	T9	71A	30779*	N15	71A			
30489	H15	71A	30567	0395	70B	30714	T9	72A	30780*	N15	70A			
30490	H15	70A	30568	0395	70C	30715	T9	72A	30781*	N15	74C			
30491	H15	70A	30569	0395	70B	30716	T9	72A	30782*	N15	70A			
30492	G16	70B	30570	0395	70B	30717	T9	72A	30783*	N15	71A			
30493	G16	70B	30571	0395	71A	30718	T9	70A	30784*	N15	71A			
30494	G16	70B	30572	0395	70B	30719	T9	72B	30785*	N15	71A			
30495	G16	70B	30573	0395	70B	30721	T9	71A	30786*	N15	73A			
30496	S15	70B	30574	0395	70C	30722	T9	71A	30787*	N15	70A			
30497	S15	70B	30575	0395	70C	30723	T9	72A	30788*	N15	71A			
30498	S15	70B	30576	0395	70C	30724	T9	72B	30789*	N15	71A			
30499	S15	70B	30577	0395	72B	30725	T9	72B	30790*	N15	71A			
30500	S15	70B	30578	0395	70C	30726	T9	71A	30791*	N15	73A			
30501	S15	70B	30579	0395	70B	30727	T9	72B	30792*	N15	73A			
30502	S15	70B	30580	0395	70C	30728	T9	71B	30793*	N15	73A			
30503	S15	70B	30581	0395	72A	30729	T9	71A	30794*	N15	73B			
30504	S15	70B	30582	0415	72A	30730	T9	72B	30795*	N15	73B			
30505	S15	70B	30583	0415	72A	30731	T9	71D	30796*	N15	73A			
30506	S15	70B	30584	0415	72A	30732	T9	70B	30797*	N15	73C			
30507	S15	70B	30585	0298	72F	30733	T9	71D	30798*	N15	73B			
30508	S15	70B	30586	0298	72F	30736*	N15	71B	30799*	N15	73B			
30509	S15	70B	30587	0298	72F	30737*	N15	71B	30800*	N15	73C			
30510	S15	70B	30588	C14	71A	30738*	N15	70B	30801*	N15	74A			
30511	S15	70B	30589	C14	71A	30739*	N15	72B	30802*	N15	74A			
30512	S15	70B	30667	M7	71A	30740*	N15	71B	30803*	N15	74A	30823	S15	72A
30513	S15	70B	30668	M7	72A	30741*	N15	71B	30804*	N15	74A	30824	S15	72A
30514	S15	70B	30669	M7	72A	30742*	N15	71B	30805*	N15	74A	30825	S15	72A
30515	S15	70B	30670	M7	72E	30743*	N15	71B	30806*	N15	74C	30826	S15	72B
30516	H16	70B	30671	M7	72A	30744*	N15	72B						
30517	H16	70B	30673	M7	71A	30745*	N15	70D						
30518	H16	70B	30674	M7	71A	30746*	N15	71B						
30519	H16	70B	30675	M7	72B	30747*	N15	70A						

No.	Class	Shed	No.	Class	Shed	No.	Class	Shed	No.	Class	Shed
30827	S15	72B	30922*	V	74E	31092	D	73D	31263	H	73A
30828	S15	72B	30923*	V	74E	31093	OI	74B	31265	H	74B
30829	S15	72B	30924*	V	74C	31102	C	73B	31266	H	73A
30830	S15	72B	30925*	V	74C	31107	RI	74C	31267	C	73D
30831	S15	72B	30926*	V	74B			(F)	31268	C	73E
30832	S15	72B	30927*	V	74C	31108	OI	74C	31269	H	74A
30833	S15	70B	30928*	V	73B	31112	C	73D	31270	C	73C
30834	S15	70B	30929*	V	73B	31113	C	74C	31271	C	74A
30835	S15	70B	30930*	V	73B	31128	RI	74C	31272	C	74D
30836	S15	70B	30931*	V	73B			(F)	31273	E	73B
30837	S15	70B	30932*	V	73B	31145	DI	73A	31274	H	74A
30838	S15	70B	30933*	V	73B	31147	RI	74C	31275	E	73B
30839	S15	70B	30934*	V	73B			(F)	31276	H	74C
30840	S15	70B	30935*	V	74E	31150	C	73C	31277	C	74D
30841	S15	72A	30936*	V	73B	31154	RI	74C	31278	H	73B
30842	S15	72A	30937*	V	73B			(F)	31279	H	74E
30843	S15	72A	30938*	V	73B	31157	E	73E	31280	C	73B
30844	S15	72A	30939*	V	73B	31158	H	74A	31287	C	73D
30845	S15	72A	30950	Z	73B	31159	EI	73C	31291	C	74C
30846	S15	72A	30951	Z	73D	31160	EI	73B	31293	C	73B
30847	S15	72A	30952	Z	71A	31161	H	74A	31294	C	73B
30850*	LN	71A	30953	Z	74A	31162	H	73B	31295	H	73A
30851*	LN	71A	30954	Z	72A	31164	H	74E	31297	C	73B
30852*	LN	71A	30955	Z	70A	31165	E	73A	31298	C	74B
30853*	LN	71A	30956	Z	71A	31166	E	73B	31305	H	74A
30854*	LN	71A	30957	Z	72B	31174	RI	74E	31306	H	74C
30855*	LN	71A	31004	C	74B	31175	E	73B	31307	H	73A
30856*	LN	71A	31005	H	73A	31176	E	73B	31308	H	73D
30857*	LN	71A	31010	RI	74A	31177	H	73A	31309	H	73B
30858*	LN	70A	31016	H	75F	31178	P	75A	31310	H	74E
30859*	LN	70A	31018	C	73C	31179	EI	73B	31311	H	73A
30860*	LN	70A	31019	EI	73A	31182	H	75F	31315	E	73B
30861*	LN	71B	31027	P	74C	31184	C	73A	31317	C	73D
30862*	LN	71B	31033	C	73B	31191	C	74C	31319	H	73A
30863*	LN	71B	31036	E	73B	31193	H	74D	31320	H	74D
30864*	LN	71B	31037	C	74E	31218	H	74A	31321	H	73A
30865*	LN	71B	31038	C	74E	31219	C	74D	31322	H	74A
30900*	V	74E	31041	OI	74A	31221	C	73D	31323	P	74C
30901*	V	74E	31044	OI	73B	31223	C	73D	31324	H	73B
30902*	V	74E	31047	RI	74C	31225	C	73D	31325	P	71A
30903*	V	74E			(F)	31227	C	73B	31326	H	73B
30904*	V	74E	31048	OI	74A	31229	C	73E	31327	H	74D
30905*	V	74E	31054	C	73C	31234	C	73A	31328	H	74E
30906*	V	74E	31057	D	70E	31239	H	74A	31329	H	73A
30907*	V	74E	31059	C	73C	31242	C	73E	31335	RI	74E
30908*	V	73B	31061	C	73C	31243	C	74C	31337	RI	74C
30909*	V	73B	31063	C	74A	31244	C	74D			(F)
30910*	V	74E	31064	OI	73B	31245	C	73C	31339	RI	74A
30911*	V	74B			(NC)	31246	DI	74C	31340	RI	74C
30912*	V	74B	31065	OI	74B	31247	DI	74C			(F)
30913*	V	74B	31066	OI	73B	31248	OI	74A	31369	OI	73E
30914*	V	74B			(NC)	31252	C	74B	31370	OI	74A
30915*	V	74B	31067	EI	73A	31253	C	73B	31373	OI	74C
30916*	V	74B	31068	C	73B	31255	C	73D	31379	OI	74A
30917*	V	74B	31069	RI	74A	31256	C	73D	31381	OI	74C
30918*	V	74B	31071	C	73B	31258	OI	73C	31383	OI	74C
30919*	V	73B	31075	D	70E	31259	H	74B	31390	OI	74B
30920*	V	73B	31086	C	73D	31260	C	74A	31391	OI	73C
30921*	V	73B	31090	C	73D	31261	H	74A			

No.	Class	Shed	No.	Class	Shed	No.	Class	Shed	No.	Class	Shed
31395	OI	73B	31519	H	74B	31613	U	70A	31700	RI	7 4D
	(NC)		31520	H	74A	31614	U	70E	31703	RI	7 4D
31400	N	74A	31521	H	74B	31615	U	70E	31704	RI	7 4D
31401	N	74A	31522	H	74B	31616	U	73C	31705	RI	73 E
31402	N	74A	31523	H	74D	31617	U	73C	31706	RI	74D
31403	N	74A	31530	H	74C	31618	U	72B	31708	RI	74C
31404	N	74A	31531	H	74C	31619	U	70A	31710	RI	74A
31405	N	74A	31532	H	74B	31620	U	70C	31711	C	74A
31406	N	74A	31533	H	73B	31621	U	70C	31712	C	73D
31407	N	72A	31540	H	74C	31622	U	71B	31713	C	73D
31408	N	72A	31541	H	73B	31623	U	70A	31714	C	73A
31409	N	73A	31542	H	73B	31624	U	70B	31715	C	73E
31410	N	73A	31543	H	74B	31625	U	70A	31716	C	73A
31411	N	73A	31544	H	73B	31626	U	72B	31717	C	73A
31412	N	73A	31545	DI	74C	31627	U	70C	31718	C	73A
31413	N	73A	31546	H	73B	31628	U	70C	31719	C	73A
31414	N	73A	31547	E	73B	31629	U	70C	31720	C	73C
31425	OI	74C	31548	H	74D	31630	U	70C	31721	C	74A
31430	OI	74C	31549	D	74D	31631	U	73E	31722	C	73A
31432	OI	73C	31550	H	74D	31632	U	71C	31723	C	73B
31434	OI	74C	31551	H	70A	31633	U	70D	31724	C	73D
31443	BI	70E	31552	H	70A	31634	U	72C	31725	C	73B
31461	C	74D	31553	H	70A	31635	U	70C	31727	DI	73E
31470	DI	74C	31554	H	70A	31636	U	72C	31728	D	74D
31477	D	74A	31555	P	74C	31637	U	70A	31729	D	73D
31480	C	73C	31556	P	75A	31638	U	73E	31730	D	74D
31481	C	73E	31557	P	74C	31639	U	73C	31731	D	74D
31486	C	73C	31558	P	73A	31658	R	73D	31732	D	73C
31487	DI	73A	31572	C	74A	31659	R	73D	31733	D	74D
31488	D	73B	31573	D	73D	31660	R	73A	31734	D	73E
31489	DI	73E	31574	D	74A	31661	R	73E	31735	DI	74C
31490	D	73B	31575	C	73A	31662	R	73D	31736	DI	74A
31491	E	70E	31576	C	73A	31663	R	73D	31737	D	74C
31492	DI	73D	31577	D	74A	31665	R	73D	31739	DI	73E
31493	D	74E	31578	C	73A	31666	R	74D	31740	D	70E
31494	DI	73D	31579	C	73D	31667	R	73A	31741	DI	73E
31495	C	73E	31580	C	74D	31670	R	74D	31743	DI	73A
31496	D	73B	31581	C	73C	31671	R	74D	31744	D	70E
31497	EI	73A	31582	C	73A	31673	R	74C	31745	DI	74D
31498	C	73A	31583	C	73D	31674	R	73E	31746	D	73B
31500	H	73B	31584	C	73B	31675	R	74D	31748	D	74A
31501	D	73E	31585	C	73D	31681	C	73A	31749	DI	73A
31502	DI	73E	31586	D	73E	31682	C	73D	31750	D	70E
31503	H	74C	31587	E	74E	31683	C	73A	31753	LI	74C
31504	EI	73A	31588	C	73D	31684	C	74D	31754	LI	74C
31505	DI	73E	31589	C	74A	31685	S	74A	31755	LI	74C
31506	EI	73A	31590	C	74D	31686	C	74D	31756	LI	74C
31507	EI	73B	31591	D	73B	31687	C	73B	31757	LI	74C
31508	C	73B	31592	C	74B	31688	C	73D	31758	LI	73B
31509	DI	74D	31593	C	74D	31689	C	73C	31759	LI	73B
31510	C	73D	31595	J	74A	31690	C	74B	31760	L	74D
31511	EI	73B	31596	J	74A	31691	C	73E	31761	L	74D
31512	H	74C	31598	J	74A	31692	C	73E	31762	L	73A
31513	C	74A	31602	T	70E	31693	C	73D	31763	L	74A
31514	E	74A	31604	T	70E	31694	C	73C	31764	L	73A
31515	E	70E	31610	U	70E	31695	C	73C	31765	L	74D
31516	E	73D	31611	U	70E	31696	RI	73E	31766	L	74E
31517	H	74D	31612	U	71D	31697	RI	73D	31767	L	73A
31518	H	74C				31698	RI	73E			

No.	Class	Shed	No.	Class	Shed	No.	Class	Shed	No.	Class	Shed
31768	L	74E	31827	N	73B	31895	UI	75B	32067	B4X	70D
31769	L	74E	31828	N	72A	31896	UI	75B	32068	B4	75G
31770	L	74A	31829	N	72A	31897	UI	75B	32070	B4X	73B
31771	L	74A	31830	N	72A	31898	UI	75B	32071	B4X	75G
31772	L	74A	31831	N	72A	31899	UI	73B	32072	B4X	75G
31773	L	74A	31832	N	72A	31900	UI	73B	32073	B4X	75G
31774	L	74A	31833	N	72A	31901	UI	73B	32075	I3	73B
31775	L	74A	31834	N	72A	31902	UI	73B			(NC)
31776	L	74B	31835	N	72A	31903	UI	73A	32076	I3	75A
31777	L	74B	31836	N	72A	31904	UI	73A	32077	I3	73B
31778	L	74D	31837	N	72A	31905	UI	73A			(NC)
31779	L	74D	31838	N	72A	31906	UI	73A	32078	I3	75E
31780	L	74B	31839	N	72A	31907	UI	73A	32079	I3	75E
31781	L	74B	31840	N	72A	31908	UI	73A	32081	I3	75G
31782	LI	73B	31841	N	72A	31909	UI	73A	32082	I3	75E
31783	LI	73B	31842	N	72E	31910	UI	73A	32083	I3	75G
31784	LI	73B	31843	N	75B	31911	W	73C	32084	I3	75E
31785	LI	73B	31844	N	75B	31912	W	73C	32086	I3	75A
31786	LI	73B	31845	N	72A	31913	W	73C	32089	I3	75G
31787	LI	73B	31846	N	72A	31914	W	73A	32090	I3	75E
31788	LI	74B	31847	N	72A	31915	W	75C	32091	I3	75E
31789	LI	73B	31848	N	75B	31916	W	75C	32094	EI/R	72D
31790	U	72C	31849	N	75B	31917	W	75C	32095	EI/R	72E
31791	U	72C	31850	N	73E	31918	W	75C	32096	EI/R	72E
31792	U	72C	31851	N	75B	31919	W	75C	32100	E2	73A
31793	U	70E	31852	N	75B	31920	W	75C	32101	E2	73A
31794	U	70E	31853	N	72A	31921	W	73C	32102	E2	73A
31795	U	70E	31854	N	73E	31922	W	73C	32103	E2	73A
31796	U	70E	31855	N	72A	31923	W	73C	32104	E2	73A
31797	U	70E	31856	N	72A	31924	W	73C	32105	E2	73A
31798	U	70C	31857	N	75B	31925	W	73C	32106	E2	73A
31799	U	70E	31858	N	75B	32002	IIX	75A	32107	E2	73A
31800	U	70C	31859	N	73A	32005	IIX	75A	32108	E2	74C
31801	U	70C	31860	N	74A	32008	IIX	73B	32109	E2	74C
31802	U	70C	31861	N	74A			(NC)	32113	EI	73B
31803	U	73A	31862	N	75B	32009	IIX	75G	32124	EI/R	72A
31804	U	70C	31863	N	75B	32021	I3	75F	32128	EI	73A
31805	U	71D	31864	N	75B	32022	I3	75F	32129	EI	71D
31806	U	73E	31865	N	75B	32023	I3	75F	32133	EI	71A
31807	U	70A	31866	N	72A	32026	I3	75F	32135	EI/R	72A
31808	U	73E	31867	N	72A	32027	I3	75F	32138	EI	70A
31809	U	71D	31868	N	73E	32028	I3	75F	32139	EI	75A
31810	N	73A	31869	N	72A	32029	I3	75G	32145	EI	74D
31811	N	73A	31870	N	72D	32030	I3	75G	32147	EI	71A
31812	N	73A	31871	N	72D	32037*	HI	73B	32151	EI	73B
31813	N	73A	31872	N	72B			(NCG)	32156	EI	71I
31814	N	73A	31873	N	72B	32038*	HI	73B	32160	EI	70D
31815	N	73A	31874	N	72A			(NCG)	32165	E3	73B
31816	N	73A	31875	N	73C	32039*	HI	75A	32166	E3	73B
31817	N	73A	31876	NI	73C	32043	B4X	75G	32167	E3	74D
31818	N	73A	31877	NI	73C	32045	B4X	70D	32168	E3	73B
31819	N	74C	31878	NI	73C	32050	B4X	73B	32169	E3	74D
31820	N	74C	31879	NI	73C	32052	B4X	70D	32170	E3	73B
31821	N	74C	31880	NI	73C	32054	B4	75G	32300	C3	71D
31822	NI	73C	31890	UI	75A	32055	B4X	75G	32301	C3	71D
31823	N	74C	31891	UI	75A	32056	B4X	73B	32302	C3	75D
31824	N	73B	31892	UI	75A	32060	B4X	75G	32303	C3	71D
31825	N	73B	31893	UI	75A	32062	B4	75G	32306	C3	71D
31826	N	73B	31894	UI	75A	32063	B4	75G	32325	JI	75A

No.	Class	Shed	No.	Class	Shed	No.	Class	Shed	No.	Class	Shed
32326	J2	75A	32417	E6	75C	32487	E4	71D	32546	C2X	75C
32327*	N15X	70D	32418	E6	75C	32488	E4	74D	32547	C2X	75C
32328*	N15X	70D	32421*	H2	75A	32489	E4X	75C	32548	C2X	75D
32329*	N15X	70D			(N)	32490	E4	70C	32549	C2X	73B
32330*	N15X	70D	32422*	H2	75A	32491	E4	71A	32550	C2X	75B
32331*	N15X	70D			(N)	32492	E4	71A	32551	C2X	73B
32332*	N15X	70D	32424*	H2	75A	32493	E4	70A	32552	C2X	75E
32333*	N15X	70D			(N)	32494	E4	75A	32553	C2X	75E
32337*	K	75G	32425*	H2	75A			(N)	32554	C2X	73B
32338	K	71D	32426*	H2	75A	32495	E4	75C	32556	E4	75D
32339	K	75A	32434	C2X	75A	32496	E4	75A	32557	E4	71A
32340	K	71D	32437	C2X	75A			(N)			(N)
32341	K	75A			(N)	32497	E4	75E	32558	E4	71A
32342	K	75A	32438	C2X	75A	32498	E4	70A	32559	E4	71A
32343	K	75A	32440	C2X	75C	32499	E4	70A	32560	E4	75B
32344	K	75A	32441	C2X	75E	32500	E4	70A	32561	E4	75B
32345	K	75A	32442	C2X	73B	32501	E4	75D	32562	E4	71A
32346	K	75E	32443	C2X	75A	32502	E4	75C	32563	E4	71A
32347	K	75A	32444	C2X	75C	32503	E4	74D	32564	E4	73B
32348	K	75E	32445	C2X	75E	32504	E4	75A	32565	E4	73B
32349	K	75E	32446	C2X	73B			(N)	32566	E4	75A
32350	K	75E	32447	C2X	75C	32505	E4	75A			(N)
32351	K	75E	32448	C2X	73B	32506	E4	75C	32568	E5	75D
32352	K	75E	32449	C2X	75B	32507	E4	75B	32570	E5X	75D
32353	K	75E	32450	C2X	75B	32508	E4	75A	32571	E5	75E
32359	D1/M	74C	32451	C2X	75E			(N)	32573	E5	75A
32364	D3	75D	32453	E3	73B	32509	E4	75A	32574	E5	75G
32365	D3	75D	32454	E3	74D	32510	E4	71A	32575	E5	75A
32368	D3	75A	32455	E3	75A	32511	E4	75D	32576	E5X	75A
32372	D3	75A	32456	E3	74D	32512	E4	75B	32577	E4	75A
32376	D3	75A	32458	E3	73B	32513	E4	75A	32578	E4	75C
32378	D3	74E	32459	E3	73B	32514	E4	75A	32579	E4	71A
32379	D3	75D	32460	E3	73B	32515	E4	75D	32580	E4	74D
32380	D3	75D	32461	E3	73B	32516	E4	75E	32581	E4	74D
32384	D3	75D	32462	E3	73B	32517	E4	75B	32582	E4	70E
32385	D3	75G	32463	E4	73B	32518	E4	75G	32583	E5	75A
32386	D3	75A	32464	E4	75D	32519	E4	75E	32584	E5	75E
32388	D3	74E	32465	E4	75A	32520	E4	75E	32585	E5	73B
32390	D3	75F	32466	E4X	75C	32521	C2X	75D			(NC)
32391	D3	74E	32467	E4	73B	32522	C2X	75E	32586	E5X	75D
32393	D3	75A	32468	E4	70A	32523	C2X	75A(N)	32587	E5	73B
32394	D3	75G	32469	E4	73B	32524	C2X	73B			(NC)
32399	E5	75A	32470	E4	75A	32525	C2X	73B	32588	E5	75G
32400	E5	75A	32471	E4	75A	32526	C2X	75C	32590	E5	73B
32401	E5X	75A	32472	E4	73B	32527	C2X	75E	32591	E5	75G
32402	E5	75A	32473	E4	73B	32528	C2X	75A	32592	E5	75B
32404	E5	75G	32474	E4	73B	32529	C2X	75E	32593	E5	75G
32405	E5	75G	32475	E4	75A	32532	C2X	75E	32594	E5	75A
32406	E5	75G			(N)	32534	C2X	75A	32595	IIX	75A
32407	E6X	75C	32476	E4	75C	32535	C2X	75C	32596	IIX	75A
32408	E6	73B	32477	E4X	75C	32536	C2X	75C			(NC)
32409	E6	71A	32478	E4X	75C	32537	C2X	75D	32602	IIX	73B
32410	E6	73B	32479	E4	75C	32538	C2X	75A	32603	IIX	75G
32411	E6X	73B	32480	E4	75E	32539	C2X	75A	32606	E1	7II
32412	E6	71A	32481	E4	73B	32540	C2X	75B	32608	E1/R	72E
32413	E6	73B	32482	E4	75D	32541	C2X	75B	32610	E1/R	72E
32414	E6	75C	32484	E4	75E	32543	C2X	75A	32636	A1X	75A
32415	E6	73B	32485	E4	75G	32544	C2X	75D			(N)
32416	E6	71A	32486	E4	75A	32545	C2X	75E	32640	A1X	74A
									32644	A1X	74A
									32646	A1X	71D

No.	Class	Shed	No.	Class	Shed	No.	Class	Shed	No.	Class	Shed
32647	AIX	75A (N)	33036	QI	74D	34046*	WC	72A	34096*	WC	74B
32655	AIX	71D	33037	QI	74D	34047*	WC	72A	34097*	WC	74B
32659	AIX	74A	33038	QI	74D	34048*	WC	72A	34098*	WC	74B
32661	AIX	71D	33039	QI	74E	34049*	BB	70A	34099*	WC	74B
32662	AIX	71D	33040	QI	74E	34050*	BB	70A	34100*	WC	74B
32670	AIX	71D	34001*	WC	72A	34051*	BB	70A	34101*	WC	73A
32677	AIX	71D	34002*	WC	72A	34052*	BB	70A	34102*	WC	73A
32678	AIX	74A	34003*	WC	72A	34053*	BB	70A	34103*	WC	73A
32689	EI	75A	34004*	WC	72A	34054*	BB	70A	34104*	WC	73A
32691	EI	71D	34005*	WC	72A	34055*	BB	70A	34105*	WC	71B
32694	EI	71D	34006*	WC	72A	34056*	BB	70A	34106*	WC	71B
32695	EI/R	72A	34007*	WC	72A	34057*	BB	70A	34107*	WC	71B
32696	EI/R	72E	34008*	WC	72A	34058*	BB	70A	34108*	WC	71B
32697	EI/R	72A	34009*	WC	72A	34059*	BB	70A	34109*	BB	71B
33001	QI	70C	34010*	WC	72A	34060*	BB	70A	34110*	BB	
33002	QI	70C	34011*	WC	72D	34061*	BB	70A	35001*	MN	72A
33003	QI	70C	34012*	WC	72D	34062*	BB	70A	35002*	MN	72A
33004	QI	70C	34013*	WC	72D	34063*	BB	70A	35003*	MN	72A
33005	QI	70C	34014*	WC	72A	34064*	BB	70A	35004*	MN	72A
33006	QI	70B	34015*	WC	72A	34065*	BB	70A	35005*	MN	70A
33007	QI	70B	34016*	WC	72A	34066*	BB	73A	35006*	MN	72B
33008	QI	70B	34017*	WC	72A	34067*	BB	73A	35007*	MN	72B
33009	QI	70B	34018*	WC	72A	34068*	BB	73A	35008*	MN	72B
33010	QI	70B	34019*	WC	72A	34069*	BB	73A	35009*	MN	72B
33011	QI	70B	34020*	WC	72A	34070*	BB	73A	35010*	MN	70A
33012	QI	70B	34021*	WC	72D	34071*	BB	73A	35011*	MN	70A
33013	QI	70C	34022*	WC	72B	34072*	BB	74C	35012*	MN	70A
33014	QI	70C	34023*	WC	72B	34073*	BB	74C	35013*	MN	70A
33015	QI	70C	34024*	WC	72A	34074*	BB	73A	35014*	MN	70A
33016	QI	70C	34025*	WC	72A	34075*	BB	73A	35015*	MN	70A
33017	QI	71A	34026*	WC	72A	34076*	BB	73A	35016*	MN	70A
33018	QI	71A	34027*	WC	72A	34077*	BB	74B	35017*	MN	70A
33019	QI	71A	34028*	WC	72A	34078*	BB	74B	35018*	MN	70A
33020	QI	71A	34029*	WC	72A	34079*	BB	74B	35019*	MN	70A
33021	QI	71A	34030*	WC	72A	34080*	BB	74B	35020*	MN	70A
33022	QI	71A	34031*	WC	72A	34081*	BB	74B	35021*	MN	72A
33023	QI	71A	34032*	WC	72B	34082*	BB	74B	35022*	MN	72A
33024	QI	71A	34033*	WC	73A	34083*	BB	73A	35023*	MN	72A
33025	QI	71A	34034*	WC	73A	34084*	BB	73A	35024*	MN	72A
33026	QI	74D	34035*	WC	75A	34085*	BB	73A	35025*	MN	73A
33027	QI	74D	34036*	WC	75A	34086*	BB	74B	35026*	MN	73A
33028	QI	74D	34037*	WC	75A	34087*	BB	74B	35027*	MN	73A
33029	QI	74D	34038*	WC	75A	34088*	BB	74B	35028*	MN	73A
33030	QI	74D	34039*	WC	75A	34089*	BB	74B	35029*	MN	74C
33031	QI	74D	34040*	WC	75A	34090*	BB		35030*	MN	74C
33032	QI	74D	34041*	WC	75A	34091*	WC	73A	36001	Lead	
33033	QI	74D	34042*	WC	72B	34092*	WC	73A	36002	Lead	
33034	QI	74D	34043*	WC	72B	34093*	WC	71B	36003	Lead	
33035	QI	74D	34044*	WC	72A	34094*	WC	71B	36004	Lead	
			34045*	WC	72A	34095*	WC	71B	36005	Lead	

Isle of Wight Locomotives

No.	Class	Shed	No.	Class	Shed	No.	Class	Shed
W1*	E1	71E	W15*	O2	71F	W23*	O2	71F
W2*	E1	71E	W16*	O2	71F	W24*	O2	71F
W3*	E1	71E	W17*	O2	71F	W25*	O2	71F
W4*	E1	71E	W18*	O2	71F	W26*	O2	71E
W14*	O2	71F	W19*	O2	71F	W27*	O2	71E
			W20*	O2	71F	W28*	O2	71E
			W21*	O2	71F	W29*	O2	71E
			W22*	O2	71F			

No.	Class	She
W30*	O2	71E
W31*	O2	71E
W32*	O2	71E
W33*	O2	71E
W34*	O2	71E
W35*	O2	71E
W36*	O2	71E

BRITISH RAILWAYS LOCOMOTIVES
Nos. 40001-58935
WITH SHED ALLOCATIONS

Cl. "3MT" 2-6-2T							
40001	8A	40050	1A	40102	6C	40154	65D
40002	2C	40051	3D	40103	6E	40155	14A
40003	8A	40052	1A	40104	6C	40156	6E
40004	1A	40053	3B	40105	21B	40157	5D
40005	84G	40054	1A	40106	9B	40158	65D
40006	1A	40055	1A	40107	9A	40159	66B
40007	8A	40056	26F	40108	10E	40160	14B
40008	84G	40057	26F	40109	1A	40161	14B
40009	1A	40058	84G	40110	6C	40162	23B
40010	1C	40059	26F	40111	14B	40163	22A
40011	3C	40060	26F	40112	14B	40164	22A
40012	26F	40061	26F	40113	9F	40165	15D
40013	26A	40062	26F	40114	14B	40166	14B
40014	26F	40063	26A	40115	21A	40167	14B
40015	26A	40064	23B	40116	22B	40168	21B
40016	11D	40065	26A	40117	21A	40169	20A
40017	1A	40066	3B	40118	9E	40170	68B
40018	1A	40067	11D	40119	14B	40171	21A
40019	3C	40068	11A	40120	16A	40172	14A
40020	1C	40069	20E	40121	6C	40173	15C
40021	23B	40070	11A	40122	5D	40174	22A
40022	14C	40071	9B	40123	7A	40175	21A
40023	14A	40072	1A	40124	7B	40176	65D
40024	14C	40073	1A	40125	8D	40177	65D
40025	14A	40074	20C	40126	5D	40178	16A
40026	14C	40075	20A	40127	6E	40179	20D
40027	14B	40076	2C	40128	5D	40180	8E*
40028	14B	40077	9A	40129	6C	40181	20C
40029	14B	40078	2C	40130	7A	40182	15C
40030	14A	40079	14B	40131	6C	40183	23B
40031	14B	40080	10E	40132	6C	40184	23B
40032	14B	40081	1A	40133	7A	40185	65D
40033	14B	40082	19B	40134	7B	40186	65D
40034	14B	40083	7A	40135	1A	40187	65D
40035	14B	40084	10E	40136	9A	40188	65D
40036	14B	40085	6E	40137	7A	40189	65D
40037	14B	40086	5F	40138	9B	40190	27C
40038	14B	40087	1A	40139	19B	40191	27C
40039	14C	40088	5D	40140	16A	40192	27C
40040	22B	40089	9F	40141	15D	40193	20C
40041	11A	40090	20A	40142 – 14B		40194	27C
40042	8B	40091	14A	40143	7B	40195	27C
40043	1C	40092	14B	40144	6A	40196	27C
40044	1A	40093	9E	40145	15C	40197	27C
40045	3C	40094	9E	40146	15C	40198	27C
40046	1A	40095	9F	40147	20C	40199	27C
40047	3B	40096	14B	40148	14B	40200	66B
40048	84G	40097	21A	40149	14B	40201	2B
40049	3B	40098	14A	40150	66C	40202	2B
		40099	14B	40151	66C	40203	2C
		40100	14B	40152	65D	40204	1A
		40101	6C	40153	65D	40205	2B

40206	1A
40207	6C
40208	2B
40209	7A

Cl. "2P" 4-4-0

40322	5C
40323	20A
40324	7D
40325	17B
40326	20A
40332	5A
40337	18C
40351	20A
40353	15A
40356	12A
40359	18C
40362	20A
40364	17B
40370	18A
40377	7D
40383	17A
40395	17B
40396	7D
40397	8E
40401	35C
40402	5A
40404	17A
40405	5C
40406	20D
40407	17A
40409	18C
40410	35C
40411	17A
40412	4B
40413	2B
40414	23A
40415	16A
40416	17A
40417	16A
40418	17A
40419	16A
40420	4B
40421	4B
40422	23A
40423	22A
40424	16D
40425	5A
40426	17A
40430	6A
40432	17B
40433	7D
40434	10C
40436	17B
40438	2B
40439	21B
40443	5C
40444	20C
40447	2B
40448	12A
40450	10C
40452	16A
40453	17B
40454	16D
40455	20E
40458	16A
40461	5C
40462	3C
40463	21B
40464	8E
40470	23B
40471	5C
40472	18C
40477	14B
40478	16A
40480	20D
40482	35C
40484	23A
40485	15C
40486	21A
40487	19B
40488	23C
40489	20E
40491	18C
40493	19B
40495	7D
40497	35C
40499	17D
40501	3C
40502	19B
40503	18C
40504	16A
40505	71G
40507	5C
40508	2B
40509	71H
40511	21A
40513	17A
40514	20A
40518	19B
40519	17B
40520	17D
40521	20C
40522	8E
40523	22B
40524	7B
40525	17B
40526	17B
40527	5A
40528	2B
40529	8E
40530	22B
40531	9D
40532	35C
40534	4B
40535	16A
40536	15C
40537	18C
40538	15C
40539	9A
40540	16A
40541	15C
40542	15C
40543	15C
40546	16A
40547	14B
40548	18C
40549	19B
40550	15B
40551	15D
40552	16A
40553	16A
40556	18C
40557	18C
40558	35C
40559	35C
40560	16A
40562	20E
40563	71H
40564	71H
40565	10B
40566	67B
40567	20E
40568	71G
40569	71G
40570	67B
40571	67B
40572	67B
40573	67B
40574	67C
40575	67C
40576	68B
40577	68B
40578	67D
40579	67D
40580	27D
40581	27A
40582	27A
40583	8E
40584	27A
40585	27A
40586	25C
40587	27D
40588	24D
40589	25C
40590	67C
40592	64D
40593	67B
40594	67A
40595	67A
40596	67A
40597	67B
40598	67A
40599	67A
40600	68C
40601	71G
40602	68A
40603	61A
40604	67A
40605	67B
40606	67D
40607	67D
40608	67D
40609	67D
40610	67C
40611	68C
40612	67B
40613	68A
40614	68B
40615	68A
40616	68C
40617	67B
40618	67B
40619	67B
40620	67A
40621	67A
40622	61A
40623	68C
40624	67D
40625	67D
40626	67D
40627	67A
40628	10C
40629	7D
40630	20D
40631	10B
40632	17A
40633	17B
40634	71H
40635	10C
40636	67A
40637	67A
40638	67C
40640	67C
40641	67A
40642	67A
40643	67B
40644	67B
40645	67B
40646	7D
40647	67C
40648	67C
40649	67A
40650	61A
40651	67A
40652	12A
40653	4B
40654	11B
40655	9D
40656	12D
40657	4B
40658	6A
40659	5A
40660	5A
40661	67B
40662	67B
40663	67B
40664	67C
40665	67B
40666	67B
40667	67D
40668	67D
40669	67D
40670	67C

40671	7D	40913	63B	41052	9E	41114	7A
40672	1C	40914	67A	41053	15B	41115	5A
40673	12B	40915	67A	41054	14B	41116	3E
40674	9A	40916	66A	41055	9E	41117	14B
40675	7D	40917	21B	41056	23C	41118	8E
40676	24A	40918	65B	41057	17A	41119	7A
40677	24A	40919	67A	41058	22B	41120	6A
40678	27D	40920	67C	41059	17A	41121	6A
40679	8E	40921	63A	41060	17A	41122	2A
40680	24A	40922	63A	41061	21B	41123	7A
40681	24A	40923	63A	41062	19B	41124	7A
40682	26E	40924	63B	41063	15B	41125	63A
40683	8E	40925	7A	41064	21B	41126	65B
40684	27D	40926	8E	41065	23C	41127	68C
40685	25C	40927	17A	41066	9E	41128	65B
40686	67B	40928	21A	41067	20E	41129	68A
40687	67B	40929	16A	41068	20A	41130	64D
40688	67B	40930	14B	41069	20E	41131	66A
40689	67B	40931	23C	41070	15D	41132	67C
40690	27E	40932	14B	41071	14B	41133	67C
40691	26E	40933	7A	41072	19B	41134	61B
40692	9D	40934	35C	41073	21B	41135	68B
40693	9A	40935	22A	41074	22B	41136	64D
40694	12D	40936	9E	41075	15C	41137	20A
40695	12D	40937	27E	41076	9E	41138	67C
40696	71G	40938	63A	41077	14B	41139	68A
40697	71G	40939	63A	41078	22B	41140	68A
40698	71G	41000	17A	41079	19B	41141	68A
40699	12A	41001	22B	41080	20E	41142	68A
40700	71G	41003	17A	41081	23C	41143	68A
		41004	20E	41082	16A	41144	20A
		41005	23C	41083	35C	41145	64D
		41006	15C	41084	17A	41146	68A
Cl. "3P" 4-4-0		41007	15D	41085	26C	41147	64D
		41008	15D	41086	7A	41148	66D
40726	19C	41009	15D	41087	15B	41149	66D
40728	19A	41011	15C	41088	17A	41150	7A
40729	19A	41012	15B	41089	15C	41151	3E
40741	71H	41013	19B	41090	2A	41152	2A
40743	20A	41014	19A	41091	15D	41153	6A
40747	20A	41015	16A	41092	68C	41154	9E
40758	20A	41016	19B	41093	7A	41155	67C
40762	15D	41019	16A	41094	15D	41156	8E
		41020	14B	41095	15C	41157	6A
		41021	19B	41096	16A	41158	6A
		41023	17A	41097	22B	41159	9A
Cl. "4P" 4-4-0		41025	22B	41098	6A	41160	5A
		41028	22A	41099	68C	41161	7A
40900	9E	41030	22A	41100	26B	41162	8E
40901	64D	41032	16A	41101	27C	41163	6A
40902	68B	41035	21A	41102	27C	41164	6A
40903	64D	41037	19B	41103	26C	41165	2A
40904	68B	41038	15D	41104	26C	41166	8E
40905	67A	41040	20A	41105	2A	41167	5A
40906	67A	41041	15C	41106	6A	41168	9A
40907	64D	41042	17A	41107	6A	41169	6A
40908	67C	41043	17A	41108	6A	41170	6A
40909	67A	41044	15D	41109	68B	41171	68B
40910	9E	41045	23C	41110	67B	41172	3E
40911	64C	41046	21A	41111	3E	41173	8E
40912	68B	41047	22B	41112	5A	41174	2A
		41048	20A	41113	9A	41175	68B
		41049	17D				
		41050	14B				
		41051	14B				

No.	Shed		No.	Shed
41176	61B		41234	2B
41177	64C		41235	2B
41178	64C		41236	2B
41179	68B		41237	2B
41180	64D		41238	2B
41181	9E		41239	2C
41182	66D		41240	71G
41183	67C		41241	71G
41184	61B		41242	71G
41185	28A		41243	71G
41186	26C		41244	15A
41187	27A		41245	19B
41188	24A		41246	19B
41189	26B		41247	17A
41190	26C		41248	14B
41191	26C		41249	14B
41192	28A		41250	25A
41193	27A		41251	25A
41194	27E		41252	25A
41195	28A		41253	25A
41196	26B		41254	25A
41197	20E		41255	25G
41198	15D		41256	25G
41199	14B		41257	25G

Cl. "2MT" 2-6-2T

No.	Shed		No.	Shed
41200	32B		41258	25G
41201	86K		41259	25G
41202	86K		41260	28B
41203	86K		41261	28B
41204	86K		41262	28B
41205	23B		41263	28B
41206	23B		41264	28B
41207	14A		41265	20E
41208	14A		41266	20E
41209	15D		41267	20A
41210	7D		41268	15C
41211	7D		41269	15D
41212	10D		41270	15D
41213	10D		41271	15D
41214	10D		41272	
41215	10D		41273	
41216	10D		41274	
41217	10D		41275	
41218	4B		41276	
41219	4B		41277	
41220	1C		41278	
41221	11B		41279	
41222	4A		41280	
41223	7B		41281	
41224	7B		41282	
41225	3B		41283	
41226	3C		41284	
41227	2C		41285	
41228	2C		41286	
41229	5A		41287	
41230	17B		41288	
41231	7D		41289	
41232	7A		41290	
41233	7B		41291	
			41292	
			41293	
			41294	
			41295	

No.	Shed
41296	
41297	
41298	
41299	

Cl. "0F" 0-4-0T

No.	Shed
41516	17B
41518	18C
41523	17B

Cl. "0F" 0-4-0T

No.	Shed
41528	18D
41529	18D
41530	22B
41531	18C
41532	18C
41533	18D
41534	18D
41535	17A
41536	17B
41537	22B

Cl. "1F" 0-6-0T

No.	Shed		No.	Shed
41660	19A		41763	18D
41661	14B		41767	23A
41664	14B		41769	87K
41666	20B		41770	17B
41671	14B		41773	17A
41672	14B		41777	18D
41682	16A		41779	17A
41686	16A		41780	6C
41690	26G		41781	19A
41695	14A		41793	20D
41699	21A		41794	20B
41702	26G		41795	17A
41706	22A		41797	19C
41708	18D		41803	18D
41710	18D		41804	18D
41711	18D		41805	19C
41712	14A		41811	14A
41713	14B		41813	18C
41720	22B		41814	26G
41724	14B		41820	23A
41725	84G		41824	87K
41726	17A		41826	14B
41727	22B		41829	18C
41734	6C		41833	17A
41739	20B		41835	19C
41745	20A		41838	20B
41747	17A		41839	17B
41748	17B		41844	20D
41749	18D		41846	16A
41752	18D		41847	17A
41753	18D		41852	87K
41754	17A		41853	6C
			41854	14C
			41855	23A
			41856	21A
			41857	19A
			41859	20B
			41860	87K
			41865	17B
			41869	20B
			41874	18C
			41875	17D
			41878	17B
			41879	21A
			41885	16D
			41889	17A
			41890	20B

Cl. "2P" 0-4-4T

No.	Shed
41900	23C
41901	23C
41902	23C
41903	17A
41904	23C
41905	9A
41906	9A
41907	9A
41908	1C
41909	1C

Cl. "2P" 4-4-2T		Cl. "3F" 0-6-2T			

Cl. "2P" 4-4-2T

41911	18A
41915	33A
41916	15A
41917	16A
41919	16A
41921	16A
41922	16A
41925	16A
41926	16A

Cl. "3P" 4-4-2T

41928	33A
41929	33A
41930	33A
41931	33A
41932	33B
41933	33B
41934	33B
41935	33B
41936	33A
41937	33A
41938	15C
41939	33A
41940	16D
41941	33A
41942	33A
41943	16D
41944	33A
41945	33A
41946	33B
41947	16D
41948	33A
41949	33B
41950	33A
41951	33A
41952	33B
41953	33B
41954	33B
41955	33B
41956	33A
41957	33B
41958	16D
41959	33B
41960	33C
41961	16D
41962	16D
41963	33C
41964	33C
41965	33A
41966	33C
41967	33A
41968	33A
41969	33A
41970	33A
41971	23A
41972	23A
41973	23A
41974	23A
41975	33A
41976	33A
41977	33A
41978	33A

Cl. "3F" 0-6-2T

41980	33B
41981	33A
41982	33A
41983	33A
41984	33A
41985	33A
41986	33A
41987	33A
41988	33A
41989	33A
41990	33A
41991	33C
41992	33C
41993	33A

Cl. "4MT" 2-6-4T

42050	21B
42051	
42052	
42053	
42054	
42055	
42056	
42057	
42058	
42059	
42060	
42061	
42062	
42063	
42064	
42065	
42066	
42067	
42068	
42069	
42070	
42071	
42072	
42073	
42074	
42075	
42076	
42077	
42078	
42079	
42080	
42081	
42082	
42083	
42084	
42085	
42086	
42087	
42088	
42089	
42090	
42091	
42092	
42093	
42094	
42095	
42096	75F
42097	75F
42098	75F
42099	75F
42100	75F
42101	75F
42102	
42103	
42104	
42105	
42106	
42107	25F
42108	25F
42109	25F
42110	25F
42111	25F
42112	25F
42113	25F
42114	25F
42115	25F
42116	25F
42117	1A
42118	1A
42119	1C
42120	1C
42121	1C
42122	67A
42123	67A
42124	67A
42125	66B
42126	66B
42127	66B
42128	66C
42129	66C
42130	66C
42131	67C
42132	14C
42133	14B
42134	14C
42135	23C
42136	23C
42137	15C
42138	14B
42139	14B
42140	16A
42141	21A
42142	20C
42143	20C
42144	23C
42145	20C
42146	20E
42147	24D
42148	29A
42149	25E
42150	25E
42151	25E
42152	25D
42153	24A
42154	24D
42155	2A
42156	7B
42157	7B
42158	24C
42159	1C
42160	14C
42161	14C
42162	64D
42163	64D
42164	66C
42165	66C
42166	66C
42167	66A
42168	66A
42169	66A
42170	66A
42171	66A
42172	66A
42173	64D
42174	66D
42175	66D
42176	66D
42177	17A
42178	1C
42179	11B
42180	23D
42181	15C
42182	15C
42183	15C
42184	16A
42185	16A
42186	21B
42187	24B
42188	25F
42189	25F
42190	67A
42191	67A
42192	67A
42193	67A
42194	67A
42195	67A
42196	67A
42197	67A
42198	63B
42199	63B
42200	66A
42201	66A
42202	66A
42203	66A
42204	66A
42205	66A
42206	66A
42207	66A
42208	66B
42209	67D
42210	67D
42211	67D

42212	67D	42274	66A	42336	17B	42398	9A
42213	66A	42275	66A	42337	21A	42399	9A
42214	66A	42276	66A	42338	21B	42400	66D
42215	66A	42277	66A	42339	16A	42401	11B
42216	66A	42278	26A	42340	17A	42402	11B
42217	64D	42279	26A	42341	17A	42403	11D
42218	33B	42280	26A	42342	21B	42404	11D
42219	33B	42281	26A	42343	5D	42405	25D
42220	33B	42282	26A	42344	5D	42406	25D
42221	33B	42283	26A	42345	5C	42407	25D
42222	33B	42284	26A	42346	5C	42408	25B
42223	33B	42285	26A	42347	5C	42409	25B
42224	33B	42286	26A	42348	4A	42410	25B
42225	33A	42287	26A	42349	5D	42411	25C
42226	33A	42288	26A	42350	9A	42412	25B
42227	33A	42289	26A	42351	9A	42413	25B
42228	16A	42290	26A	42352	9B	42414	25B
42229	16A	42291	27C	42353	9B	42415	66D
42230	33C	42292	27C	42354	9B	42416	66D
42231	33A	42293	27C	42355	9C	42417	66D
42232	33A	42294	27C	42356	9C	42418	66D
42233	5D	42295	24A	42357	9C	42419	66D
42234	5D	42296	24C	42358	5F	42420	66D
42235	5D	42297	27D	42359	11B	42421	66D
42236	5D	42298	24C	42360	9C	42422	66D
42237	14B	42299	27D	42361	16A	42423	66D
42238	66A	42300	14C	42362	9C	42424	11D
42239	66A	42301	11C	42363	9C	42425	6A
42240	66A	42302	14C	42364	5D	42426	8A
42241	66A	42303	4A	42365	9D	42427	9A
42242	66A	42304	1C	42366	9D	42428	11A
42243	66A	42305	87K	42367	9D	42429	11A
42244	66A	42306	9D	42368	9C	42430	9A
42245	66A	42307	87K	42369	9C	42431	5D
42246	66A	42308	5A	42370	9D	42432	11A
42247	66A	42309	5E	42371	9D	42433	24A
42248	33A	42310	25B	42372	11B	42434	24C
42249	33A	42311	25B	42373	16A	42435	24C
42250	33A	42312	25B	42374	33A	42436	24C
42251	33A	42313	11C	42375	5D	42437	24A
42252	33A	42314	11C	42376	5D	42438	24B
42253	33A	42315	9D	42377	20E	42439	24D
42254	33A	42316	1A	42378	1C	42440	5D
42255	33A	42317	11C	42379	9B	42441	3D
42256	33A	42318	9D	42380	20E	42442	10A
42257	33A	42319	9C	42381	9C	42443	5D
42258	7B	42320	5C	42382	9C	42444	3C
42259	7B	42321	11B	42383	14B	42445	5D
42260	7B	42322	9A	42384	25B	42446	4A
42261	7B	42323	5D	42385	87K	42447	5E
42262	3E	42324	25D	42386	9C	42448	3C
42263	3E	42325	14B	42387	87K	42449	5D
42264	3E	42326	21A	42388	87K	42450	6A
42265	3E	42327	21B	42389	1C	42451	6A
42266	10A	42328	33A	42390	87K	42452	3C
42267	3E	42329	14B	42391	5C	42453	10A
42268	64C	42330	15C	42392	11B	42454	10A
42269	64C	42331	15C	42393	11B	42455	6A
42270	64C	42332	9B	42394	87K	42456	10A
42271	64C	42333	16A	42395	11B	42457	11C
42272	64C	42334	14C	42396	11D	42458	5D
42273	64C	42335	14C	42397	9A	42459	8A

42460	7B	42527	33C	42589	1C	42651	26E
42461	9A	42528	33C	42590	1C	42652	26C
42462	11B	42529	33C	42591	4A	42653	26C
42463	9B	42530	33A	42592	27D	42654	26C
42464	11C	42531	33A	42593	1C	42655	26C
42465	10A	42532	33A	42594	9A	42656	26C
42466	3C	42533	33A	42595	6A	42657	26C
42467	9A	42534	33A	42596	8A	42658	8A
42468	1C	42535	33A	42597	8A	42659	4A
42469	3E	42536	33A	42598	1C	42660	7B
42470	3D	42537	27D	42599	9A	42661	24A
42471	5E	42538	3D	42600	4A	42662	10C
42472	26C	42539	10A	42601	11A	42663	5F
42473	26D	42540	6A	42602	8A	42664	5D
42474	26D	42541	2A	42603	5D	42665	5F
42475	24B	42542	9A	42604	3C	42666	4A
42476	26D	42543	5D	42605	5D	42667	5D
42477	26A	42544	11A	42606	8B	42668	5D
42478	9A	42545	26C	42607	8B	42669	4A
42479	5D	42546	24B	42608	9A	42670	5D
42480	24C	42547	24B	42609	5D	42671	2C
42481	24C	42548	24A	42610	10A	42672	5D
42482	3C	42549	24A	42611	5E	42673	2A
42483	24D	42550	26A	42612	8A	42674	2C
42484	24D	42551	26A	42613	11C	42675	26G
42485	24D	42552	3D	42614	27D	42676	5D
42486	26A	42553	25D	42615	11A	42677	5A
42487	2A	42554	27D	42616	3D	42678	33A
42488	3C	42555	24B	42617	7B	42679	33A
42489	3E	42556	24C	42618	26A	42680	16A
42490	24D	42557	27D	42619	26E	42681	33A
42491	24C	42558	24D	42620	26E	42682	20E
42492	24C	42559	24D	42621	26A	42683	5D
42493	11B	42560	10C	42622	26A	42684	33A
42494	5D	42561	10C	42623	26A	42685	20E
42500	33C	42562	3C	42624	26A	42686	16A
42501	33C	42563	10A	42625	26A	42687	33A
42502	33C	42564	8A	42626	26A	42688	66A
42503	33C	42565	26C	42627	3C	42689	66A
42504	33C	42566	4A	42628	7B	42690	66A
42505	33C	42567	5D	42629	26D	42691	66A
42506	33C	42568	6A	42630	26A	42692	66A
42507	33C	42569	27D	42631	27D	42693	66A
42508	33C	42570	8A	42632	27D	42694	66A
42509	33C	42571	11B	42633	26C	42695	66A
42510	33C	42572	10A	42634	24A	42696	66A
42511	33C	42573	11A	42635	26A	42697	66D
42512	33C	42574	10C	42636	28A	42698	66A
42513	33C	42575	9A	42637	28A	42699	66A
42514	33C	42576	2A	42638	28A		
42515	33C	42577	2A	42639	25E		
42516	33C	42578	3D	42640	27D	**Cl. "5MT" 2-6-0**	
42517	33C	42579	3E	42641	27D		
42518	33C	42580	9A	42642	27D	42700	25D
42519	33C	42581	11B	42643	24A	42701	26A
42520	33C	42582	5D	42644	27D	42702	26A
42521	33C	42583	8A	42645	26B	42703	26A
42522	33C	42584	6A	42646	26B	42704	26A
42523	33C	42585	2A	42647	26B	42705	26A
42524	33C	42586	3C	42648	26B	42706	24B
42525	33C	42587	6A	42649	26E	42707	26A
42526	33C	42588	7B	42650	26E	42708	26A

42709	26A	42771	14A	42833	68A	42895	23C
42710	26A	42772	9A	42834	68A	42896	17B
42711	26A	42773	5B	42835	68A	42897	17A
42712	25D	42774	14A	42836	68A	42898	26G
42713	26A	42775	9A	42837	68A	42899	68A
42714	26A	42776	9A	42838	26B	42900	21A
42715	26A	42777	2B	42839	14A	42901	26A
42716	24A	42778	9A	42840	28B	42902	17D
42717	24A	42779	3A	42841	28B	42903	21A
42718	24A	42780	68A	42842	28B	42904	19A
42719	25D	42781	2B	42843	24A	42905	68A
42720	68A	42782	3D	42844	28B	42906	68A
42721	26B	42783	2B	42845	26A	42907	68A
42722	26B	42784	23B	42846	17B	42908	68B
42723	26B	42785	5B	42847	17A	42909	68B
42724	26B	42786	1A	42848	9A	42910	67B
42725	26B	42787	1A	42849	8C	42911	67A
42726	25F	42788	9A	42850	66C	42912	67B
42727	25F	42789	26A	42851	3A	42913	68A
42728	25F	42790	21A	42852	8C	42914	67A
42729	28B	42791	17B	42853	3A	42915	68B
42730	25G	42792	15C	42854	9A	42916	67A
42731	25G	42793	68A	42855	14A	42917	67A
42732	25F	42794	14A	42856	5B	42918	68B
42733	24B	42795	20A	42857	21A	42919	68B
42734	26B	42796	26B	42858	9A	42920	5B
42735	66C	42797	19A	42859	9B	42921	3D
42736	65F	42798	20A	42860	26B	42922	17B
42737	65F	42799	17B	42861	25B	42923	9A
42738	63C	42800	63C	42862	25B	42924	9A
42739	67C	42801	63C	42863	25B	42925	9A
42740	66C	42802	68A	42864	26B	42926	5B
42741	66C	42803	68A	42865	25F	42927	67C
42742	63A	42804	64C	42866	25B	42928	23C
42743	63A	42805	67C	42867	28B	42929	3A
42744	67B	42806	67C	42868	26B	42930	9A
42745	67B	42807	64C	42869	25B	42931	1A
42746	65B	42808	67C	42870	1A	42932	2B
42747	1A	42809	67C	42871	26A	42933	2B
42748	68A	42810	5B	42872	17A	42934	9B
42749	68A	42811	5B	42873	17D	42935	9A
42750	26A	42812	1A	42874	17D	42936	9A
42751	68A	42813	2B	42875	68A	42937	9A
42752	68A	42814	2B	42876	68A	42938	9A
42753	26B	42815	5B	42877	68A	42939	5B
42754	21A	42816	20A	42878	26A	42940	1A
42755	26B	42817	1A	42879	67C	42941	2B
42756	17B	42818	21A	42880	66C	42942	9D
42757	68A	42819	26B	42881	68A	42943	9D
42758	21A	42820	26A	42882	68A	42944	2B
42759	14A	42821	24B	42883	68A	42945	6B
42760	17D	42822	21A	42884	68A	42946	3D
42761	17B	42823	16A	42885	1A	42947	3D
42762	20E	42824	21A	42886	9A	42948	3D
42763	17B	42825	21A	42887	9A	42949	8E
42764	21A	42826	21A	42888	2B	42950	5B
42765	26G	42827	21A	42889	9A	42951	3D
42766	26A	42828	25F	42890	21A	42952	5B
42767	17B	42829	21A	42891	3A	42953	6C
42768	17D	42830	64C	42892	8C	42954	3D
42769	17B	42831	68A	42893	23C	42955	5B
42770	23B	42832	68A	42894	3A	42956	5B

42957	3D	43031	17A	43093	43235	18B
42958	3D	43032	19A	43094	43237	8B
42959	6B	43033	16A	43095	43239	16D
42960	2B	43034	23C	43096	43240	16A
42961	6C	43035	23C	43097	43241	19A
42962	8C	43036	71G	43098	43242	18A
42963	3D	43037	19A	43099	43243	19C
42964	8C	43038	19A	43100	43244	17B
42965	8C	43039	20A	43101	43245	14C
42966	3D	43040	16A	43102	43246	21A
42967	6C	43041	19A	43103	43247	17B
42968	5B	43042	19A	43104	43248	71H
42969	6C	43043	21A	43105	43249	16A
42970	6C	43044	21A	43106	43250	20C
42971	8C	43045	15C	43107	43251	18A
42972	5B	43046	22A	43108	43252	18A
42973	3D	43047	22A	43109	43253	18B
42974	3D	43048	21A	43110	43254	18B
42975	6B	43049	17A	43111	43256	17B
42976	6B	43050	51A		43257	21A
42977	8C	43051	51A	**Cl. "3F" 0-6-0**	43258	22B
42978	9A	43052	50E		43259	17A
42979	9A	43053	53A	43137	17A	43261	14A
42980	5B	43054	51A	43174	15D	43263	21B
42981	6C	43055	51A	43178	20E	43266	18B
42982	8C	43056		43180	19C	43267	20B
42983	5B	43057		43181	19C	43268	9D
42984	5B	43058		43183	15C	43271	9D
		43059		43185	17A	43273	17D
Cl. "4MT" 2-6-0	43060		43186	18A	43274	9D
		43061		43187	23C	43275	9A
43000	4A	43062		43188	17B	43277	21D
43001	4A	43063		43189	5B	43278	9D
43002	4A	43064		43191	17A	43281	9B
43003	4A	43065		43192	16A	43282	8B
43004	4A	43066		43193	15A	43283	8B
43005	4A	43067		43194	71H	43284	21A
43006	12D	43068		43200	17A	43286	17B
43007	12D	43069		43201	21A	43287	18A
43008	12D	43070	52B	43203	21B	43290	17D
43009	12D	43071	51A	43204	71H	43292	18D
43010	17A	43072	51A	43205	15C	43293	23C
43011	21A	43073		43207	5B	43294	18D
43012	22A	43074		43208	19C	43295	23A
43013	71G	43075		43210	21A	43296	9D
43014	21A	43076		43211	18C	43298	18D
43015	19A	43077		43212	18C	43299	18D
43016	20A	43078		43213	22B	43300	16A
43017	71G	43079		43214	21A	43301	20D
43018	16A	43080		43216	71H	43305	18A
43019	16A	43081		43218	71H	43306	17B
43020	2B	43082		43219	18C	43307	14A
43021	2B	43083		43222	15D	43308	3D
43022	2B	43084		43223	21A	43309	18D
43023	2B	43085		43224	18D	43310	18D
43024	2B	43086		43225	21A	43312	17A
43025	2B	43087		43226	17A	43313	14A
43026	10E	43088		43228	71H	43314	8B
43027	10E	43089		43231	3E	43315	17A
43028	10E	43090		43232	15C	43317	18B
43029	10E	43091		43233	20C	43318	17A
43030	20A	43092		43234	18D	43319	35C

43321	21A	43440	14A	43584	17A	43686	21C
43323	17A	43441	21A	43585	23B	43687	21B
43324	17A	43443	21A	43586	23B	43690	21A
43325	19C	43444	22A	43587	19C	43693	21D
43326	15C	43446	20C	43593	71H	43698	21A
43327	18A	43448	14A	43594	21A	43705	20B
43329	8B	43449	20B	43595	19A	43709	17B
43330	23C	43453	18A	43596	16C	43710	15C
43331	18B	43454	15C	43598	17A	43711	16A
43332	20C	43456	20B	43599	18A	43712	22A
43333	15C	43457	9A	43600	84G	43714	20D
43334	19A	43459	17A	43604	19A	43715	20A
43335	19A	43462	22A	43605	19A	43717	9A
43336	21A	43463	19A	43607	19A	43721	15D
43337	22B	43464	22A	43608	17B	43723	16A
43339	21A	43468	16C	43612	26G	43724	16A
43340	17B	43469	17A	43615	8B	43727	16D
43341	19B	43474	15D	43618	8B	43728	15C
43342	17D	43476	20B	43619	17B	43729	16A
43344	22B	43482	17A	43620	21A	43731	19A
43351	20E	43484	21A	43621	21A	43734	22A
43355	21B	43490	21A	43622	18C	43735	17A
43356	71H	43491	21A	43623	17B	43737	20B
43357	84G	43494	16C	43624	21A	43742	20E
43359	21B	43496	17A	43627	21A	43745	17A
43361	17A	43497	20D	43629	14A	43747	19C
43364	17A	43499	18A	43630	26G	43748	15C
43367	15A	43502	3C	43631	18A	43749	19A
43368	17A	43506	22B	43633	3C	43751	18D
43369	16A	43507	21A	43634	16D	43753	15C
43370	17D	43509	20D	43636	19A	43754	22B
43371	16A	43510	17A	43637	16A	43755	19A
43373	22B	43514	20D	43638	26G	43756	26G
43374	21A	43515	18D	43639	20D	43757	84G
43378	16A	43520	21D	43644	21A	43759	21A
43379	18B	43521	21D	43645	22B	43760	84G
43381	21D	43522	16D	43650	18A	43762	21A
43386	18D	43523	21D	43651	35C	43763	17A
43387	9D	43524	18D	43652	17B	43765	20C
43388	17B	43529	16D	43653	15C	43766	15D
43389	8B	43531	21A	43656	20D	43767	21D
43392	20B	43538	16A	43657	8B	43770	20E
43394	84G	43540	21A	43658	17A	43771	18C
43395	17B	43544	21A	43660	19C	43773	16C
43396	7D	43546	18D	43661	19A	43775	19A
43398	8B	43548	17A	43662	19A	43776	17A
43399	16A	43550	17A	43664	19C	43777	15D
43400	14A	43553	20C	43665	20A	43778	18A
43401	16A	43558	16A	43667	21C	43779	17C
43402	17A	43562	9D	43668	21B	43781	20B
43405	18A	43565	14A	43669	19C	43782	14C
43406	17A	43568	21D	43673	21A	43784	23A
43410	3C	43570	84G	43674	21A	43785	15D
43411	15C	43572	17A	43675	21B	43786	3C
43419	71H	43574	17A	43676	15C	43787	3C
43427	22A	43575	18D	43678	20B	43789	20C
43428	15D	43578	17A	43679	84G	43790	15C
43429	17C	43579	20B	43680	21A	43791	21A
43431	16D	43580	18B	43681	20B	43792	71H
43433	21A	43581	84G	43682	17C	43793	18A
43435	21A	43582	17B	43683	19A	43795	18A
43436	22A	43583	21B	43684	21A	43797	15A

43798	18A	43863	35C	43925	17D	43987	20B
43799	18A	43864	35C	43926	22A	43988	18A
43800	21A	43865	17C	43927	26G	43989	20B
43801	14A	43866	18B	43928	22A	43990	18A
43802	18C	43867	18B	43929	17D	43991	17B
43803	18A	43868	68A	43930	15A	43992	18B
43804	18A	43869	21A	43931	20A	43993	18D
43805	18A	43870	15C	43932	22B	43994	18A
43806	15C	43871	20B	43933	23C	43995	18A
43807	15C	43872	17C	43934	14A	43996	68A
43808	15A	43873	21D	43935	14B	43997	16D
43809	17C	43874	16D	43936	18C	43998	18B
43810	18A	43875	71G	43937	15C	43999	23A
43811	9F	43876	15C	43938	17B	44000	23A
43812	21A	43877	7A	43939	21A	44001	68A
43814	19C	43878	20B	43940	21A	44002	17B
43815	17B	43879	21A	43941	21A	44003	20C
43817	18A	43880	18B	43942	20C	44004	16D
43818	18A	43881	17D	43943	18A	44005	16C
43819	18A	43882	17C	43944	23A	44006	18D
43820	18A	43883	65F	43945	9F	44007	23A
43821	18A	43884	66B	43946	21A	44008	68A
43822	21D	43885	18B	43947	14A	44009	68A
43823	18A	43886	18D	43948	17B	44010	21A
43824	18A	43887	22B	43949	21A	44011	63B
43825	18A	43888	15D	43950	19C	44012	18A
43826	18A	43889	15B	43951	21A	44013	19C
43827	18A	43890	23C	43952	26G	44014	18B
43828	18A	43891	21A	43953	20A	44015	19C
43829	15C	43892	17B	43954	16A	44016	68A
43832	18A	43893	23A	43955	17A	44017	17D
43833	18A	43894	17C	43956	16A	44018	17D
		43895	16C	43957	35C	44019	26G
Cl. "4F" 0-6-0		43896	9E	43958	16A	44020	20B
		43897	24D	43959	18C	44021	16C
43835	17C	43898	15B	43960	23A	44022	26G
43836	9F	43899	67A	43961	18A	44023	21A
43837	17B	43900	18A	43962	14A	44024	17D
43838	17A	43901	14A	43963	20B	44025	26G
43839	17A	43902	68A	43964	14B	44026	21A
43840	17A	43903	16C	43965	17B	44027	3B
43841	4A	43904	23A	43966	18B	44028	14A
43842	9D	43905	14A	43967	15D	44029	14A
43843	21A	43906	19C	43968	21A	44030	16A
43844	19A	43907	16C	43969	22A	44031	17A
43845	21A	43908	9E	43970	18A	44032	23C
43846	22B	43909	14B	43971	15D	44033	15A
43847	22A	43910	15D	43972	17B	44034	15C
43848	65B	43911	21A	43973	68A	44035	22B
43849	65B	43912	21A	43974	18A	44036	19C
43850	18B	43913	23A	43975	15A	44037	15A
43851	20B	43914	18D	43976	17B	44038	24B
43852	20B	43915	5D	43977	15C	44039	16A
43853	22A	43916	17B	43978	22B	44040	26G
43854	35C	43917	23A	43979	18A	44041	23A
43855	21A	43918	17D	43980	35C	44042	23B
43856	18C	43919	17B	43981	35C	44043	15B
43857	18D	43920	18D	43982	14A	44044	20A
43858	21A	43921	17C	43983	16D	44045	22B
43859	18A	43922	68A	43984	23A	44046	17D
43860	18B	43923	15D	43985	18A	44047	17B
43861	15A	43924	22B	43986	21A	44048	17B
43862	18D						

44049	21A	44111	19C	44173	19C	44235	71G
44050	17D	44112	21A	44174	17D	44236	9E
44051	14A	44113	16A	44175	22B	44237	10D
44052	14B	44114	26G	44176	21A	44238	35C
44053	35C	44115	3C	44177	17A	44239	35C
44054	18C	44116	1A	44178	9F	44240	24D
44055	16A	44117	35C	44179	21A	44241	19C
44056	25D	44118	5D	44180	17C	44242	15A
44057	3E	44119	26G	44181	68A	44243	14B
44058	2A	44120	5D	44182	18D	44244	18C
44059	11B	44121	12A	44183	68A	44245	20B
44060	11A	44122	18D	44184	21A	44246	17D
44061	3D	44123	15C	44185	21A	44247	16A
44062	25C	44124	17B	44186	21D	44248	21A
44063	5E	44125	5E	44187	21A	44249	15A
44064	12D	44126	18B	44188	18B	44250	18A
44065	6B	44127	19C	44189	68A	44251	63A
44066	18D	44128	19C	44190	21A	44252	17C
44067	5D	44129	18D	44191	18B	44253	63A
44068	5D	44130	18B	44192	11A	44254	63A
44069	5D	44131	14A	44193	63A	44255	65B
44070	18D	44132	16A	44194	63A	44256	65B
44071	19C	44133	18A	44195	14A	44257	63A
44072	4B	44134	17D	44196	66A	44258	63A
44073	6B	44135	22A	44197	23A	44259	14A
44074	9B	44136	18A	44198	67A	44260	17C
44075	11A	44137	21A	44199	68A	44261	10D
44076	4B	44138	21B	44200	21A	44262	17D
44077	5D	44139	14A	44201	23C	44263	21A
44078	3C	44140	16C	44202	16C	44264	16A
44079	5E	44141	20C	44203	21A	44265	17B
44080	9F	44142	17A	44204	21D	44266	22A
44081	12A	44143	17B	44205	16C	44267	22A
44082	16C	44144	9F	44206	16C	44268	16C
44083	11D	44145	21A	44207	20A	44269	22A
44084	21A	44146	71H	44208	1A	44270	17B
44085	17C	44147	18D	44209	17D	44271	9A
44086	12C	44148	17C	44210	14B	44272	22B
44087	22B	44149	23B	44211	19A	44273	35C
44088	21A	44150	21A	44212	19A	44274	18C
44089	19C	44151	20D	44213	21A	44275	17B
44090	9F	44152	35C	44214	17A	44276	23B
44091	18A	44153	20B	44215	16A	44277	23A
44092	21A	44154	18D	44216	20E	44278	15B
44093	5D	44155	35C	44217	20D	44279	17C
44094	20B	44156	17C	44218	35C	44280	23C
44095	16A	44157	18A	44219	3D	44281	65B
44096	71G	44158	16A	44220	25C	44282	23B
44097	35C	44159	67A	44221	24B	44283	63B
44098	20D	44160	15C	44222	23A	44284	19A
44099	20D	44161	20C	44223	16A	44285	19A
44100	17B	44162	18C	44224	21A	44286	9F
44101	17A	44163	17D	44225	24D	44287	15C
44102	71H	44164	17A	44226	17B	44288	18C
44103	17C	44165	21A	44227	17C	44289	21A
44104	18D	44166	17B	44228	33A	44290	19C
44105	25C	44167	22B	44229	18B	44291	24D
44106	18A	44168	17D	44230	16A	44292	11D
44107	18C	44169	22A	44231	15C	44293	35C
44108	21A	44170	17B	44232	19C	44294	18C
44109	17C	44171	17B	44233	18A	44295	17B
44110	35C	44172	17D	44234	65B	44296	35C

44297	14A	44359	5E	44421	9F	44483	24D
44298	14B	44360	3C	44422	71G	44484	5D
44299	18D	44361	3E	44423	15C	44485	25C
44300	5B	44362	21A	44424	22A	44486	24A
44301	5B	44363	5D	44425	16A	44487	11B
44302	3D	44364	12D	44426	19A	44488	3C
44303	9A	44365	12D	44427	21A	44489	5D
44304	14A	44366	21B	44428	17B	44490	3D
44305	7B	44367	6B	44429	17D	44491	4B
44306	11B	44368	11B	44430	18B	44492	3B
44307	5F	44369	5D	44431	20A	44493	6B
44308	9A	44370	1D	44432	17A	44494	9G
44309	5D	44371	18A	44433	17B	44495	12D
44310	5D	44372	1A	44434	17B	44496	5D
44311	26A	44373	5D	44435	17B	44497	1A
44312	67B	44374	11A	44436	17B	44498	5D
44313	16A	44375	5D	44437	19A	44499	5D
44314	63A	44376	18A	44438	5D	44500	5D
44315	68A	44377	5D	44439	3B	44501	20A
44316	17B	44378	5D	44440	14B	44502	5D
44317	21A	44379	10E	44441	1C	44503	5D
44318	63A	44380	5D	44442	1A	44504	5F
44319	67B	44381	5D	44443	1C	44505	12D
44320	65F	44382	9D	44444	9B	44506	3E
44321	18B	44383	5D	44445	7B	44507	5D
44322	63B	44384	10D	44446	20C	44508	5D
44323	67B	44385	11A	44447	4A	44509	35C
44324	68A	44386	5B	44448	5D	44510	11A
44325	67B	44387	4B	44449	12D	44511	11B
44326	68A	44388	5D	44450	5E	44512	3C
44327	17D	44389	7A	44451	1A	44513	5D
44328	63A	44390	12A	44452	5B	44514	3E
44329	67A	44391	5D	44453	5E	44515	21A
44330	63B	44392	2A	44454	10D	44516	21A
44331	63B	44393	5D	44455	5D	44517	3D
44332	17B	44394	16D	44456	2A	44518	35C
44333	21B	44395	2A	44457	19C	44519	35C
44334	19A	44396	5D	44458	35C	44520	21A
44335	22A	44397	14B	44459	11D	44521	35C
44336	20D	44398	24D	44460	24A	44522	35C
44337	20D	44399	11A	44461	12E	44523	71G
44338	20D	44400	20E	44462	27B	44524	21A
44339	9D	44401	16A	44463	16C	44525	21A
44340	9B	44402	17A	44464	24B	44526	17B
44341	5E	44403	15C	44465	15B	44527	17B
44342	5E	44404	20A	44466	22A	44528	17B
44343	5D	44405	23C	44467	20B	44529	14A
44344	5E	44406	21A	44468	23A	44530	33A
44345	3C	44407	9F	44469	11D	44531	14B
44346	12A	44408	16A	44470	16C	44532	14B
44347	11B	44409	11A	44471	25D	44533	16A
44348	1D	44410	18C	44472	16A	44534	22A
44349	9A	44411	22A	44473	10D	44535	71G
44350	3D	44412	16A	44474	25D	44536	22A
44351	11B	44413	21A	44475	21A	44537	22A
44352	2B	44414	16A	44476	35C	44538	21A
44353	5D	44415	16D	44477	19C	44539	17C
44354	2A	44416	16D	44478	5D	44540	17D
44355	71G	44417	71H	44479	24A	44541	27B
44356	10D	44418	21A	44480	16A	44542	17A
44357	9A	44419	17A	44481	27B	44543	26A
44358	5D	44420	17A	44482	18B	44544	24B

44545	21A	**Cl. "5MT" 4-6-0**		44718	68A	44780 25B
44546	16A			44719	68A	44781 26B
44547	16C	44658	14B	44720	68A	44782 26B
44548	5D	44659	21A	44721	68A	44783 60A
44549	12E	44660	21A	44722	68A	44784 60A
44550	19A	44661	21A	44723	68A	44785 60A
44551	17B	44662	20A	44724	68A	44786 65B
44552	16C	44663	15C	44725	68A	44787 66A
44553	22A	44664	19B	44726	68A	44788 60A
44554	17C	44665	19B	44727	68A	44789 60A
44555	20E	44666	21A	44728	27C	44790 66A
44556	19A	44667	17A	44729	27C	44791 65C
44557	71G	44668	68A	44730	28A	44792 66A
44558	71G	44669	68A	44731	28A	44793 66A
44559	71G	44670	68A	44732	28A	44794 66A
44560	71G	44671	68A	44733	28A	44795 68A
44561	71G	44672	68A	44734	26A	44796 63A
44562	20D	44673	68A	44735	26A	44797 63A
44563	14B	44674	68A	44736	26A	44798 60A
44564	17D	44675	68A	44737	27C	44799 60A
44565	17A	44676	68A	44738	7A	44800 6B
44566	17A	44677	68A	44739	7A	44801 63A
44567	21A	44678	5A	44740	7A	44802 19A
44568	19A	44679	5A	44741	7A	44803 26G
44569	22A	44680	5A	44742	7A	44804 21A
44570	20E	44681	5A	44743	22A	44805 21A
44571	21A	44682	5A	44744	22A	44806 15C
44572	17C	44683	5A	44745	22A	44807 9A
44573	19A	44684	5A	44746	22A	44808 7C
44574	15A	44685	5A	44747	22A	44809 17A
44575	15A	44686		44748	9A	44810 21A
44576	19C	44687		44749	9A	44811 21B
44577	16A	44688	27A	44750	9A	44812 15C
44578	16A	44689		44751	9A	44813 21A
44579	23B	44690		44752	9A	44814 21A
44580	21A	44691		44753	20A	44815 17A
44581	14A	44692		44754	20A	44816 14B
44582	17B	44693		44755	20A	44817 14B
44583	15C	44694		44756	20A	44818 17A
44584	20A	44695		44757	20A	44819 17A
44585	16A	44696		44758	5A	44820 17A
44586	20D	44697		44759	9A	44821 20A
44587	21D	44698	63A	44760	9A	44822 14B
44588	17D	44699	63A	44761	5A	44823 26B
44589	16C	44700	64D	44762	5A	44824 26B
44590	18D	44701	64D	44763	5A	44825 16A
44591	21A	44702	65B	44764	5A	44826 71G
44592	3E	44703	65B	44765	5A	44827 19A
44593	12D	44704	63A	44766	5A	44828 20A
44594	11B	44705	63A	44767	27A	44829 3E
44595	5E	44706	67A	44768	8A	44830 71G
44596	5D	44707	66A	44769	8A	44831 2A
44597	17B	44708	10B	44770	5A	44832 9A
44598	16A	44709	11A	44771	5A	44833 1A
44599	17B	44710	2A	44772	8A	44834 9A
44600	17B	44711	2A	44773	16A	44835 84G
44601	17A	44712	2A	44774	20A	44836 2A
44602	17A	44713	2A	44775	20A	44837 9A
44603	20D	44714	2A	44776	17A	44838 9A
44604	20D	44715	2A	44777	14B	44839 71G
44605	18B	44716	2A	44778	28A	44840 6A
44606	21D	44717	21A	44779	28A	44841 16A

223

44842	21A	44904	11A	44966	21A	45028	7C
44843	20A	44905	11B	44967	65B	45029	64C
44844	6A	44906	8A	44968	67A	45030	5B
44845	19A	44907	8A	44969	66B	45031	26G
44846	14B	44908	84G	44970	65B	45032	8B
44847	17A	44909	2A	44971	7A	45033	2A
44848	17A	44910	2A	44972	63A	45034	2A
44849	20A	44911	1A	44973	63A	45035	8B
44850	20A	44912	25F	44974	63A	45036	64A
44851	17A	44913	7B	44975	63A	45037	10C
44852	21B	44914	3A	44976	63A	45038	5B
44853	20A	44915	2A	44977	63A	45039	11A
44854	20A	44916	4A	44978	63A	45040	20A
44855	22A	44917	17A	44979	63A	45041	1A
44856	20A	44918	16A	44980	63A	45042	10C
44857	20A	44919	21A	44981	14B	45043	28A
44858	19A	44920	21A	44982	27A	45044	5B
44859	19B	44921	26G	44983	20A	45045	6A
44860	2A	44922	65B	44984	14B	45046	11B
44861	16A	44923	65B	44985	14B	45047	67A
44862	2A	44924	63A	44986	19B	45048	5B
44863	2A	44925	63A	44987	26A	45049	67A
44864	4A	44926	27C	44988	28A	45050	11A
44865	4A	44927	28A	44989	27C	45051	3D
44866	4A	44928	28A	44990	25F	45052	3D
44867	2A	44929	28A	44991	60A	45053	60A
44868	7C	44930	28A	44992	60A	45054	11B
44869	12A	44931	63A	44993	68A	45055	10C
44870	2A	44932	28A	44994	68A	45056	19A
44871	12A	44933	26A	44995	65B	45057	4A
44872	3D	44934	26A	44996	65B	45058	3D
44873	3C	44935	9A	44997	63A	45059	16A
44874	10B	44936	12A	44998	63A	45060	5B
44875	1A	44937	9A	44999	63A	45061	27C
44876	12A	44938	9E	45000	2A	45062	25G
44877	68A	44939	12A	45001	8B	45063	25G
44878	68A	44940	26A	45002	2A	45064	1A
44879	63A	44941	8A	45003	2A	45065	12A
44880	65B	44942	3D	45004	2A	45066	60A
44881	65B	44943	20A	45005	8A	45067	5B
44882	68A	44944	19A	45006	5B	45068	27A
44883	68A	44945	71G	45007	63A	45069	3C
44884	68A	44946	27A	45008	66B	45070	7C
44885	63A	44947	28A	45009	66B	45071	1A
44886	68A	44948	28B	45010	65A	45072	8B
44887	27C	44949	25B	45011	63A	45073	5B
44888	26A	44950	28A	45012	60A	45074	19A
44889	26A	44951	25F	45013	5B	45075	25G
44890	26A	44952	64D	45014	12B	45076	25G
44891	26A	44953	64D	45015	3E	45077	28A
44892	10B	44954	62B	45016	63B	45078	25G
44893	26A	44955	64D	45017	8A	45079	26A
44894	26A	44956	65B	45018	60B	45080	25G
44895	26A	44957	65B	45019	10A	45081	68A
44896	25G	44958	63A	45020	2A	45082	68A
44897	8B	44959	63A	45021	4B	45083	68A
44898	68A	44960	63A	45022	64C	45084	68A
44899	68A	44961	63A	45023	64C	45085	64A
44900	68A	44962	19B	45024	1A	45086	63A
44901	68A	44963	19B	45025	1A	45087	64D
44902	68A	44964	19B	45026	10C	45088	15C
44903	68A	44965	19B	45027	1A	45089	1A

45090	60A
45091	4B
45092	2A
45093	5B
45094	3D
45095	6A
45096	12B
45097	1A
45098	60A
45099	25B
45100	68A
45101	25A
45102	26A
45103	26A
45104	26A
45105	26A
45106	12A
45107	28A
45108	5B
45109	8B
45110	7C
45111	7C
45112	84G
45113	7C
45114	5D
45115	65B
45116	65B
45117	64D
45118	63A
45119	63A
45120	60A
45121	66B
45122	60A
45123	60A
45124	60A
45125	63A
45126	68A
45127	63A
45128	19A
45129	12A
45130	4A
45131	5B
45132	6B
45133	12A
45134	5B
45135	10C
45136	60A
45137	10C
45138	60A
45139	12A
45140	1A
45141	10A
45142	10C
45143	84G
45144	7B
45145	84G
45146	1A
45147	10C
45148	5B
45149	8B
45150	2A
45151	66B
45152	66B
45153	65B
45154*	65B
45155	65B
45156*	65B
45157*	65B
45158*	65B
45159	65B
45160	60A
45161	64D
45162	63A
45163	67A
45164	63A
45165	63A
45166	63A
45167	63A
45168	67A
45169	63A
45170	63A
45171	63A
45172	63A
45173	63A
45174	67A
45175	63A
45176	66B
45177	65B
45178	65B
45179	60A
45180	84G
45181	8A
45182	10C
45183	84G
45184	64C
45185	5B
45186	21A
45187	2A
45188	10C
45189	5B
45190	84G
45191	4B
45192	60A
45193	11A
45194	67A
45195	5B
45196	8B
45197	12A
45198	5B
45199	10C
45200	27C
45201	25F
45202	26A
45203	26A
45204	25A
45205	25A
45206	25A
45207	25F
45208	25F
45209	25A
45210	26A
45211	26A
45212	28B
45213	63A
45214	28A
45215	25B
45216	27A
45217	5A
45218	25G
45219	26A
45220	26A
45221	25A
45222	26A
45223	26A
45224	26A
45225	19A
45226	27A
45227	27A
45228	27A
45229	27A
45230	12A
45231	10C
45232	26A
45233	26A
45234	26A
45235	10A
45236	21B
45237	25B
45238	25B
45239	5B
45240	5B
45241	7A
45242	8A
45243	8A
45244	12A
45245	84G
45246	12A
45247	6A
45248	8A
45249	7C
45250	2A
45251	67A
45252	8B
45253	14B
45254	5B
45255	8B
45256	8A
45257	5D
45258	12A
45259	10C
45260	19B
45261	25A
45262	19A
45263	15C
45264	19B
45265	21A
45266	63A
45267	14B
45268	21A
45269	21A
45270	5B
45271	5B
45272	20A
45273	21A
45274	21B
45275	6B
45276	8A
45277	14B
45278	5D
45279	14B
45280	15C
45281	84G
45282	2A
45283	84G
45284	26G
45285	14B
45286	6B
45287	3B
45288	6B
45289	9A
45290	10C
45291	11B
45292	7A
45293	12A
45294	5B
45295	12A
45296	12A
45297	19B
45298	84G
45299	12A
45300	5B
45301	5B
45302	10C
45303	8A
45304	10C
45305	8B
45306	11A
45307	9A
45308	3C
45309	63A
45310	3A
45311	12A
45312	10C
45313	10A
45314	4A
45315	6B
45316	4A
45317	11B
45318	84G
45319	60A
45320	60A
45321	8B
45322	3D
45323	12A
45324	5D
45325	5D
45326	5D
45327	10C
45328	8B
45329	10C
45330	84G
45331	4B
45332	10B
45333	11A
45334	27C
45335	27A
45336	27A
45337	10B

45338	26B	45400	84G	45462	66B	45518*	12A
45339	25A	45401	10C	45463	63A	45519*	10B
45340	25B	45402	6B	45464	63A	45520*	9A
45341	25G	45403	10C	45465	63A	45521*	8B
45342	15C	45404	2A	45466	63A	45522*	1B
45343	11A	45405	3B	45467	63A	45523*	5A
45344	3C	45406	84G	45468	65B	45524*	3B
45345	12A	45407	19A	45469	63A	45525*	12A
45346	7C	45408	10C	45470	63A	45526*	12A
45347	8A	45409	12A	45471	65B	45527*	8A
45348	12A	45410	10C	45472	63A	45528	5A
45349	3D	45411	10C	45473	63A	45529*	5A
45350	8A	45412	12A	45474	63A	45530*	9A
45351	12A	45413	10A	45475	63A	45531*	8A
45352	8A	45414	12A	45476	60A	45532*	1B
45353	1A	45415	27C	45477	60A	45533*	8A
45354	8B	45416	12A	45478	60A	45534*	7C
45355	65B	45417	3A	45479	60A	45535*	5A
45356	65B	45418	3E	45480	65B	45536*	9A
45357	63A	45419	2A	45481	65B	45537*	10B
45358	63B	45420	10C	45482	65B	45538*	8A
45359	63B	45421	10C	45483	63A	45539*	9A
45360	60A	45422	84G	45484	66A	45540*	9A
45361	60A	45423	65B	45485	66A	45541*	1B
45362	64C	45424	10C	45486	66A	45542	12A
45363	68A	45425	10A	45487	66A	45543*	5A
45364	68A	45426	10C	45488	63A	45544	10B
45365	63A	45427	11A	45489	67A	45545*	3B
45366	63A	45428	10C	45490	67A	45546*	5A
45367	24A	45429	2A	45491	67A	45547	10B
45368	12A	45430	2A	45492	63A	45548*	5A
45369	5B	45431	2A	45493	2A	45549	12A
45370	8B	45432	68A	45494	12A	45550	12A
45371	12A	45433	3A	45495	10C	45551	12A
45372	2A	45434	3B	45496	63A		
45373	10C	45435	27C	45497	63A		
45374	2A	45436	84G	45498	66B	**Cl. "5XP"**	
45375	2A	45437	3B	45499	65B	**"Jubilee"**	
45376	7C	45438	10C			**4-6-0**	
45377	10C	45439	12A			45552*	12A
45378	10C	45440	71G	**Cl. "5XP"**		45553*	9E
45379	2A	45441	2A	**"Patriot"**		45554*	16A
45380	8A	45442	10C	**4-6-0**		45555*	12A
45381	5D	45443	65B			45556*	9A
45382	7C	45444	10C	45500*	9A	45557*	14B
45383	11B	45445	12A	45501*	9A	45558*	5A
45384	84G	45446	3D	45502*	5A	45559*	10C
45385	6A	45447	21A	45503*	5A	45560*	67A
45386	11B	45448	3D	45504*	5A	45561*	22A
45387	9A	45449	10A	45505*	12A	45562*	20A
45388	12A	45450	26G	45506*	5A	45563*	10C
45389	63A	45451	12A	45507*	5A	45564*	63A
45390	3E	45452	63A	45508	10B	45565*	20A
45391	2A	45453	60A	45509	1A	45566*	20A
45392	11A	45454	12B	45510	5A	45567*	8A
45393	8A	45455	68A	45511*	5A	45568*	20A
45394	2A	45456	63A	45512*	12A	45569*	20A
45395	3C	45457	63A	45513	5A	45570*	22A
45396	24A	45458	63A	45514*	1B	45571*	28A
45397	3D	45459	63A	45515*	8A	45572*	22A
45398	8A	45460	63A	45516*	10B	45573*	20A
45399	8A	45461	60A	45517	12A	45574*	28A

45575* 63A	45637* 8A	45699* 22A	46109* 20A
45576* 67A	45638* 9A	45700* 26A	46110* 12A
45577* 68A	45639* 17A	45701* 26A	46111* 8A
45578* 12A	45640* 16A	45702* 25G	46112* 7C
45579* 66A	45641* 14B	45703* 3B	46113* 5A
45580* 68A	45642* 26A	45704* 25G	46114* 9A
45581* 68A	45643* 67A	45705* 25G	46115* 9A
45582* 68A	45644* 63A	45706* 26A	46116* 1B
45583* 66A	45645* 67A	45707* 28A	46117* 20A
45584* 66A	45646* 67A	45708* 25G	46118* 1B
45585* 17A	45647* 5A	45709* 9A	46119* 7C
45586* 5A	45648* 14B	45710* 26A	46120* 9A
45587* 20A	45649* 14B	45711* 25G	46121* 66A
45588* 28A	45650* 14B	45712* 26A	46122* 9A
45589* 20A	45651* 20A	45713* 68A	46123* 8A
45590* 19B	45652* 9E	45714* 68A	46124* 8A
45591* 1A	45653* 28A	45715* 68A	46125* 8A
45592* 5A	45654* 14B	45716* 68A	46126* 1B
45593* 9A	45655* 9A	45717* 27A	46127* 7C
45594* 19B	45656* 17A	45718* 3B	46128* 5A
45595* 12A	45657* 14B	45719* 26A	46129* 9A
45596* 25B	45658* 20A	45720* 10C	46130* 5A
45597* 20A	45659* 20A	45721* 8A	46131* 9A
45598* 14B	45660* 22A	45722* 3B	46132* 7C
45599* 10B	45661* 26A	45723* 9A	46133* 20A
45600* 10C	45662* 22A	45724* 3B	46134* 8A
45601* 1B	45663* 22A	45725* 19B	46135* 8A
45602* 17A	45664* 19B	45726* 3B	46136* 12A
45603* 9A	45665* 14B	45727* 68A	46137* 8A
45604* 20A	45666* 5A	45728* 68A	46138* 8A
45605* 20A	45667* 17A	45729* 68A	46139* 1B
45606* 5A	45668* 10C	45730* 68A	46140* 1B
45607* 19B	45669* 1B	45731* 68A	46141* 1B
45608* 20A	45670* 8A	45732* 68A	46142* 1B
45609* 14B	45671* 26A	45733* 3B	46143* 9A
45610* 17A	45672* 1B	45734* 9A	46144* 8A
45611* 16A	45673* 8A	45735* 1B	46145* 9A
45612* 14B	45674* 5A	45736* 1B	46146* 5A
45613* 8A	45675* 20A	45737* 8A	46147* 12A
45614* 14B	45676* 1B	45738* 5A	46148* 1B
45615* 14B	45677* 12A	45739* 20A	46149* 9A
45616* 14B	45678* 5A	45740* 9A	46150* 9A
45617* 9A	45679* 19B	45741* 3B	46151* 1B
45618* 9E	45680* 9A	45742* 3B	46152* 1B
45619* 20A	45681* 8A		46153* 8A
45620* 16A	45682* 22A		46154* 1B
45621* 19B	45683* 19B		46155* 5A
45622* 9E	45684* 5A	**Cl. "6P"**	46156* 8A
45623* 8A	45685* 22A	**"Royal Scot"**	46157* 5A
45624* 12A	45686* 5A	**4-6-0**	46158* 7C
45625* 1A	45687* 12A		46159* 1B
45626* 20A	45688* 9A		46160* 9A
45627* 9A	45689* 5A		46161* 7C
45628* 9E	45690* 22A		46162* 1B
45629* 9E	45691* 66A	46100* 1B	46163* 12A
45630* 12A	45692* 66A	46101* 1B	46164* 8A
45631* 9A	45693* 67A	46102* 66A	46165* 7C
45632* 9A	45694* 20A	46103* 20A	46166* 7C
45633* 9A	45695* 28A	46104* 66A	46167* 9A
45634* 5A	45696* 17A	46105* 66A	46168* 1B
45635* 26A	45697* 28A	46106* 8A	46169* 9A
45636* 16A	45698* 27A	46107* 66A	46170* 1B
		46108* 20A	

Cl. "7P" "Princess Royal" 4-6-2

46200*	8A
46201*	8A
46202	1B
46203*	8A
46204*	8A
46205*	8A
46206*	5A
46207*	5A
46208*	5A
46209*	5A
46210*	5A
46211*	5A
46212*	5A

Cl. "7P" "Princess Coronation" 4-6-2

46220*	66A
46221*	66A
46222*	66A
46223*	66A
46224*	66A
46225*	12A
46226*	12A
46227*	66A
46228*	12A
46229*	12A
46230*	66A
46231*	66A
46232*	66A
46233*	5A
46234*	5A
46235*	5A
46236*	5A
46237*	1B
46238*	1B
46239*	1B
46240*	1B
46241*	1B
46242*	1B
46243*	5A
46244*	1B
46245*	1B
46246*	1B
46247*	1B
46248*	5A
46249*	1B
46250*	1B
46251*	1B
46252*	1B
46253*	1B
46254*	12A
46255*	12A
46256*	1B
46257*	1B

Cl. "2MT" 2-6-0

46400	15B
46401	15B
46402	15B
46403	15B
46404	15B
46405	25C
46406	27A
46407	25C
46408	25C
46409	25C
46410	28A
46411	28A
46412	28A
46413	28A
46414	27A
46415	27A
46416	27A
46417	27A
46418	26A
46419	26A
46420	8D
46421	8D
46422	8D
46423	8D
46424	8D
46425	3A
46426	3A
46427	3A
46428	9F
46429	10B
46430	10B
46431	1A
46432	1A
46433	1A
46434	9F
46435	28A
46436	27E
46437	25C
46438	25A
46439	25A
46440	23A
46441	23C
46442	23A
46443	17A
46444	17A
46445	2D
46446	2D
46447	12D
46448	12D
46449	12C
46450	19A
46451	19A
46452	20E
46453	20E
46454	17A
46455	12C
46456	12D
46457	5A
46458	5A
46459	2A
46460	64A
46461	64A
46462	64A
46463	62B
46464	62B
46465	
46466	
46467	
46468	
46469	
46470	
46471	
46472	
46473	
46474	
46475	
46476	
46477	
46478	
46479	
46480	
46481	
46482	
46483	
46484	
46485	
46486	
46487	
46488	
46489	
46490	
46491	
46492	
46493	
46494	
46495	
46496	
46497	
46498	
46499	
46500	
46501	
46502	

Cl. "1P" 2-4-2T

46601	4A
46603	8B
46604	7A
46616	9D
46620	87K
46628	10E
46643	10E
46654	8B
46656	68D
46658	10E
46666	4B
46680	5A
46683	2C
46688	8B
46701	8B
46712	3C
46727	10E
46749	2C
46757	3C

Cl. "2P" 2-4-2T

46762	10B

Cl. "2MT" 0-6-2T

46899	7B
46900	3E
46906	7B
46912	3E
46922	3E

Cl. "0F" 0-4-0T

47000	17B
47001	27A
47002	27A
47003	18C
47004	18C
47005	
47006	
47007	
47008	
47009	

Cl. "2F" 0-6-0T

47160	6C
47161	28B
47162	64A
47163	64C
47164	6C
47165	28B
47166	6C
47167	66D
47168	66D
47169	66D

"Sentinel" 0-4-0T

47180	10E
47181	10E
47182	67C
47183	84G
47184	6E
47190	22A
47191	71G

Cl. "3F" 0-6-0T

47200	14B	47260	14B	47322	11B	47384	5B
47201	23C	47261	14C	47323	11B	47385	8A
47202	14B	47262	14B	47324	6C	47386	24B
47203	14A	47263	18D	47325	8A	47387	8B
47204	14A	47264	15A	47326	12A	47388	8C
47205	14A	47265	15A	47327	12A	47389	6A
47206	14A	47266	5B	47328	33A	47390	12E
47207	14A	47267	9A	47329	67A	47391	12A
47208	14A	47268	8B	47330	5B	47392	8A
47209	14A	47269	35C	47331	66A	47393	10E
47210	14A	47270	35C	47332	66A	47394	7A
47211	14A	47271	20B	47333	15A	47395	3A
47212	14A	47272	18C	47334	20D	47396	3A
47213	14A	47273	15A	47335	20D	47397	3B
47214	14A	47274	15C	47336	26G	47398	3B
47215	14A	47275	71G	47337	12E	47399	3B
47216	14A	47276	21A	47338	5D	47400	9A
47217	14A	47277	16A	47339	11A	47401	10D
47218	14A	47278	18C	47340	12A	47402	8A
47219	14A	47279	15A	47341	9A	47403	12A
47220	14A	47280	5B	47342	1A	47404	8A
47221	14A	47281	5D	47343	9A	47405	20D
47222	20E	47282	14B	47344	5B	47406	11A
47223	15D	47283	14B	47345	9A	47407	8A
47224	14A	47284	8C	47346	9B	47408	12A
47225	14A	47285	2B	47347	9A	47409	11A
47226	14A	47286	2B	47348	1D	47410	11A
47227	14A	47287	11B	47349	1D	47411	1D
47228	14A	47288	4A	47350	1D	47412	1A
47229	14B	47289	9B	47351	33A	47413	3C
47230	87K	47290	12D	47352	8B	47414	5B
47231	17B	47291	10B	47353	8A	47415	12A
47232	87K	47292	12D	47354	1B	47416	8A
47233	17B	47293	10B	47355	1C	47417	17A
47234	21C	47294	8A	47356	1B	47418	20A
47235	19A	47295	12A	47357	8A	47419	20E
47236	19A	47296	10B	47358	1B	47420	20A
47237	22B	47297	6A	47359	1B	47421	20C
47238	15A	47298	4A	47360	2A	47422	16A
47239	20D	47299	4B	47361	1A	47423	18C
47240	14A	47300	33A	47362	8C	47424	18D
47241	14B	47301	21A	47363	3D	47425	21C
47242	14B	47302	1D	47364	3D	47426	18D
47243	14A	47303	21C	47365	3D	47427	23A
47244	14B	47304	1D	47366	3D	47428	14B
47245	14B	47305	21C	47367	2B	47429	14B
47246	14B	47306	1D	47368	7C	47430	1A
47247	18A	47307	1D	47369	9A	47431	5B
47248	14A	47308	21C	47370	5D	47432	19A
47249	20B	47309	8A	47371	6B	47433	14A
47250	17A	47310	1D	47372	6B	47434	14A
47251	14A	47311	33A	47373	8C	47435	14A
47252	15D	47312	1D	47374	6A	47436	18A
47253	17B	47313	21A	47375	6A	47437	15B
47254	20A	47314	1D	47376	8B	47438	16A
47255	20E	47315	1D	47377	12A	47439	8C
47256	87K	47316	71G	47378	2A	47440	26G
47257	17B	47317	11A	47379	2A	47441	15C
47258	87K	47318	4B	47380	1A	47442	15C
47259	87K	47319	10B	47381	23C	47443	20B
		47320	8A	47382	3A	47444	10E
		47321	7C	47383	6A	47445	5E

47446	15A	47509	25E	47572	25A	47636	15A
47447	17D	47510	25A	47573	25A	47637	16A
47448	20C	47511	1D	47574	26B	47638	21A
47449	17C	47512	33A	47575	24B	47639	23C
47450	5B	47513	19A	47576	24B	47640	20B
47451	10E	47514	1D	47577	26A	47641	17B
47452	4A	47515	1D	47578	26B	47642	15A
47453	10E	47516	1D	47579	26B	47643	17B
47454	18A	47517	1D	47580	25A	47644	14B
47455	18D	47518	1D	47581	20C	47645	14B
47457	17D	47519	3A	47582	25A	47646	6B
47458	33A	47520	1A	47583	26B	47647	5D
47459	17D	47521	4A	47584	26B	47648	5D
47460	17D	47522	1B	47585	26B	47649	5C
47461	17D	47523	5B	47586	26A	47650	6B
47462	20C	47524	5B	47587	5D	47651	8C
47463	20B	47525	12E	47588	5C	47652	8B
47464	17B	47526	5B	47589	20B	47653	5C
47465	71G	47527	1B	47590	5B	47654	8B
47466	18B	47528	9A	47591	8B	47655	87K
47467	18A	47529	1B	47592	C. Wks.	47656	6B
47468	23C	47530	6C	47593	12D	47657	8B
47469	23C	47531	1A	47594	2B	47658	5D
47470	23C	47532	23C	47595	5B	47659	35C
47471	23C	47533	15C	47596	5D	47660	17A
47472	6C	47534	15C	47597	8A	47661	5B
47473	3B	47535	18C	47598	5C	47662	5B
47474	1A	47536	66A	47599	5D	47663	12A
47475	1A	47537	66A	47600	6A	47664	5C
47476	7C	47538	20B	47601	9B	47665	12A
47477	87K	47539	16A	47602	5E	47666	12A
47478	87K	47540	66A	47603	8B	47667	1B
47479	87K	47541	66A	47604	12E	47668	1B
47480	87K	47542	71G	47605	11A	47669	1B
47481	87K	47543	15A	47606	5C	47670	5B
47482	1D	47544	22A	47607	22B	47671	1B
47483	1D	47545	18A	47608	5E	47672	6C
47484	33A	47546	19C	47609	5D	47673	9A
47485	16A	47547	19C	47610	5D	47674	6C
47486	1D	47548	19A	47611	19A	47675	1A
47487	1D	47549	15D	47612	4B	47676	1A
47488	1D	47550	22A	47613	12A	47677	2A
47489	1D	47551	18A	47614	12A	47678	22A
47490	1D	47552	16A	47615	6B	47679	17D
47491	1A	47554	15A	47616	5E	47680	5B
47492	1D	47555	18A	47617	12A	47681	87K
47493	1D	47556	12A	47618	12A		
47494	1D	47557	71G	47619	22B		
47495	1D	47558	1D	47620	22B		
47496	71G	47559	1D	47621	35C		
47497	1D	47560	1D	47622	35C		
47498	1D	47561	1D	47623	16A		
47499	1D	47562	23A	47624	19A		
47500	1D	47563	19A	47625	18D		
47501	1D	47564	1D	47626	18D		
47502	18D	47565	21C	47627	6C		
47503	11C	47566	35C	47628	6C		
47504	6A	47567	25G	47629	16A		
47505	1A	47568	25G	47630	18A		
47506	1D	47569	25G	47631	16A		
47507	6C	47570	25G	47632	16A		
47508	25E	47571	25G	47633	5B		
				47634	20C		
				47635	22B		

Cl. "1F" 0-4-2T

47862	C. Wks.
47865	C Wks.

Cl. "6F" 0-8-2T

47877	10A
47881	10A
47884	10A
47896	10A

Cl. "7F" 0-8-4T

47931	8A
47937	8A
47939	8A

Beyer-Garratt 2-6-0 + 0-6-2

47967	18A
47968	18C
47969	18A
47970	18A
47971	18C
47972	18A
47973	18C
47974	18A
47975	18A
47976	18A
47977	18A
47978	18A
47979	18A
47980	18C
47981	18A
47982	18A
47983	18C
47984	18C
47985	18A
47986	18A
47987	18A
47988	18A
47989	18A
47990	18C
47991	18A
47992	18C
47993	18C
47994	18A
47995	18A
47996	18A
47997	18C
47998	18A
47999	18A

Cl. "8F" 2-8-0

48000	16C
48001	23C
48002	18D
48003	16A
48004	16C
48005	23A
48006	16C
48007	18A
48008	17C
48009	16C
48010	15A
48011	1A
48012	2C
48016	2B
48017	6B

48018	2C
48020	2B
48024	15A
48026	19C
48027	21A
48029	16C
48033	18A
48035	15A
48036	2B
48037	18A
48039	2A
48045	9G
48046	9G
48050	15A
48053	18D
48054	9D
48055	19C
48056	18B
48057	18B
48060	18B
48061	2B
48062	20C
48063	18B
48064	16A
48065	19C
48067	20A
48069	15B
48070	20A
48073	16C
48074	12B
48075	18A
48076	18B
48077	2B
48078	20C
48079	17A
48080	20C
48081	16C
48082	15A
48083	18B
48084	20D
48085	2A
48088	16D
48089	9F
48090	9D
48092	16C
48093	20C
48094	6B
48095	20C
48096	16C
48097	16C
48098	16C
48099	9F
48100	16C
48101	16C
48102	16A
48103	20C
48104	20A
48105	23B
48106	6C
48107	17C
48108	16C
48109	14A

48110	26G
48111	18D
48112	18A
48113	20C
48114	16C
48115	18B
48116	19A
48117	18A
48118	18B
48119	16D
48120	3A
48121	17A
48122	1A
48123	20B
48124	15B
48125	18B
48126	20A
48127	9F
48128	15A
48129	1A
48130	20D
48131	20D
48132	14A
48133	18A
48134	9F
48135	9G
48136	18B
48137	16C
48138	16C
48139	16C
48140	19C
48141	15B
48142	6B
48143	15B
48144	16A
48145	23A
48146	20D
48147	1A
48148	23C
48149	15A
48150	15A
48151	15A
48152	18B
48153	17A
48154	9F
48155	9F
48156	16D
48157	20A
48158	20A
48159	20A
48160	20D
48161	23C
48162	20C
48163	14A
48164	20D
48165	2A
48166	9D
48167	15A
48168	18A
48169	20C
48170	16A
48171	1A

48172	1A
48173	2A
48174	1A
48175	3A
48176	18A
48177	15D
48178	18A
48179	19A
48180	15A
48181	15A
48182	18A
48183	15A
48184	18B
48185	18B
48186	18B
48187	18A
48188	26G
48189	23B
48190	9F
48191	15A
48192	15A
48193	16C
48194	18A
48195	18D
48196	18A
48197	18A
48198	15A
48199	18A
48200	18A
48201	18A
48202	18A
48203	18A
48204	18A
48205	18A
48206	16A
48207	84G
48208	9F
48209	19C
48210	18D
48211	15C
48212	18B
48213	18D
48214	16C
48215	16C
48216	19A
48217	16A
48218	16A
48219	19A
48220	9F
48221	18A
48222	15A
48223	16C
48224	16C
48225	16C
48246	6B
48247	6C
48248	5B
48249	5B
48250	5B
48251	5B
48252	5B
48253	5B

231

48254	5B	48319	24B	48381	16A	48443	20C
48255	5B	48320	2A	48382	16C	48444	6B
48256	5B	48321	68A	48383	16C	48445	4B
48257	5B	48322	9D	48384	18A	48446	6B
48258	9G	48323	12B	48385	15A	48447	6B
48259	9G	48324	18A	48386	15A	48448	6C
48260	5B	48325	3A	48387	18A	48449	25C
48261	5B	48326	9D	48388	21A	48450	19C
48262	5B	48327	1A	48389	9A	48451	9D
48263	5B	48328	84G	48390	17A	48452	6B
48264	15A	48329	9F	48391	18B	48453	26C
48265	17C	48330	26G	48392	16C	48454	20A
48266	20D	48331	18A	48393	16C	48455	6C
48267	16C	48332	18D	48394	20D	48456	25G
48268	16C	48333	18B	48395	20D	48457	8A
48269	15A	48334	18A	48396	20D	48458	6B
48270	16C	48335	3A	48397	15C	48459	6B
48271	20D	48336	21A	48398	2A	48460	18D
48272	16C	48337	20C	48399	20A	48461	18A
48273	18A	48338	15A	48400	18A	48462	8D
48274	20D	48339	21A	48401	21A	48463	18A
48275	9F	48340	1A	48402	16A	48464	68A
48276	20B	48341	18D	48403	16C	48465	9D
48277	20B	48342	6B	48404	17A	48466	8B
48278	1A	48343	2A	48405	16C	48467	6B
48279	16A	48344	6C	48406	9F	48468	26C
48280	18B	48345	2B	48407	19C	48469	8B
48281	15A	48346	18D	48408	16C	48470	6B
48282	16C	48347	84G	48409	16C	48471	15B
48283	20A	48348	26G	48410	14A	48472	68A
48284	19A	48349	26G	48411	9E	48473	8B
48285	15B	48350	18A	48412	20C	48474	84G
48286	5B	48351	21A	48413	16C	48475	17C
48287	5B	48352	20D	48414	14A	48476	1A
48288	5B	48353	18B	48415	14A	48477	6B
48289	5B	48354	1A	48416	1A	48478	84G
48290	5B	48355	15B	48417	21A	48479	2A
48291	5B	48356	15B	48418	18A	48490	18A
48292	5B	48357	20D	48419	20C	48491	6C
48293	16A	48358	18B	48420	21A	48492	15A
48294	5B	48359	15A	48421	9D	48493	18D
48295	5B	48360	15A	48422	4B	48494	18B
48296	5B	48361	18A	48423	4B	48495	18B
48297	5B	48362	18A	48424	21A	48500	9A
48301	15B	48363	15A	48425	9A	48501	9A
48302	17A	48364	15A	48426	4B	48502	25A
48303	18A	48365	15A	48427	2A	48503	9F
48304	18A	48366	8B	48428	9A	48504	25A
48305	15A	48367	18A	48429	9A	48505	2A
48306	15C	48368	1A	48430	18B	48506	25A
48307	84G	48369	84G	48431	20C	48507	20D
48308	84G	48370	18A	48432	17A	48508	20D
48309	1A	48371	1A	48433	1A	48509	2A
48310	1A	48372	2A	48434	19C	48510	8A
48311	20B	48373	84G	48435	24B	48511	25A
48312	1A	48374	15A	48436	8B	48512	8A
48313	18A	48375	3A	48437	2A	48513	8A
48314	19A	48376	20C	48438	1A	48514	25A
48315	9F	48377	20C	48439	20C	48515	27B
48316	9F	48378	15A	48440	9E	48516	9A
48317	21A	48379	16C	48441	18D	48517	15C
48318	3A	48380	16A	48442	16C	48518	3A

48519	9D	48621	16D	48683	9F	48745	9D
48520	8C	48622	20B	48684	6C	48746	9D
48521	8C	48623	18B	48685	18A	48747	8C
48522	8C	48624	1A	48686	3A	48748	8C
48523	27B	48625	15A	48687	21A	48749	9D
48524	27B	48626	1A	48688	84G	48750	6B
48525	27B	48627	15A	48689	8B	48751	25D
48526	2B	48628	1A	48690	18A	48752	26A
48527	9F	48629	1A	48691	6C	48753	8D
48528	8C	48630	8C	48692	15A	48754	26A
48529	8C	48631	8C	48693	4B	48755	25D
48530	16C	48632	1A	48694	18A	48756	9G
48531	26G	48633	1A	48695	15A	48757	5B
48532	20C	48634	1A	48696	16A	48758	1A
48533	15A	48635	16A	48697	9G	48759	15B
48534	18B	48636	18A	48698	9E	48760	26B
48535	18B	48637	18A	48699	15A	48761	26A
48536	68A	48638	18A	48700	21A	48762	26C
48537	20A	48639	16A	48701	16D	48763	21A
48538	18D	48640	17A	48702	20D	48764	8D
48539	18D	48641	20B	48703	20B	48765	26C
48540	20C	48642	19A	48704	15B	48766	26B
48541	14A	48643	16D	48705	26A	48767	26C
48542	20C	48644	15A	48706	9G	48768	25C
48543	17C	48645	15B	48707	26A	48769	26A
48544	12B	48646	19C	48708	8D	48770	6B
48545	18D	48647	17A	48709	15C	48771	8D
48546	18D	48648	1A	48710	26C	48772	8D
48547	20D	48649	1A	48711	26C		
48548	19C	48650	18B	48712	9D		
48549	18B	48651	15A	48713	27B		
48550	4B	48652	20B	48714	26A		
48551	1A	48653	16A	48715	26A		
48552	16C	48654	17A	48716	2B		
48553	18A	48655	18A	48717	9G		
48554	8D	48656	1A	48718	9G		
48555	9G	48657	1A	48719	26A		
48556	3A	48658	1A	48720	25D		
48557	1A	48659	1A	48721	18B		
48558	8D	48660	1A	48722	26A		
48559	2A	48661	18B	48723	2B		
48600	1A	48662	18A	48724	26B		
48601	1A	48663	18D	48725	26B		
48602	1A	48664	8B	48726	26A		
48603	1A	48665	1A	48727	26A		
48604	18D	48666	16A	48728	15C		
48605	1A	48667	9G	48729	2A		
48606	18A	48668	15A	48730	26A		
48607	18A	48669	21A	48731	9D		
48608	23B	48670	20D	48732	26B		
48609	23A	48671	15A	48733	26A		
48610	1A	48672	18A	48734	9D		
48611	15B	48673	6C	48735	26A		
48612	68A	48674	3A	48736	2A		
48613	9G	48675	16A	48737	9D		
48614	16A	48676	9F	48738	25C		
48615	18A	48677	17A	48739	26A		
48616	23B	48678	15A	48740	9D		
48617	15A	48679	1A	48741	9D		
48618	18A	48680	9E	48742	9D		
48619	15A	48681	18A	48743	8C		
48620	18B	48682	9F	48744	6B		

Cl. "6F" and "7F" 0-8-0

48893	87K
48895	10A
48898	8A
48899	86K
48901	84G
48902	3B
48905	3A
48907	3A
48914	4B
48915	1C
48917	3A
48920	10C
48921	86K
48922	5C
48926	10C
48927	2B
48930	10A
48932	8A
48933	8A
48936	4B
48940	3B
48942	8C
48943	8A
48944	8C
48945	84G
48950	3A
48951	4A

48952	4A	49101	10D	49191	10B	49293	8C
48953	4A	49104	10B	49193	3C	49296	1A
48964	4A	49105	8C	49196	3B	49300	3C
49002	9B	49106	3A	49198	3C	49301	8A
49005	4A	49108	9B	49199	10C	49302	8C
49006	86K	49109	11A	49200	10B	49304	2B
49007	4A	49112	11A	49202	3A	49306	10A
49008	8B	49113	86K	49203	4B	49307	4A
49009	3A	49114	3A	49204	3B	49308	3A
49010	9B	49115	5C	49205	10E	49310	10A
49014	4A	49116	8D	49208	3C	49311	10A
49017	3D	49117	1A	49209	10C	49312	10E
49018	10A	49119	8B	49210	5B	49313	3A
49020	8D	49120	8C	49212	8C	49314	11A
49021	1A	49121	86K	49213	3C	49315	10D
49022	3A	49122	1A	49214	9D	49316	86K
49023	10A	49125	8C	49216	3A	49318	2B
49024	10A	49126	8A	49218	8C	49319	5B
49025	3A	49129	10A	49219	8C	49321	4B
49027	10C	49130	11A	49222	3C	49322	3C
49028	86K	49132	9D	49223	3A	49323	1C
49030	10A	49134	10B	49224	8A	49326	3C
49031	3C	49137	8A	49226	86K	49327	3A
49033	87K	49138	84G	49228	10A	49328	3A
49034	10A	49139	1A	49229	5C	49330	2D
49035	87K	49140	3D	49230	5B	49331	10A
49037	3B	49141	10B	49234	10C	49334	3A
49044	3B	49142	3A	49239	8A	49335	10C
49045	3A	49143	8C	49240	3B	49339	2B
49046	86K	49144	4A	49241	11A	49340	10C
49047	5C	49145	1C	49243	86K	49341	10A
49048	3C	49146	86K	49244	8C	49342	1A
49049	4A	49147	10D	49245	3A	49343	8D
49050	10A	49148	87K	49246	3A	49344	1A
49051	86K	49149	8B	49247	8B	49345	86K
49057	9D	49150	10B	49249	8C	49346	3B
49061	4A	49151	11A	49252	11A	49347	9D
49062	1A	49153	4B	49253	8C	49348	9D
49063	3A	49154	4A	49254	10C	49350	2B
49064	86K	49155	4A	49257	11A	49352	10A
49066	3C	49156	9B	49258	3C	49354	3A
49068	2B	49157	1C	49260	87K	49355	8A
49070	4A	49158	5C	49261	3D	49356	1A
49071	3A	49160	10A	49262	10E	49357	4B
49073	8D	49161	86K	49264	10A	49358	87K
49074	8C	49162	3B	49265	3A	49359	3A
49077	3A	49163	1A	49266	3A	49361	3A
49078	1A	49164	1A	49267	10B	49364	3C
49079	8D	49167	3B	49268	10A	49366	4B
49081	3A	49168	86K	49270	4B	49367	3A
49082	10A	49171	3C	49271	4B	49368	2B
49087	10C	49172	8C	49275	1A	49370	3D
49088	4A	49173	4A	49276	84G	49371	3A
49089	3A	49174	86K	49277	1A	49373	3C
49090	10A	49177	87K	49278	6B	49375	1C
49092	10A	49178	10C	49281	9B	49376	87K
49093	3A	49180	3A	49282	3A	49377	10E
49094	10C	49181	2B	49287	4A	49378	10A
49096	3A	49186	2B	49288	4A	49381	10A
49098	9B	49187	9B	49289	4A	49382	10B
49099	3A	49189	3A	49292	4A	49385	2B

49386	10C
49387	9D
49388	3C
49389	10E
49390	10B
49391	4A
49392	2A
49393	1C
49394	10A

Cl. "7F" "G2" 0-8-0

49395	8C
49396	2B
49397	2B
49398	2A
49399	8A
49400	10C
49401	3C
49402	10A
49403	86K
49404	8A
49405	2D
49406	4A
49407	5B
49408	2A
49409	86K
49410	5C
49411	2A
49412	8A
49413	2A
49414	2B
49415	2A
49416	2A
49417	4A
49418	2B
49419	8A
49420	8C
49421	10C
49422	86K
49423	2A
49424	2B
49425	2A
49426	10C
49427	4A
49428	9A
49429	2B
49430	2C
49431	2A
49432	2B
49433	2A
49434	2B
49435	2B
49436	2B
49437	8A
49438	11A
49439	9A
49440	84G
49441	2D
49442	2D
49443	4A
49444	2D
49445	8A
49446	2D
49447	2A
49448	4A
49449	8A
49450	9D
49451	2B
49452	2A
49453	2B
49454	9D

Cl. "7F" 0-8-0

49502	26B
49503	27B
49505	27B
49506	27B
49508	26D
49509	26F
49510	26C
49511	26B
49515	27B
49523	27B
49524	27B
49531	26A
49532	26B
49535	27B
49536	26A
49538	26B
49540	25E
49544	26B
49545	26A
49547	27B
49548	26F
49552	27B
49554	26A
49555	26B
49557	26D
49558	26A
49560	26A
49563	27B
49566	27B
49568	27D
49570	26B
49571	27B
49578	26B
49580	26A
49582	27B
49585	27D
49586	27B
49587	27D
49590	26F
49591	26D
49592	27B
49593	26F
49594	26D
49595	27B
49598	25D
49600	27B
49602	25D
49603	27B
49608	26A
49609	27B
49610	27D
49612	26A
49617	27B
49618	25D
49620	25D
49623	27B
49624	27B
49625	25A
49627	26B
49631	27B-
49635	27B
49637	26A
49638	26B
49640	26C
49641	27B
49648	25B
49649	27B
49650	26A
49651	26A
49657	26A
49659	25D
49660	25D
49661	25D
49662	25D
49663	25D
49664	26C
49666	26D
49667	26D
49668	26F
49671	27B
49672	26C
49673	26A
49674	26A

Cl. "5P" 4-6-0

50455	28A

Cl. "2P" and "3P" 2-4-2T

50621	20D
50622	20A
50623	20E
50625	23B
50630	20E
50633	20E
50634	20E
50636	20E
50639	10B
50640	28B
50642	28B
50643	11B
50644	10D
50646	28B
50647	26C
50648	27B
50650	25A
50651	26E
50652	26E
50653	24B
50654	24B
50655	27B
50656	25A
50660	26C
50671	20E
50676	10B
50678	7D
50681	20E
50686	23B
50687	7D
50689	20E
50695	10B
50697	8B
50703	8B
50705	8B
50712	25A
50714	20E
50715	25A
50720	28B
50721	28A
50725	28A
50731	25B
50735	25B
50736	25B
50746	28A
50749	28A
50752	28A
50757	28A
50762	25A
50764	25A
50765	25E
50766	28B
50777	28A
50778	28B
50781	28B
50788	25A
50795	20E
50799	25A
50802	28B
50806	25F
50807	26C
50812	28B
50815	26C
50818	26C
50829	26C
50831	26C
50840	28B
50842	20E
50850	28B
50852	24C
50855	26A

50859	26A	51379	25C			52137	26A
50865	26C	51381	25E	**Cl. "1F" 0-6-0T**		52138	28A
50869	25A	51390	26B			52139	26A
50872	26C	51396	27A	51535	27A	52140	26B
50873	25A	51397	10E	51536	27A	52141	2B
50886	25A	51404	25F	51537	27A	52143	8C
50887	25B	51408	25B	51544	27B	52150	25A
50892	25A	51410	24A	51546	27A	52154	25A
50897†	Rugby Test	51412	C. Wks.			52156	26A
	Plant	51413	27B			52157	28A
50898	25A	51415	24D	**Cl. "2F" 0-6-0**		52159	26D
50909	25F	51419	26D			52160	24C
50925	25E	51423	24C	52016	10C	52161	27C
		51424	26A	52021	10A	52162	27C
		51425	26A	52022	10C	52163	8C
Cl. "0F" 0-4-0T		51429	26A	52024	10C	52164	26D
		51432	25C	52030	10C	52165	26D
51202	71G	51436	26A	52031	10C	52166	25D
51204	5B	51439	8C	52034	10C	52167	7D
51206	27A	51441	6C	52037	25C	52169	27D
51207	25C	51444	C. Wks.	52041	25A	52171	24C
51212	22A	51445	8A	52043	25A	52172	7D
51216	27A	51446	C. Wks.	52044	25A	52174	28A
51217	17B	51447	25A	52045	10A	52175	8C
51218	10B	51453	25D	52051	10A	52176	7B
51221	5B	51457	26A	52053	10A	52177	10E
51222	25C	51458	26A	52056	25C	52179	27B
51227	27A	51460	27B	52059	10C	52182	28A
51229	27A	51462	27B	52064	10C	52183	27C
51230	26B	51464	26B			52186	25A
51231	27A	51470	26A			52189	25E
51232	27A	51471	10E	**Cl. "3F" 0-6-0**		52191	25D
51234	27A	51472	26A			52194	28A
51235	17A	51474	27D	52088	8B	52196	27B
51237	27A	51477	28B	52089	20D	52197	27D
51240	27A	51479	25E	52091	10E	52201	12E
51241	25C	51481	28B	52092	25F	52203	24D
51244	25C	51484	26G	52093	27B	52207	26A
51246	27A	51486	26D	52094	26A	52208	6C
51253	27A	51488	25E	52095	20C	52212	26C
		51489	26D	52098	10A	52215	28A
		51490	27C	52099	26F	52216	24C
		51491	10E	52100	8C	52217	25E
		51496	26A	52102	26A	52218	27B
Cl. "2F" 0-6-0T		51497	24B	52104	25F	52219	26B
		51498	28B	52105	10B	52220	24C
51307	27A	51499	24D	52107	10A	52225	6C
51313	6C	51500	26B	52108	20C	52230	7B
51316	10E	51503	25E	52111	8A	52231	26C
51319	10E	51504	26D	52112	27B	52232	6C
51321	28B	51506	24D	52118	8A	52233	7D
51323	25C	51510	26A	52119	7B	52235	25A
51336	24B	51511	26C	52120	25A	52236	26C
51338	26A	51512	26B	52121	16A	52237	25F
51343	27B	51513	26C	52123	16A	52238	24C
51345	24C	51514	24A	52124	25D	52239	26A
51348	25E	51516	25C	52125	7D	52240	28A
51353	8A	51519	26C	52126	10A	52243	25E
51358	25D	51521	25C	52129	26D	52244	27B
51361	25C	51524	25B	52132	26A	52245	26D
51371	27A	51526	24C	52133	25C	52246	26D
51375	27A	51530	27B	52135	16A	52248	26F
51376	26D			52136	26C		

† Not included in L.M.R. stock.

52250-54472

52250	10A	52378	26F	52515	25D	**Cl. "7F" 2-8-0**	
52252	20C	52379	27D	52517	26A		
52255	25D	52381	27B	52521	25A	53800	71G
52258	20C	52382	26D	52522	24C	53801	71G
52260	24D	52386	25A	52523	24C	53802	71G
52262	24D	52387	26F	52524	24C	53803	71G
52266	26A	52388	25D	52525	84G	53804	71G
52268	24D	52389	26F	52526	24D	53805	71G
52269	7B	52390	27D	52527	24C	53806	71G
52270	6C	52393	10E	52529	24D	53807	71G
52271	27E	52397	10E			53808	71G
52272	24C	52399	24C			53809	71G
52273	25C	52400	25E			53810	71G
52275	28A	52404	26C				
52278	27C	52405	27B				
52279	26B	52407	7B	**Cl. "3F" 0-6-0**			
52280	10E	52408	25D			**Cl. "2P" 4-4-0**	
52284	25A	52410	25F	52549	27D		
52285	12E	52411	25F	52551	84G	54398*	60D
52288	27D	52412	27B	52554	26D	54399*	60D
52289	24D	52413	27D	52557	27B	54404*	60D
52290	28B	52414	84G	52558	26A		
52293	26B	52415	28A	52559	20C		
52296	24C	52416	26E	52561	25A	**Cl. "3P" 4-4-0**	
52299	26E	52418	12E	52569	26A		
52300	26A	52427	25F	52572	28A	54438	64D
52304	26A	52428	84G	52575	25E	54439	60A
52305	25A	52429	2B	52576	25A	54440	66D
52309	25F	52430	28A	52579	24D	54441	66B
52311	26C	52431	24D	52580	26D	54443	68B
52312	27B	52432	6C	52581	26D	54444	68B
52317	24C	52433	25A	52582	27C	54445	60D
52319	25A	52435	25A	52583	26A	54446	60D
52321	8A	52437	27E	52587	25E	54447	63A
52322	2B	52438	8C	52588	28B	54448	63A
52328	27E	52440	26E	52590	25F	54449	64D
52330	8A	52441	24D	52592	25C	54450	63C
52331	25F	52443	26E	52598	8B	54451	64C
52333	27E	52444	24D	52608	8B	54452	64C
52334	28A	52445	24D	52615	26D	54453	66B
52336	24C	52446	26C	52616	25E	54454	63C
52338	7D	52447	28A	52619	10B	54455	60B
52341	10A	52448	25D			54456	67B
52343	26A	52449	10E			54457	66D
52345	25A	52450	27D			54458	63A
52348	26C	52452	25E	**Cl. "6F" 0-8-0**		54459	63A
52349	10E	52453	7D			54460	66B
52350	26C	52455	26A	52727	27D		
52351	25A	52456	24C	52822	27D		
52353	25A	52458	28B	52831	27D	**Cl. "3P" 4-4-0**	
52355	26A	52459	28A				
52356	7D	52460	24D			54461	64D
52357	28A	52461	25F			54462	66A
52358	26A	52464	26F	**Cl. "7F" 0-8-0**		54463	60A
52360	27D	52465	2B			54464	66B
52362	27B	52466	28A	52857	25F	54465	66B
52363	24D	52494	12E	52870	27D	54466	60B
52365	26F	52499	12E	52906	27D	54467	63A
52366	10E	52501	12D	52910	27D	54468	66D
52368	24C	52508	12D	52916	27D	54469	63A
52369	25A	52509	12D	52945	27D	54470	60A
52376	25E	52510	12E			54471	60A
						54472	60A

54473	60E
54474	65B
54475	65B
54476	63A
54477	64D
54478	64C
54479	66D
54480	60C
54481	60E
54482	60E
54483	65F
54484	60A
54485	63A
54486	63C
54487	60A
54488	60B
54489	63A
54490	64D
54491	60A
54492	66D
54493	60B
54494	63A
54495	60C
54496	60A
54497	66D
54498	66D
54499	63A
54500	63A
54501	63A
54502	63A
54503	63A
54504	67B
54505	64D
54506	66D
54507	68B
54508	66D

Cl. "4MT" 4-6-0

54630	66B
54634	66B
54635	66B
54636	66B
54638	66C
54639	66C
54640	66B
54647	66B
54648	66B
54649	66B
54650	66B
54654	66B

Cl. "1P" 0-4-4T

55051	60C
55053	60C

Cl. "2P" 0-4-4T

55119	65F
55121	65B
55122	63B
55124	68B
55125	68C
55126	63B
55132	67C
55134	66B
55135	67A
55136	63C
55138	66B
55139	64C
55140	67A
55141	66A
55142	68D
55143	67A
55144	63A
55145	63B
55146	66C
55160	60A
55161	63C
55162	63C
55164	68B
55165	64C
55166	64C
55167	66A
55168	65D
55169	63C
55170	66A
55171	63A
55172	63C
55173	62B
55174	60B
55175	63A
55176	63A
55177	64C
55178	68D
55179	66A
55181	68D
55182	67A
55185	63C
55186	62B
55187	63E
55188	66B
55189	64C
55191	66B
55192	62B
55193	63C
55194	63C
55195	63C
55196	63E
55197	66A
55198	63E
55199	60A
55200	63C
55201	66A
55202	64C
55203	67B
55204	65B
55206	67A
55207	66A
55208	63A
55209	63A
55210	64C
55211	67A
55212	63A
55213	63A
55214	63C
55215	63E
55216	63A
55217	62B
55218	63A
55219	67A
55220	68D
55221	66C
55222	63B
55223	62B
55224	66A
55225	67A
55226	62B
55227	62B
55228	66A
55229	64C
55230	63C
55231	62B
55232	68D
55233	68D
55234	68D
55235	67A
55236	67B
55237	68D
55238	65F
55239	68D
55240	67C
55260	67B
55261	64D
55262	67C
55263	63E
55264	67C
55265	66A
55266	67A
55267	66A
55268	66A
55269	67A

Cl. "4P" 4-6-2T

55350	68D
55352	68D
55353	68D
55359	68D
55360	68D
55361	68D

Cl. "0F" 0-4-0T

56011	60A
56020	17B
56025	St. R. Wks.
56027	84G
56028	66D
56029	65D
56030	65G
56031	66D
56032	C. Wks.
56035	66D
56038	60A
56039	65G

Cl. "2F" 0-6-0T

56151	65B
56152	65F
56153	66A
56154	66A
56155	66B
56156	66D
56157	66D
56158	65G
56159	66A
56160	66A
56161	65G
56162	66A
56163	66D
56164	65F
56165	66D
56166	66D
56167	66A
56168	65G
56169	65D
56170	65G
56171	65D
56172	66B
56173	66D

Cl. "3F" 0

56230	65F
56231	68A
56232	63B
56233	65B
56234	68C
56235	68A
56236	67B
56237	66C
56238	65G
56239	66A
56240	61B
56241	66B
56242	66C
56243	65F
56244	66A
56245	66B
56246	63A
56247	66B
56248	68A
56249	67A
56250	65G
56251	61B
56252	65B
56253	64C
56254	63B
56255	66C

56256	66C	56319	66C	57233	63B	57306	65D

56256	66C	56319	66C	57233	63B	57306	65D
56257	67C	56320	66C	57234	66A	57307	66C
56258	66B	56321	66C	57235	67C	57309	67A
56259	67D	56322	62B	57236	67B	57311	65B
56260	66A	56323	62B	57237	66B	57312	67C
56261	66A	56324	66A	57238	66A	57314	65D
56262	60A	56325	62B	57239	66A	57315	67C
56263	66A	56326	61B	57240	65B	57317	66A
56264	66B	56327	63A	57241	67A	57318	65B
56265	66B	56328	63A	57242	67A	57319	66A
56266	68A	56329	67A	57243	63B	57320	66A
56267	65F	56330	65B	57244	66C	57321	66A
56268	66B	56331	63A	57245	65D	57322	65D
56269	66B	56332	68A	57246	63B	57323	64D
56271	66B	56333	68A	57247	66B	57324	63C
56272	67C	56334	66B	57249	67A	57325	66B
56273	67C	56335	66B	57250	66C	57326	66B
56274	67C	56336	65F	57251	65B	57328	66B
56275	65F	56337	66B	57252	63B	57329	68B
56276	66B	56338	66B	57253	65B	57331	67B
56277	66B	56339	65G	57254	63E	57332	66B
56278	61B	56340	68A	57255	67A	57334	65F
56279	67D	56341	66A	57256	66B	57335	66B
56280	66A	56342	66A	57257	63B	57336	65D
56281	66A	56343	65D	57258	65D	57337	68B
56282	67D	56344	66A	57259	65G	57338	65F
56283	64C	56345	66B	57260	66C	57339	63A
56284	66C	56346	66A	57261	65B	57340	64D
56285	66B	56347	63A	57262	67C	57341	65D
56286	66A	56348	61B	57263	67D	57344	68B
56287	66C	56349	66A	57264	63B	57345	63A
56288	66D	56350	67A	57265	65F	57346	65D
56289	65B	56352	63A	57266	67A	57347	66A
56290	63A	56353	63A	57267	66B	57348	67D
56291	60A	56354	68A	57268	66A	57349	68B
56292	60A	56355	68A	57269	65B	57350	65B
56293	60A	56356	66B	57270	66B	57352	65B
56294	66A	56357	66B	57271	66A	57353	67B
56295	66A	56358	66B	57272	66B	57354	67C
56296	66C	56359	63A	57273	65D	57355	67D
56297	65G	56360	66C	57274	67D	57356	67D
56298	66C	56361	67A	57275	66A	57357	67D
56299	60A	56362	66C	57276	67D	57359	67A
56300	65F	56363	67C	57277	67B	57360	66A
56301	60E	56364	67D	57278	66B	57361	66A
56302	65D	56365	63B	57279	67C	57362	68B
56303	66C	56366	63B	57280	66C	57363	66B
56304	66A	56367	67C	57282	67D	57364	67C
56305	66A	56368	67B	57283	63B	57365	66A
56306	66A	56369	67B	57284	67C	57366	65F
56307	66A	56370	65B	57285	65F	57367	66A
56308	66A	56371	66C	57287	65F	57368	63C
56309	66C	56372	68C	57288	66A	57369	66D
56310	65B	56373	68A	57289	66B	57370	66A
56311	67D	56374	68A	57291	66B	57372	65D
56312	64C	56375	65F	57292	66A	57373	65D
56313	64C	56376	65F	57295	67C	57375	68C
56314	66A			57296	65D	57377	68B
56315	65G	**Cl. "2F" 0-6-0**		57299	66B	57378	68B
56316	66A			57300	67A	57379	66B
56317	68A	57230	66A	57302	68B	57383	67B
56318	66A	57232	63B	57303	66B	57384	66C

57385	64D	57451	64D	57581	66A	57635	64D
57386	64D	57453	65B	57582	66B	57637	67B
57387	66A	57454	65B	57583	64D	57638	66B
57388	66A	57455	65B	57585	60D	57640	67C
57389	66A	57456	65D	57586	60B	57642	60A
57391	68B	57457	65B	57587	60C	57643	67B
57392	67C	57458	68C	57588	66B	57644	67C
57394	65D	57459	66A	57589	67A	57645	64C
57395	66C	57460	63B	57590	67D	57650	67B
57396	63E	57461	66B	57591	60A	57651	67B
57397	68B	57462	66B	57592	65D	57652	65D
57398	66C	57463	66A	57593	66B	57653	62B
57404	66B	57464	66A	57594	67C	57654	64C
57405	68B	57465	66A	57595	66B	57655	64D
57407	66C	57468	63B	57596	67A	57658	67C
57410	66C	57470	65D	57597	60A	57659	66B
57411	65B	57472	65D	57599	66B	57661	66A
57412	66A	57473	63A	57600	68B	57663	66C
57413	66C			57601	68B	57665	66C
57414	66B	**Cl. "3F" 0-6-0**		57602	68B	57666	66B
57416	66B			57603	64D	57667	66F
57417	66B	57550	64C	57604	64D	57668	66B
57418	66B	57552	66D	57605	65D	57669	67B
57419	66B	57553	64C	57607	65D	57670	64D
57423	63B	57554	65B	57608	64D	57671	67B
57424	63B	57555	66A	57609	66C	57672	67B
57425	63B	57556	66D	57611	67C	57673	67D
57426	65D	57557	65B	57612	65D	57674	66A
57429	65D	57558	65B	57613	64D	57679	64D
57430	66C	57559	64C	57614	67C	57681	66B
57431	66C	57560	67A	57615	67C	57682	66D
57432	66A	57562	67A	57617	65B	57684	67C
57433	66A	57563	68B	57618	64D	57686	65B
57434	65B	57564	66A	57619	66A	57688	67B
57435	66B	57565	64C	57620	60E	57689	66F
57436	66B	57566	67A	57621	68B	57690	66A
57437	66B	57568	62B	57622	66A	57691	65F
57438	64D	57569	67C	57623	68B	57695	67A
57439	66A	57570	67B	57625	66A	57697	67C
57441	63C	57571	67B	57626	64D	57698	67A
57443	66A	57572	67B	57627	67D		
57444	66A	57573	67B	57628	67C	**Cl. "4F" 4-6-0**	
57445	68C	57575	67A	57630	66A		
57446	66A	57576	64C	57631	65B	57951	60A
57447	66A	57577	67D	57632	68A	57954	60A
57448	66A	57579	67D	57633	67C	57955	60A
57450	63A	57580	67A	57634	60A	57956	60A

Cl. "1P" 2-4-0

New No.	Old No.	
58020	20155	16A

Cl. "1P" 0-4-4T

58034	1251	22B
58038	1261	33A
58040	1273	15D

New No.	Old No.	
58042	1278	9D
58043	1287	33A
58045	1295	15A
58046	1298	71H
58047	1303	71H
58050	1324	16A
58051	1330	15D
58052	1337	20C
58053	1340	15A
58054	1341	15D
58056	1344	16A

58058-58195

New No.	Old No.	
58058	1350	17A
58059	1353	15D
58060	1357	20A
58061	1358	23A
58062	1360	33A
58063	1365	22B
58065	1367	33A
58066	1368	20C
58067	1370	19B
58068	1371	19B
58069	1373	20E
58070	1375	20E
58071	1377	19B
58072	1379	15C
58073	1382	15C
58075	1390	20C
58076	1396	19B
58077	1397	23A
58080	1411	17B
58083	1420	2A
58084	1421	9D
58085	1422	15A
58086	1423	71H
58087	1424	17B
58088	1425	71H
58089	1426	33A
58090	1429	20C
58091	1430	15D

Cl. "1P" 2-4-0T

58092	26428	9D

0-10-0

58100	22290	21C

Cl. "2F" 0-6-0

58110	22630	17A
58114	22900	19C
58115	22901	11B
58116	22902	3C
58117	22904	3D
58118	22907	2B
58119	22911	3B
58120	22912	11B
58121	22913	11B
58122	22915	3C
58123	22918	3C
58124	22920	3E
58125	22921	17A
58126	22924	21B
58127	22926	19C
58128	22929	9F
58129	22931	33B
58130	22932	17B

New No.	Old No.	
58131	22933	14B
58132	22934	17A
58133	22935	16A
58135	22944	16A
58136	22945	20B
58137	22946	16C
58138	22947	21B
58139	22950	19A
58140	22951	19A
58142	22954	15C
58143	22955	21B
58144	22958	17A
58145	22959	17B
58146	22963	18A
58147	22965	19C
58148	22967	17A
58149	22968	15D
58151	22970	19A
58152	22971	3B
58153	22974	18A
58154	22975	20E
58156	22977	20C
58157	22978	3C
58158	22982	14B
58159	22983	18A
58160	22984	17B
58161	2987	14A
58162	2988	15B
58163	2989	17C
58164	2990	15B
58165	2992	19A
58166	2993	18B
58167	2994	21A
58168	2995	18B
58169	2996	18A
58170	2997	19C
58171	2998	18A
58172	2999	15B
58173	23000	18A
58174	23001	17C
58175	23002	19A
58176	23003	18A
58177	23005	3E
58178	23006	3E
58179	23007	3E
58180	23008	3D
58181	23009	2A
58182	23010	3D
58183	23011	15B
58184	23012	33A
58185	23013	3D
58186	23014	17B
58187	23018	11B
58188	3023	20C
58189	3027	17D
58190	3031	19A
58191	3035	33A
58192	3037	18A
58193	3038	15B
58194	3039	15B
58195	3042	15B

New No.	Old No.		New No.	Old No.	
58196	3044	18B	58272	3493	1C
58197	3045	18A	58273	3503	3E
58198	3047	19C	58274	3508	14A
58199	3048	11B	58276	3512	19A
58200	3049	14A	58277	3516	3A
58201	3051	16A	58278	3517	2D
58203	3054	17A	58279	3525	3D
58204	3058	19C	58280	3526	1A
58206	3062	22B	58281	3527	4B
58207	3064	17B	58282	3533	19D
58209	3071	19B	58283	3536	1A
58211	3074	84G	58285	3539	1A
58212	3078	20B	58286	3543	1A
58213	3084	84G	58287	3545	3B
58214	3090	15B	58288	3551	3C
58215	3094	14B	58289	3559	33A
58216	3095	17A	58290	3561	2C
58217	3096	2D	58291	3564	11B
58218	3098	4B	58293	3571	2D
58219	3099	17D	58295	3603	3D
58220	3101	19A	58296	3617	18A
58221	3103	17B	58298	3648	15C
58224	3113	17D	58299	3655	11B
58225	3118	19A	58300	3688	15C
58226	3119	17D	58302	3691	1A
58228	3127	17D	58303	3696	1A
58229	3130	14B	58304	3703	17B
58230	3134	21A	58305	3707	15D
58231	3138	21A	58306	3725	2D
58232	3140	19A	58307	3726	3E
58233	3144	19C	58308	3738	2C
58234	3149	14B	58309	3739	11B
58235	3150	14A	58310	3764	14C
58236	3151	17B	58321	28091	C. Wks.
58237	3154	20C	58322	28093	84G
58238	3156	19C	58323	28100	C. Wks.
58240	3161	2B	58326	28106	C. Wks.
58241	3164	15D	58327	28107	84G
58242	3166	15C	58328	28115	C. Wks.
58244	3171	19C	58330	28128	84G
58245	3173	20B	58332	28141	C. Wks.
58246	3175	17A	58333	28152	84G
58247	3176	17C	58335	28166	11B
58248	3177	16A	58336	28172	C. Wks.
58249	3190	15C	58340	28205	11B
58252	3262	16A	58343	28227	C. Wks.
58254	3270	17D	58346	28239	11B
58257	3372	3A	58347	28245	C. Wks.
58258	3377	17B	58349	28247	11B
58259	3385	33A	58350	28251	11B
58260	3420	20C	58352	28256	11B
58261	3423	21A	58354	28263	11B
58262	3425	17B	58360	28312	11B
58264	3445	17C	58362	28318	12D
58265	3451	20C	58363	28333	8D
58267	3477	17B	58364	28335	7A
58268	3479	18A	58365	28337	7A
58269	3485	2A	58368	28345	3B
58271	3492	21A	58375	28408	7B

New No.	Old No.	
58376	28417	12A
58377	28428	9B
58378	28430	3B
58381	28450	7B
58382	28451	5D
58383	28457	8D
58388	28487	5A
58389	28492	12C
58392	28505	7D
58393	28507	8D
58394	28509	10E
58396	28512	12D
58398	28515	10A
58400	28525	5D
58409	28548	12C
58410	28549	10E
58412	28553	12C
58413	28555	8D
58415	28559	8D
58418	28580	12D
58419	28583	12A
58420	28585	7D
58421	28589	12D
58426	28611	9B
58427	28616	5D
58429	28619	5A
58430	28622	8D

Cl. "2F" 0-6-0T

New No.	Old No.	
58850	27505	17D
58851	27509	6C
58852	27510	1D
58853	27512	1D
58854	27513	6C
58855	27514	1D
58856	27515	17D
58857	27517	6C
58858	27520	1D
58859	27522	1D
58860	27527	17D
58861	27528	6C
58862	27530	17D
58863	27532	6C

Crane Engine 0-4-2ST

New No.	Old No.	
58865	27217	1D

Cl. "2F" 0-6-2T

New No.	Old No.	
58880	27553	86K
58881	27561	84G
58887	27596	8A
58888	27602	86K
58889	27603	7D
58891	27621	86K
58892	27625	87F
58895	27654	86K
58897	27674	4A
58899	7692	86K
58900	7699	10E
58902	7710	86K
58903	7711	7B
58904	7720	84G
58908	7737	4A
58910	7741	87K
58911	7746	8A
58912	7751	86K
58913	7752	86K
58915	7757	86K
58916	7759	86K
58919	7773	86K
58921	7782	8A
58924	7791	7D
58925	7794	86K
58926	7799	4A
58928	7803	3E
58932	7822	7D
58933	7829	86K
58935	7833	86K

Diesel Rail-cars (Leyland)

(Numbered in coach stock series)

29950	66C	
29951	66C	
29952	66C	

WITH SHED ALLOCATIONS

A4
4-6-2

60001*	52A
60002*	52A
60003*	34A
60004*	64B
60005*	52A
60006*	34A
60007*	34A
60008*	34A
60009*	64B
60010*	34A
60011*	64B
60012*	64B
60013*	34A
60014*	34A
60015*	35B
60016*	52A
60017*	34A
60018*	52A
60019*	52A
60020*	52A
60021*	34A
60022*	34A
60023*	52A
60024*	64B
60025*	34A
60026*	35B
60027*	64B
60028*	34A
60029*	34A
60030*	34A
60031*	64B
60032*	34A
60033*	34A
60034*	34A

A3
4-6-2

60035*	64B
60036*	50B
60037*	64B
60038*	52A
60039*	34A
60040*	52A
60041*	64B
60042*	52A
60043*	64B
60044*	37B

60045*	52A
60046*	37B
60047*	36A
60048*	38C
60049*	38C
60050*	34E
60051*	34E
60052*	38C
60053*	35B
60054*	38C
60055*	36A
60056*	37B
60057*	64B
60058*	36A
60059*	34A
60060*	52A
60061*	36A
60062*	37B
60063*	34A
60064*	36A
60065*	34A
60066*	36A
60067*	34A
60068*	12B
60069*	52B
60070*	51A
60071*	52A
60072*	52B
60073*	52B
60074*	50B
60075*	52A
60076*	51A
60077*	52B
60078*	52A
60079*	12B
60080*	52B
60081*	50B
60082*	52A
60083*	52B
60084*	50B
60085*	52B
60086*	50B
60087*	64B
60088*	52B
60089*	34A
60090*	64B
60091*	52B
60092*	52B
60093*	12B
60094*	64B
60095*	12B

60096*	64B
60097*	64B
60098*	64B
60099*	64B
60100*	64B
60101*	64B
60102*	38C
60103*	38C
60104*	38C
60105*	34A
60106*	35B
60107*	38C
60108*	34A
60109*	34A
60110*	34A
60111*	34E
60112*	37B

A1
4-6-2

60113*	35A
60114*	37B
60115*	52A
60116*	52B
60117*	37B
60118*	37B
60119*	37B
60120*	37B
60121*	50A
60122*	34A
60123*	37B
60124*	52A
60125*	37B
60126*	52B
60127*	52B
60128*	34A
60129*	52A
60130*	34A
60131*	34A
60132*	52A
60133*	37B
60134*	37B
60135*	52A
60136*	34A
60137*	52A
60138*	50A
60139*	34A
60140*	50A
60141*	37B
60142*	52A

60143*	52A
60144*	34A
60145*	52A
60146*	50A
60147*	52A
60148*	34A
60149*	34A
60150*	52A
60151*	64B
60152*	64B
60153*	50A
60154*	52A
60155*	52A
60156*	34A
60157*	34A
60158*	34A
60159*	64B
60160*	64B
60161*	64B
60162*	64B

A2
4-6-2

60500*	35A
60501*	50A
60502*	50A
60503*	50A
60504*	35A
60505*	35A
60506*	35A
60507*	64B
60508*	35A
60509*	64B
60510*	64B
60511*	52B
60512*	52B
60513*	35A
60514*	35A
60515*	52B
60516*	52B
60517*	52B
60518*	52A
60519*	64B
60520*	35A
60521*	52A
60522*	50A
60523*	35A
60524*	50A
60525*	61B
60526*	50A

60527*	62B	60838	62B	60900	34A	60962	50A
60528*	62B	60839	50A	60901	36A	60963	50A
60529*	64B	60840	62B	60902	36A	60964	52A
60530*	64B	60841	35A	60903	34A	60965	52A
60531*	61B	60842	35A	60904	50A	60966	35A
60532*	64B	60843	50A	60905	35A	60967	52A
60533*	35A	60844	62B	60906	35A	60968	50A
60534*	64B	60845	38E	60907	50A	60969	62B
60535*	64B	60846	36A	60908	35A	60970	61B
60536*	64B	60847*	50A	60909	34A	60971	62B
60537*	61B	60848	64A	60910	52B	60972	64B
60538*	52A	60849	36A	60911	35A	60973	61B
60539*	52B	60850	35A	60912	35A	60974	50A
		60851	61B	60913	35A	60975	50A
		60852	36A	60914	34A	60976	50A
W1		60853	38E	60915	34A	60977	50A
4-6-4		60854	35A	60916	35A	60978	50A
		60855	35A	60917	36A	60979	50A
60700	34A	60856	50A	60918	50A	60980	64A
		60857	36A	60919	61B	60981	50A
		60858	35A	60920	62B	60982	50A
V2		60859	35A	60921	36A	60983	34A
2-6-2		60860*	52B	60922	34A		
		60861	36A	60923	52A		
60800*	34A	60862	34A	60924	35A	**B1**	
60801	52B	60863	35A	60925	50A	**4-6-0**	
60802	52B	60864	50A	60926	52A		
60803	35A	60865	35A	60927	64B	61000*	30A
60804	52B	60866	35A	60928	36A	61001*	30A
60805	52B	60867	36A	60929	50A	61002*	64A
60806	52B	60868	52B	60930	36A	61003*	30F
60807	52B	60869	35A	60931	62B	61004*	30F
60808	52B	60870	36A	60932	52D	61005*	30F
60809*	52B	60871	35A	60933	50A	61006*	30F
60810	52B	60872*	36A	60934	50A	61007*	64B
60811	52B	60873*	34A	60935	36A	61008*	30A
60812	52B	60874	35A	60936	35A	61009*	30A
60813	34A	60875	36A	60937	62B	61010*	53B
60814	34A	60876	35A	60938	35A	61011*	52A
60815	38E	60877	36A	60939	52B	61012*	52A
60816	64A	60878	35A	60940	52A	61013*	52A
60817	38E	60879	35A	60941	50A	61014*	52A
60818	38E	60880	36A	60942	52B	61015*	50A
60819	61B	60881	36A	60943	36A	61016*	50A
60820	38E	60882	64B	60944	52B	61017*	51E
60821	34A	60883	52A	60945	52B	61018*	51E
60822	61B	60884	52A	60946	50A	61019*	52D
60823	34A	60885	52A	60947	52B	61020*	50A
60824	61B	60886	52B	60948	36A	61021*	51A
60825	64A	60887	52B	60949	52B	61022*	51A
60826	38E	60888	61B	60950	35A	61023*	51A
60827	61B	60889	36A	60951	64B	61024*	52D
60828	35A	60890	36A	60952	52B	61025*	52D
60829	35A	60891	52B	60953	64A	61026*	36A
60830	38E	60892	34A	60954	50A	61027*	35A
60831	38E	60893	35A	60955	61B	61028*	34E
60832	38E	60894	64A	60956	36A	61029*	37A
60833	52B	60895	52B	60957	52B	61030*	51E
60834	64B	60896	36A	60958	62B	61031*	37A
60835*	52B	60897	35A	60959	64B	61032*	51E
60836	64A	60898	61B	60960	50A	61033*	37A
60837	50A	60899	35A	60961	50A	61034*	51E

61035*	50B	61098	30A	61160	39A	61222	12B
61036*	36A	61099	34D	61161	39A	61223	39A
61037*	51E	61100	52A	61162	39A	61224	51A
61038*	50A	61101	52B	61163	34E	61225	39A
61039*	51A	61102	62B	61164	34E	61226	30F
61040*	32A	61103	62A	61165	36B	61227	30A
61041	32A	61104	30A	61166	36B	61228	39A
61042	32A	61105	34D	61167	36B	61229	37C
61043	32A	61106	38C	61168	36B	61230	37C
61044	32A	61107	36A	61169	39B	61231	36E
61045	32A	61108	38C	61170	36A	61232	30F
61046	32A	61109	30A	61171	30A	61233	30A
61047	32A	61110	38A	61172	65A	61234	30A
61048	32A	61111	38A	61173	51A	61235	30A
61049	32A	61112	40A	61174	36B	61236	30A
61050	32A	61113	34A	61175	30A	61237*	50B
61051	32A	61114	39A	61176	51A	61238*	52A
61052	32A	61115	50A	61177	30A	61239	50A
61053	32B	61116	65A	61178	64B	61240*	50B
61054	32B	61117	65A	61179	39B	61241*	52D
61055	32B	61118	62A	61180	65A	61242*	64A
61056	32B	61119	30A	61181	39B	61243*	65A
61058	32B	61120	36A	61182	39A	61244*	64B
61059	32B	61121	31A	61183	39B	61245*	64B
61060	53A	61122	38A	61184	39A	61246*	36A
61061	64A	61123	38A	61185	38C	61247*	36A
61062	50B	61124	36A	61186	38C	61248*	36A
61063	36A	61125	36A	61187	38C	61249*	36A
61064	65A	61126	36A	61188	38C	61250*	36A
61065	50B	61127	36A	61189*	51E	61251*	34A
61066	38B	61128	36A	61190	40B	61252	32B
61067	64A	61129	34A	61191	40B	61253	32B
61068	53A	61130	30A	61192	30A	61254	32B
61069	50B	61131	38A	61193	36A	61255	51A
61070	35A	61132	61B	61194	36B	61256	50B
61071	50A	61133	61B	61195	40B	61257	50B
61072	62A	61134	61A	61196	36A	61258	50B
61073	35A	61135	30F	61197	65A	61259	50B
61074	53A	61136	34A	61198	51A	61260	65A
61075	35A	61137	34A	61199	52D	61261	65A
61076	64B	61138	34A	61200	34A	61262	62A
61077	34E	61139	34A	61201	32B	61263	62B
61078	38A	61140	34E	61202	40B	61264	30F
61079	40B	61141	38C	61203	34A	61265	36A
61080	53A	61142	40B	61204	40B	61266	34A
61081	64B	61143	35A	61205	30A	61267	37C
61082	40B	61144	30A	61206	35A	61268	37C
61083	34E	61145	39B	61207	35A	61269	40A
61084	50A	61146	62A	61208	36E	61270	32A
61085	37A	61147	62B	61209	38B	61271	32A
61086	36A	61148	62A	61210	35A	61272	32A
61087	36A	61149	30F	61211	36E	61273	51A
61088	38C	61150	39B	61212	36E	61274	51A
61089	30A	61151	39B	61213	36E	61275	51A
61090	34D	61152	39B	61214	51E	61276	51A
61091	34D	61153	39B	61215*	53B	61277	64A
61092	38C	61154	39B	61216	50B	61278	62B
61093	34D	61155	39A	61217	12B	61279	40A
61094	34D	61156	39A	61218	50B	61280	40A
61095	34D	61157	39A	61219	12B	61281	40A
61096	37A	61158	39A	61220	51E	61282	30A
61097	34D	61159	39A	61221*	64B	61283	38A

61284	40B	61346	61C	61408	40B	
61285	31A	61347	61C	61409	40B	
61286	31A	61348	61A			
61287	31A	61349	61A			
61288	31A	61350	61A	**B16**		
61289	51A	61351	61A	**4–6–0**		
61290	51E	61352	61A			
61291	51A	61353	61C	61410	50B	
61292	62B	61354	64A	61411	50B	
61293	62B	61355	64A	61412	50B	
61294	37C	61356	64A	61413	50B	
61295	37B	61357	64A	61414	50B	
61296	37C	61358	64A	61415	50B	
61297	37A	61359	64A	61416	50A	
61298	38C	61360	30A	61417	50A	
61299	38C	61361	30A	61418	50A	
61300	31A	61362	30A	61419	50A	
61301	31A	61363	30A	61420	50A	
61302	31A	61364	40A	61421	50A	
61303	51E	61365	40B	61422	50A	
61304	53B	61366	40B	61423	50A	
61305	53B	61367	38A	61424	50A	
61306	53B	61368	38A	61425	50B	
61307	61A	61369	38A	61426	50A	
61308	61C	61370		61427	50B	
61309	37A	61371		61428	50B	
61310	37A	61372		61429	50B	
61311	39B	61373		61430	50B	
61312	39B	61374		61431	50B	
61313	39B	61375		61432	50B	
61314	39B	61376		61433	50B	
61315	39B	61377		61434	50A	
61316	39B	61378		61435	50A	
61317	39B	61379		61436	50A	
61318	40B	61380		61437	50A	
61319	54C	61381		61438	50A	
61320	54C	61382		61439	50A	
61321	54C	61383		61440	50B	
61322	52D	61384	To	61441	50A	
61323	61A	61385	be	61442	50B	
61324	61A	61386	built	61443	50A	
61325	40B	61387		61444	50A	
61326	26A	61388		61445	50B	
61327	39B	61389		61446	50B	
61328	40B	61390		61447	50B	
61329	40A	61391		61448	50A	
61330	35A	61392		61449	50A	
61331	35A	61393		61450	50A	
61332	32A	61394		61451	50A	
61333	31A	61395		61452	50A	
61334	31A	61396		61453	50A	
61335	30A	61397		61454	50A	
61336	30A	61398		61455	50A	
61337	50A	61399		61456	50A	
61338	50B	61400	61A	61457	50A	
61339	50B	61401	61A	61458	50A	
61340	65A	61402	62B	61459	50A	
61341	64A	61403	62B	61460	50A	
61342	65A	61404	61A	61461	50A	
61343	61A	61405	40A	61462	50A	
61344	65A	61406	40B	61463	50A	
61345	61A	61407	40B	61464	50A	

61465	50A
61466	50A
61467	50A
61468	50A
61469	50B
61470	50B
61471	50B
61472	50A
61473	50A
61474	50A
61475	50A
61476	50A
61477	50A
61478	50B

B4
4–6–0

61482*	37A

B12
4–6–0

61501	61C
61502	61C
61503	61C
61505	61A
61507	61A
61508	61A
61511	61A
61512	30E
61513	61A
61514	30A
61515	30A
61516	30A
61519	30A
61520	32F
61521	61A
61523	30E
61524	61A
61525	30A
61526	61A
61528	61A
61530	32F
61532	61A
61533	31D
61535	32B
61537	31D
61538	35B
61539	61A
61540	31D
61541	35B
61542	30A
61543	61A
61545	32F
61546	30A
61547	31D
61549	30A
61550	30A

61552	61A		
61553	35B		
61554	35B		
61555	30E		
61556	30E		
61557	30E		
61558	30E		
61559	30A		
61560	61A		
61561	32B		
61562	32B		
61563	61A		
61564	32B		
61565	35B		
61566	32B		
61567	30A		
61568	30A		
61569	32B		
61570	32B		
61571	30A		
61572	30A		
61573	30A		
61574	30A		
61575	30A		
61576	30A		
61577	32B		
61578	30A		
61579	30A		
61580	30A		

B2 & B17
4-6-0

61600	32B
61601*	32B
61602*	30A
61603*	30E
61604*	32B
61605*	30A
61606*	30A
61607*	30E
61608*	30A
61609*	32A
61610*	30A
61611*	30A
61612*	30A
61613*	30A
61614*	30E
61615*	30E
61616*	30E
61617*	31A
61618*	32B
61619*	31A
61620*	31A
61621*	31A
61622*	31A
61623*	31A
61624*	31A
61625*	31A
61626*	31B

61627*	31A
61628*	31A
61629*	32A
61630*	31B
61631*	31A
61632*	30E
61633*	31A
61634*	32B
61635*	31A
61636*	31A
61637*	31A
61638*	31A
61639*	30E
61640*	31A
61641*	31B
61642*	31A
61643*	31A
61644*	30E
61645*	32B
61646*	31B
61647*	32B
61648*	30A
61649*	32B
61650*	38E
61651*	38E
61652*	38A
61653*	38A
61654*	30A
61655*	30A
61656*	31B
61657*	38A
61658*	30A
61659*	32A
61660*	31B
61661*	32D
61662*	38A
61663*	31A
61664*	38E
61665*	32D
61666*	31B
61667*	38E
61668*	32B
61669*	32B
61670*	32A
61671*	31A
61672*	31B

B13
4-6-0

61699S Rugby Plant

V4
2-6-2

61700*	65A
61701	65A

K2
2-6-0

61720	40B
61721	30A
61722	40B
61723	38A
61724	40B
61725	40F
61726	38A
61727	40B
61728	40B
61729	35A
61730	35A
61731	40F
61732	38A
61733	40B
61734	30A
61735	35A
61736	35A
61737	30A
61738	31D
61739	35A
61740	35A
61741	38A
61742	31D
61743	31D
61744	40F
61745	30A
61746	30A
61747	35A
61748	31D
61749	38A
61750	40F
61751	38A
61752	30A
61753	30A
61754	30A
61755	40F
61756	40F
61757	31D
61758	38A
61759	30A
61760	40F
61761	30A
61762	40F
61763	38A
61764*	65A
61765	30A
61766	31D
61767	30A
61768	38A
61769	38A
61770	40F
61771	30A
61772*	65C
61773	38A
61774*	65A
61775*	65A
61776	65A
61777	30A
61778	30A

61779	65A
61780	30A
61781*	65A
61782*	63D
61783*	63D
61784	65A
61785	65A
61786	65A
61787*	63D
61788*	63D
61789*	63D
61790*	63D
61791*	63D
61792	65A
61793	65A
61794*	65A

K3 & K1
2-6-0

61800	40B
61801	40B
61802	40B
61803	40B
61804	35A
61805	30A
61806	40B
61807	40A
61808	39A
61809	39A
61810	30A
61811	35A
61812	38A
61813	53A
61814	53A
61815	30A
61816	38A
61817	30A
61818	52B
61819	53A
61820	38A
61821	38A
61822	40A
61823	64B
61824	38A
61825	40B
61826	38A
61827	40B
61828	39A
61829	39A
61830	30A
61831	30A
61832	39A
61833	38A
61834	30A
61835	30A
61836	40B
61837	40B
61838	40B
61839	39A
61840	30A

61841	35A	61903	53A	61965	53A	62009	51A
61842	40B	61904	52B	61966	40A	62010	52B
61843	35A	61905	40B	61967	35A	62011	31B
61844	31B	61906	52B	61968	64A	62012	31B
61845	40B	61907	36A	61969	52B	62013	31B
61846	31B	61908	39A	61970	32A	62014	31B
61847	31B	61909	64A	61971	32A	62015	31B
61848	39A	61910	39A	61972	35A	62016	31B
61849	30A	61911	64A	61973	32C	62017	31B
61850	35A	61912	40B	61974	38B	62018	31B
61851	12B	61913	39A	61975	38B	62019	31B
61852	39A	61914	39A	61976	38B	62020	31B
61853	35A	61915	35A	61977	38B	62021	52C
61854	12B	61916	64A	61978	36A	62022	52C
61855	64A	61917	52B	61979	38B	62023	52C
61856	39A	61918	36A	61980	38B	62024	52C
61857	64A	61919	39A	61981	32A	62025	52C
61858	12B	61920	53A	61982	40A	62026	52C
61859	40A	61921	32A	61983	64A-	62027	52C
61860	31B	61922	53A	61984	52B	62028	52C
61861	36A	61923	53A	61985	52B	62029	52C
61862	35A	61924	64A	61986	52B	62030	52C
61863	35A	61925	40A	61987	52B	62031	31B
61864	31B	61926	32C	61988	64A	62032	31B
61865	39A	61927	53A	61989	32A	62033	31B
61866	31B	61928	64A	61990	64A	62034	31B
61867	35A	61929	35A	61991	64A	62035	31B
61868	35A	61930	52B	61992	64A	62036	31B
61869	31B	61931	64A			62037	31B
61870	39A	61932	53A			62038	31B
61871	53A	61933	64A	**K4 & K1**		62039	31B
61872	53A	61934	53A	**2–6–0**		62040	31B
61873	31B	61935	53A			62041	51E
61874	53A	61936	12B	61993*	65A	62042	51E
61875	52B	61937	12B	61994*	65A	62043	51E
61876	64A	61938	31B	61995*	63D	62044	51A
61877	39A	61939	32A	61996*	63D	62045	51A
61878	64A	61940	31B	61997*	65A	62046	51A
61879	64A	61941	53A	61998*	65A	62047	51A
61880	30A	61942	32A			62048	51A
61881	64A	61943	38B			62049	51A
61882	12B	61944	40A			62050	51A
61883	53A	61945	53A	**D3**		62051	31B
61884	52B	61946	31B	**4–4–0**		62052	31B
61885	64A	61947	32A			62053	31B
61886	31B	61948	31B	62000	35B	62054	31B
61887	31B	61949	32C			62055	51A
61888	31B	61950	39A			62056	51A
61889	31B	61951	35A			62057	51A
61890	35A	61952	52B	**K1**		62058	51A
61891	40B	61953	32A	**2–6–0**		62059	51A
61892	53A	61954	35A			62060	51E
61893	31B	61955	64A			62061	51A
61894	40A	61956	39A	62001	51E	62062	51A
61895	31B	61957	32A	62002	52B	62063	51E
61896	39A	61958	32C	62003	52B	62064	51E
61897	64A	61959	32C	62004	51A	62065	51E
61898	12B	61960	40A	62005	52B	62066	31B
61899	53A	61961	31B	62006	51A	62067	31B
61900	64A	61962	52B	62007	52B	62068	31B
61901	52B	61963	40B	62008	51A	62069	31B
61902	53A	61964	40A			62070	31B

D3
4-4-0

62132	40C
62148	38A

D2
4-4-0

62154	40F
62172	38A
62181	40F

DI
4-4-0

62209	63B

D41
4-4-0

62225	61A
62227	61C
62228	61A
62229	61A
62230	61A
62231	61A
62232	61A
62241	61C
62242	61C
62243	61C
62246	61C
62247	61C
62248	61C
62249	61C
62251	61C
62252	61C
62255	61C
62256	61C

D40
4-4-0

62260	61A
62261	61A
62262	61C
62264	61C
62265	61A
62267	61C
62268	61A
62269	61A
62270	61A
62271	61C
62272	61A
62273*	61A
62274*	61A
62275*	61A

62276*	61A
62277*	61A
62278*	61A
62279*	61A

D31
4-4-0

62281	12B
62283	64F

D20
4-4-0

62340	50C
62341	50C
62342	50D
62343	50D
62344	52D
62345	53B
62347	51J
62348	50C
62349	52D (A)
62351	52D (A)
62352	52D (A)
62353	53D
62354	52D (A)
62355	53D
62357	52D (A)
62358	52D (A)
62359	51J
62360	52D (A)
62361	50C
62362	52D (A)
62363	50C
62365	53D
62366	50C
62369	50A
62370	50D
62371	52D (A)
62372	51C
62373	50D
62374	50C
62375	53D
62376	50C
62378	50C
62379	51C
62380	52D (A)
62381	50C
62382	50C
62383	53B
62384	50D
62386	50C
62387	52D (A)
62388	51J
62389	50D
62391	51J
62392	50D
62395	50C
62396	53B
62397	50D

D29
4-4-0

62405*	64B
62410*	62A
62411*	62A

D30
4-4-0

62417*	64G
62418*	62A
62419*	62A
62420*	64G
62421*	62A
62422*	64G
62423*	62A
62424*	64A
62425*	62A
62426*	63B
62427*	62B
62428*	64G
62429*	62A
62430*	62A
62431*	62A
62432*	64A
62434*	62B
62435*	64A
62436*	62B
62437*	64B
62438*	62B
62439*	64F
62440*	64G
62441*	62C
62442*	62A

D32
4-4-0

62451	64A

D33
4-4-0

62457	62B
62459	62C
62460	65A
62461	63B
62462	65A
62464	62C
62466	62B

D34
4-4-0

62467*	62A
62468*	62A
62469*	65A

62470*	65A
62471*	64A
62472*	65A
62474*	65A
62475*	52A
62477*	65A
62478*	62A
62479*	65A
62480*	65A
62482*	65A
62483*	64A
62484*	64A
62485*	62B
62487*	64A
62488*	64A
62489*	65A
62490*	64A
62492*	62A
62493*	65A
62494*	64A
62495*	64F
62496*	65A
62497*	65A
62498*	65A

D15 & D16
4-4-0

62501	31C
62502	31C
62503	31E
62505	31C
62506	31C
62507	31C
62508	31E
62509	32G
62510	32A
62511	32D
62513	31C
62514	31C
62515	32G
62516	31A
62517	32D
62518	31C
62519	32G
62520	32G
62521	32D
62522	32A
62523	32G
62524	32D
62525	31A
62526	32B
62527	31A
62528	32G
62529	31B
62530	31A
62531	31A
62532	9E
62533	32G
62534	31D
62535	9E

62536	9E	62608	30E	62689*	65A	62751*	50E
62538	32G	62609	9E	62690*	64B	62752*	50D
62539	31B	62610	32A	62691*	64B	62753*	50D
62540	32A	62611	32D	62692*	64B	62754*	53B
62541	32A	62612	32A	62693*	64B	62755*	50D
62542	31B	62613	32D	62694*	64B	62756*	50B
62543	31D	62614	31C			62757*	53B
62544	32D	62615	31E			62758*	50D
62545	32A	62616	32A	**D49**		62759*	50A
62546*	32D	62617	32A	**4-4-0**		62760*	50A
62547	31B	62618	31A			62761*	50A
62548	31B	62619	32A	62700*	53B	62762*	50D
62549	31A	62620	32G	62701*	53D	62763*	50D
62551	31A			62702*	64A	62764*	50E
62552	32A			62703*	53B	62765*	50D
62553	32A			62704*	62A	62766*	53D
62554	32A	**D10**		62705*	64B	62767*	53B
62555	32A	**4-4-0**		62706*	64B	62768*	50D
62556	32A			62707*	53D	62769*	50E
62557	31D	62650*	9G	62708*	62A	62770*	50E
62558	31D	62651*	9E	62709*	64B	62771*	52C
62559	31C	62652*	9G	62710*	53B	62772*	50D
62561	32F	62653*	9E	62711*	64A	62773*	50D
62562	32G	62654*	9E	62712*	64A	62774*	**50F (P)**
62564	32F	62655*	9E	62713*	62B	62775*	50B
62565	30A	62656*	9E	62714*	63A		
62566	31E	62657*	9E	62715*	64A		
62567	31A	62658*	9E	62716*	62A	**E4**	
62568	9E	62659*	9E	62717*	62A	**2-4-0**	
62569	31C			62718*	62B		
62570	32A			62719*	64B	62780	32A
62571	31A			62720*	53B	62781	31A
62572	30E	**D11**		62721*	64A	62782	32A
62573	31D	**4-4-0**		62722*	53B	62783	31A
62574	31A			62723*	53B	62784	31A
62575	31A	62660*	40B	62724*	53B	62785	31A
62576	32D	62661*	40B	62725*	63A	62786	31E
62577	32A	62662*	40B	62726*	50A	62787	32A
62578	32G	62663*	9F	62727*	50A	62788	31A
62579	31B	62664*	40B	62728*	62B	62789	32A
62580	32D	62665*	9F	62729*	62A	62790	31A
62581	32A	62666*	40B	62730*	12B	62791	30A
62582	31C	62667*	40B	62731*	12B	62792	32A
62584	32A	62668*	40B	62732*	12B	62793	32A
62585	32A	62669*	40B	62733*	64B	62794	31A
62586	32D	62670*	9E	62734*	12B	62795	31E
62587	9E	62671*	65A	62735*	12B	62796	32A
62588	9E	62672*	65A	62736*	50A	62797	32A
62589	31B	62673*	65A	62737*	53B		
62590	32B	62674*	65A	62738*	50D		
62592	32F	62675*	65A	62739*	50B	**C1**	
62593	32A	62676*	65A	62740*	50A	**4-4-2**	
62596	32F	62677*	64B	62741*	53B		
62597	32D	62678*	64B	62742*	50A	62822	35B
62598	30E	62679*	64B	62743*	53B		
62599	9E	62680*	65A	62744*	50A		
62601	31C	62681*	65A	62745*	50A	**C4**	
62603	31B	62682*	65A	62746*	50B	**4-4-2**	
62604	32D	62683*	64B	62747*	52C		
62605	31B	62684*	64B	62748*	50B	62900	40F
62606	32A	62685*	64B	62749*	50D	62901	40F
62607	31E	62686*	64B	62750*	53D	62908	40A
		62687*	65A				
		62688*	65A				

62909	40B	63346	54D	63408	50C	63465	54B
62918	40A	63347	51B	63409	51D	63466	54B
62919	40B	63348	50C	63410	51C	63467	54B

Q4
0-8-0

63201	36D	63349	51D	63411	51D	63468	54B
63202	37A	63350	54C	63412	52C	63469	54B
63203	36D	63351	51D	63413	51C	63470	54B
63204	37A	63352	54B	63414	51C	63471	54B
63205	37A	63353	54C	63415	51C	63472	54B
63217	37A	63354	54C	63416	51G	63473	54B
63220	36D	63355	51C	63417	51D	63474	54B
63221	37A	63356	52C	63418	54D		
63223	37A	63357	54D	63419	51C		
63225	37A	63358	54C	63420	51D		
63226	37A	63359	54D	63421	51C		
63227	37A	63360	51B	63422	51G		

O3
2-8-0

63229	36D	63361	54D	63423	51G	63475	36E
63234	37A	63362	50B	63424	51C	63476	36A
63235	36D	63363	54C	63425	51G	63477	36A
63236	37A	63364	51D	63426	51B	63478	36A
63240	37A	63365	54C	63427	51C	63479	36A
63243	37A	63366	54C	63428	52C	63480	36A
		63367	51G	63429	50C	63481	36A
		63368	51D	63430	51B	63482	36E
		63369	51D	63431	50C	63483	36A
		63370	51B	63432	52C	63484	36A

Q5
0-8-0

63251	54C	63371·	51B	63433	54D	63485	36A
63257	54C	63372	54D	63434	54D	63486	36A
63259	54C	63373	51D	63435	51C	63488	36A
63261	54C	63374	51G	63436	50C	63491	36A
63267	54C	63375	51D	63437	54B	63493	36A
63270	50A (N)	63376	52C	63438	51C		
63271	54C	63377	52C	63439	54D		
63274	51B	63378	50C	63440	50C		
63280	50C	63379	54B	63441	51C		
63282	51D	63380	51D	63442	51D		
63283	51D	63381	51G	63443	51G		

O1 & O4
2-8-0

63284	54C	63382	50C	63444	52C	63570	40D
63285	50C	63383	51C	63445	51B	63571	38B
63287	54C	63384	54C	63446	51G	63572	36C
63303	54C	63385	52C	63447	51B	63573	38A
63311	51G	63386	54C	63448	50C	63574	39B
63314	51G	63387	50C	63449	50C	63575	39A
63319	50C	63388	51B	63450	50B	63576	36C
63326	54C	63389	51B	63451	50C	63577	40E
63328	51D	63390	52C	63452	51C	63578	38B
63333	51D	63391	52C	63453	51G	63579	38B
63336	50C	63392	51C	63454	51C	63580	38B
		63393	51D	63455	54D	63581	39B
		63394	52C	63456	50C	63582	39A
		63395	50C	63457	51C	63583	39B
		63396	51C	63458	54C	63584	36C
		63397	51C	63459	51D	63585	40E
		63398	52C			63586	40B
		63399	52C			63587	38B
		63400	51C			63588	40D

Q6
0-8-0

				Q7			
		63401	51C	**0-8-0**		63589	38B
		63402	54C			63590	39A
63340	51G	63403	52C	63460	54B	63591	39A
63341	51B	63404	54D	63461	54B	63592	39A
63342	54C	63405	51G	63462	54B	63593	40B
63343	51B	63406	50C	63463	54B	63594	38B
63344	51B	63407	51G	63464	54B	63595	36C
63345	51B					63596	38B

63597	40E	63659	36C	63721	38B	63783	39B
63598	39A	63660	36C	63722	38B	63784	39A
63599	38A	63661	39B	63723	38B	63785	36E
63600	39A	63662	38B	63724	40E	63786	39A
63601	36C	63663	39A	63725	39A	63787	38A
63602	36C	63664	53A	63726	36C	63788	36C
63603	53A	63665	40E	63727	36D	63789	39A
63604	39B	63666	40E	63728	36C	63790	39B
63605	39B	63667	53E	63729	38A	63791	36B
63606	36C	63668	36B	63730	31B	63792	38B
63607	40B	63669	36C	63731	36C	63793	36C
63608	36E	63670	39A	63732	53A	63794	39A
63609	39B	63671	36C	63733	39B	63795	38B
63610	38B	63672	36B	63734	39B	63796	39A
63611	36B	63673	53A	63735	38A	63797	39B
63612	36B	63674	38B	63736	36E	63798	38B
63613	38D	63675	39B	63737	39B	63799	38B
63614	38B	63676	53A	63738	40B	63800	40E
63615	40E	63677	40E	63739	38B	63801	38A
63616	39A	63678	39A	63740	53A	63802	40B
63617	36C	63679	40E	63741	40E	63803	38B
63618	38B	63680	39B	63742	38B	63804	38A
63619	39A	63681	38B	63743	38B	63805	39A
63620	53E	63682	36B	63744	36C	63806	38B
63621	40B	63683	40E	63745	36C	63807	40E
63622	39B	63684	36C	63746	38B	63808	38B
63623	36D	63685	39B	63747	36C	63809	40E
63624	40B	63686	39A	63748	38B	63812	53A
63625	40E	63687	38B	63749	38D	63813	36B
63626	36C	63688	36E	63750	40E	63816	53A
63627	36B	63689	38B	63751	53E	63817	39A
63628	53A	63690	36C	63752	38B	63818	36C
63629	39B	63691	40D	63753	53A	63819	40B
63630	39A	63692	40B	63754	53A	63821	39B
63631	39A	63693	40B	63755	53A	63822	39B
63632	40E	63694	38D	63756	38A	63823	53A
63633	39A	63695	39A	63757	40E	63824	36C
63634	40D	63696	36C	63758	40E	63827	38B
63635	38B	63697	36D	63759	40E	63828	53A
63636	38A	63698	40B	63760	53A	63832	36C
63637	36E	63699	38B	63761	38A	63835	53A
63638	39A	63700	38B	63762	38A	63836	40B
63639	38B	63701	31B	63763	36E	63837	40E
63640	36C	63702	38D	63764	53A	63838	38B
63641	39A	63703	40E	63765	40E	63839	39A
63642	36C	63704	31B	63766	39B	63840	40E
63643	36C	63705	39A	63767	38B	63841	38B
63644	40E	63706	38B	63768	39A	63842	40E
63645	36C	63707	40E	63769	53A	63843	53E
63646	38B	63708	39A	63770	53A	63845	53A
63647	40B	63709	40E	63771	39B	63846	39B
63648	40E	63710	39B	63772	53A	63847	36C
63649	36C	63711	39A	63773	39A	63848	39A
63650	39A	63712	53A	63774	36B	63849	53E
63651	40B	63713	39A	63775	36B	63850	39B
63652	39A	63714	39B	63776	40E	63851	38A
63653	36C	63715	40E	63777	39A	63852	40D
63654	36E	63716	38B	63778	36C	63853	38B
63655	36C	63717	40E	63779	36B	63854	39A
63656	40E	63718	36C	63780	39A	63855	53A
63657	40B	63719	39A	63781	38A		
63658	40E	63720	38D	63782	36E		

No.	Code		No.	Code		No.	Code		No.	Code
63856	53A		63926	36A		**J3 & J4**			64193	36A
63857	53A		63927	36B		**0–6–0**			64194	38A
63858	38B		63928	36A					64195	38A
63859	38D		63929	35B		64105	34D		64196	40F
63860	39B		63930	35B		64112	35A		64197	38A
63861	40D		63931	35B		64114	34D		64198	40F
63862	39A		63932	35B		64115	40F		64199	38A
63863	38B		63933	35A		64116	37A		64200	38A
63864	39A		63934	36C		64117	34D		64201	40F
63865	39A		63935	35A		64118	35A		64202	38A
63867	38B		63936	35B		64119	37A		64203	37C
63868	38B		63937	36C		64120	35A		64204	40F
63869	38B		63938	35B		64121	35A		64205	37C
63870	40E		63939	36C		64122	34D		64206	35B
63872	39A		63940	35B		64123	35A		64207	35A
63873	38B		63941	36A		64124	36A		64208	37A
63874	53A		63942	36A		64125	36E		64209	36A
63876	39A		63943	36A		64128	35A		64210	40F
63877	36E		63944	36C		64129	37A		64211	35A
63878	40B		63945	36A		64131	35A		64212	38A
63879	38B		63946	36A		64132	40F		64213	38A
63880	39A		63947	36A		64133	36E		64214	37A
63881	53A		63948	35A		64135	35A		64215	38A
63882	39B		63949	35B		64137	40F		64216	35A
63883	36D		63950	35B		64140	34D		64217	35A
63884	40E		63951	36A		64141	36E		64218	36A
63885	40D		63952	36A		64142	37A		64219	36A
63886	39A		63953	36A		64148	36E		64220	35A
63887	39A		63954	36A		64150	36E		64221	35A
63888	39B		63955	36A		64151	35A		64222	38A
63889	39B		63956	36A		64153	34D		64223	38A
63890	39A		63957	36A		64158	35A		64224	38A
63891	39A		63958	36A		64160	35A		64225	35A
63893	38B		63959	36A		64162	35A		64226	37C
63894	38A		63960	35B					64227	35B
63895	39A		63961	36A					64228	35A
63897	31B		63962	36A					64229	40F
63898	36B		63963	36C		**J6**			64230	38A
63899	39A		63964	36A		**0–6–0**			64231	38A
63900	40E		63965	35B					64232	36A
63901	38B		63966	35B		64170	37C		64233	38A
63902	40E		63967	36A		64171	35A		64234	34B
63904	36D		63968	36A		64172	35B		64235	35A
63905	36E		63969	36B		64173	37B		64236	36A
63906	36C		63970	36B		64174	37A		64237	35B
63907	36E		63971	36B		64175	34D		64238	35A
63908	36E		63972	36B		64176	35A		64239	34B
63911	36C		63973	36A		64177	35A		64240	34D
63912	38B		63974	36A		64178	35B		64241	36E
63913	36D		63975	36B		64179	36A		64242	40F
63914	36E		63976	36B		64180	40F		64243	36A
63915	39A		63977	36B		64181	40F		64244	40F
63917	36C		63978	36B		64182	37A		64245	35A
63920	36C		63979	36B		64183	36A		64246	35A
			63980	36B		64184	35A		64247	40F
O2			63981	36B		64185	36A		64248	40F
2–8–0			63982	36B		64186	35A		64249	35A
			63983	36B		64187	35A		64250	37B
63922	36C		63984	36B		64188	34B		64251	34B
63923	35A		63985	36B		64189	35A		64252	35A
63924	36B		63986	36A		64190	40F		64253	38A
63925	36A		63987	36A		64191	35A		64254	35A
						64192	35A			

64255	36A	64312	40B	64374	36B	64436	36D
64256	34B	64313	34E	64375	39A	64437	39A
64257	35A	64314	40B	64376	8E	64438	38E
64258	36A	64315	40A	64377	36B	64439	40D
64259	36A	64316	39A	64378	40E	64440	39A
64260	37B	64317	38D	64379	40E	64441	39B
64261	36A	64318	38B	64380	36E	64442	36B
64262	36A	64319	36B	64381	6E	64443	39B
64263	36A	64320	40C	64382	39A	64444	38D
64264	36A	64321	40E	64383	39A	64445	39B
64265	35A	64322	38D	64384	38D	64446	40B
64266	35A	64323	40B	64385	36E	64447	39B
64267	37A	64324	38E	64386	38D	64448	36D
64268	37C	64325	40B	64387	39B	64449	36B
64269	38A	64326	39A	64388	38E	64450	39A
64270	36A	64327	38E	64389	40E	64451	36E
64271	37C	64328	40C	64390	38E	64452	36D
64272	37A	64329	34E	64391	36D	64453	9G
64273	35A	64330	38E	64392	40D		
64274	37C	64331	38D	64393	36E		
64275	37C	64332	39A	64394	34E	**J35**	
64276	40F	64333	39A	64395	36C	**0-6-0**	
64277	37A	64334	36B	64396	38D		
64278	35A	64335	36E	64397	27E	64460	65E
64279	36A	64336	39B	64398	36D	64461	63B
		64337	40D	64399	36D	64462	64A
		64338	6E	64400	36B	64463	64G
		64339	36C	64401	39A	64464	62A
J11		64340	36E	64402	36E	64466	62A
0-6-0		64341	36E	64403	36B	64468	64F
		64342	39A	64404	36B	64470	65E
64280	36E	64343	36E	64405	8E	64471	63B
64281	40E	64344	40D	64406	8E	64472	65E
64282	36E	64345	38D	64407	36C	64473	65E
64283	36B	64346	39A	64408	38E	64474	62A
64284	40B	64347	36E	64409	39A	64475	62C
64285	36A	64348	36E	64410	36A	64476	62A
64286	40D	64349	36A	64411	40B	64477	62A
64287	36E	64350	40A	64412	39B	64478	12B
64288	36B	64351	40A	64413	36E	64479	64A
64289	40E	64352	36B	64414	40E	64480	62C
64290	36D	64353	40D	64415	39A	64482	62B
64291	39B	64354	38B	64416	36E	64483	62C
64292	38B	64355	40B	64417	8E	64484	64A
64293	40D	64356	36B	64418	40E	64485	62B
64294	39A	64357	39A	64419	39B	64486	64A
64295	36E	64358	40E	64420	8E	64487	62C
64296	36B	64359	40A	64421	36E	64488	62A
64297	40E	64360	39B	64422	36E	64489	64A
64298	39A	64361	38B	64423	36E	64490	64E
64299	40D	64362	36A	64424	40D	64491	64F
64300	38B	64363	39A	64425	40D	64492	64A
64301	38A	64364	38E	64426	40E	64493	62C
64302	36B	64365	40A	64427	40E	64494	64G
64303	40A	64366	36D	64428	38D	64495	62A
64304	8E	64367	9G	64429	36C	64496	62C
64305	40B	64368	39A	64430	40A	64497	63B
64306	36E	64369	38E	64431	38B	64498	65E
64307	40B	64370	38B	64432	36B	64499	12B
64308	36C	64371	40A	64433	38D	64500	62A
64309	36C	64372	40B	64434	38D	64501	63B
64310	40E	64373	39B	64435	39A	64502	64E
64311	39A						

64504	64F
64505	62C
64506	64A
64507	65E
64509	64G
64510	64F
64511	12B
64512	64A
64513	62C
64514	62A
64515	64A
64516	62A
64517	64A
64518	64A
64519	64A
64520	63B
64521	62A
64522	62A
64523	64A
64524	64A
64525	62C
64526	12B
64527	64A
64528	64E
64529	64F
64530	62B
64531	65E
64532	64A
64533	64A
64534	65E
64535	64A

J37
0–6–0

64536	64C
64537	64E
64538	64A
64539	64G
64540	65A
64541	65A
64542	63B
64543	64A
64544	63B
64545	62C
64546	62A
64547	64A
64548	65C
64549	62A
64550	62A
64551	64E
64552	64A
64553	64E
64554	62C
64555	64A
64556	62C
64557	64A
64558	65A
64559	65C
64560	62C
64561	62C
64562	64A
64563	65C
64564	62A
64565	62A
64566	64A
64567	62C
64568	62C
64569	63B
64570	64E
64571	64E
64572	64A
64573	65C
64574	62C
64575	62B
64576	64A
64577	64A
64578	65A
64579	65A
64580	65A
64581	65A
64582	64A
64583	65A
64584	65C
64585	63B
64586	64A
64587	62B
64588	64E
64589	64E
64590	62C
64591	64C
64592	64E
64593	64E
64594	64A
64595	64A
64596	62A
64597	62A
64598	62B
64599	64A
64600	62A
64601	65A
64602	62A
64603	64A
64604	62C
64605	64A
64606	64A
64607	64A
64608	64A
64609	65C
64610	65C
64611	65A
64612	62A
64613	64E
64614	64A
64615	62B
64616	62A
64617	62C
64618	62A
64619	62B
64620	62B
64621	65C
64622	65A
64623	65A
64624	64A
64625	64A
64626	65C
64627	62B
64628	65A
64629	62A
64630	62C
64631	62B
64632	65A
64633	65A
64634	62B
64635	62A
64636	64A
64637	64A
64638	65A
64639	65A

J19
0–6–0

64640	31C
64641	31B
64642	31C
64643	31B
64644	32A
64645	31D
64646	31D
64647	31B
64648	31B
64649	31D
64650	30A
64651	30A
64652	30A
64653	31D
64654	31C
64655	31B
64656	31B
64657	30A
64658	31D
64659	31B
64660	30A
64661	31B
64662	30A
64663	30A
64664	30A
64665	30A
64666	31B
64667	31B
64668	31C
64669	31B
64670	30A
64671	31B
64672	31C
64673	31D
64674	32A

J20
0–6–0

64675	30A
64676	30A
64677	30A
64678	31A
64679	31A
64680	30A
64681	30A
64682	30A
64683	31A
64684	31A
64685	30A
64686	30A
64687	31A
64688	31B
64689	31B
64690	30A
64691	30A
64692	31B
64693	31B
64694	31B
64695	30A
64696	30A
64697	31B
64698	31B
64699	31B

J39
0–6–0

64700	52C
64701	52A
64702	40A
64703	52C
64704	52A
64705	52C
64706	50D
64707	52A
64708	30A
64709	52B
64710	51A
64711	52D
64712	39A
64713	36A
64714	39A
64715	40A
64716	38A
64717	39A
64718	39A
64719	38A
64720	38A
64721	36A
64722	40A
64723	9E
64724	32A
64725	40A
64726	32A
64727	9F
64728	40A
64729	38A
64730	40A
64731	32A
64732	14A
64733	9F
64734	40A

64735	38A	64797	32A	64859	50D	64921	50B
64736	40A	64798	38E	64860	50D	64922	50D
64737	36A	64799	37A	64861	50D	64923	52B
64738	40A	64800	32B	64862	51C	64924	52D (A)
64739	38A	64801	37A	64863	50B	64925	52D
64740	39A	64802	32A	64864	53A	64926	53A
64741	39A	64803	32B	64865	52B	64927	53A
64742	39A	64804	40A	64866	50D	64928	53A
64743	39A	64805	38A	64867	53A	64929	54C
64744	39A	64806	37A	64868	52D (A)	64930	12B
64745	39A	64807	38A	64869	52A	64931	53A
64746	39B	64808	39B	64870	53A	64932	12B
64747	38A	64809	39B	64871	52A	64933	51A
64748	39A	64810	39A	64872	37A	64934	50B
64749	37A	64811	37A	64873	30F	64935	50E
64750	38A	64812	52C	64874	30A	64936	54C
64751	37A	64813	52D	64875	12B	64937	40A
64752	32B	64814	52C	64876	30A	64938	50D
64753	39B	64815	52DA	64877	12B	64939	53A
64754	37A	64816	52C	64878	39B	64940	52C
64755	39A	64817	52B	64879	39A	64941	53A
64756	51F	64818	50D	64880	12B	64942	50D
64757	38A	64819	50B	64881	40A	64943	50B
64758	36A	64820	32B	64882	32A	64944	50D
64759	36E	64821	51D	64883	40A	64945	52B
64760	37A	64822	62B	64884	12B	64946	64A
64761	32A	64823	9E	64885	36A	64947	52B
64762	38A	64824	39A	64886	40A	64948	12B
64763	38A	64825	37A	64887	40A	64949	50B
64764	30A	64826	32B	64888	12B	64950	62B
64765	30A	64827	38A	64889	32A	64951	36A
64766	30A	64828	38A	64890	39B	64952	36A
64767	30A	64829	32B	64891	36A	64953	30F
64768	30A	64830	36E	64892	62B	64954	9E
64769	30A	64831	38A	64893	36A	64955	38A
64770	30F	64832	38A	64894	32B	64956	36E
64771	30A	64833	32A	64895	12B	64957	32B
64772	30A	64834	32B	64896	37A	64958	32B
64773	30A	64835	36A	64897	53A	64959	32A
64774	30A	64836	37A	64898	36E	64960	39B
64775	30A	64837	38A	64899	12B	64961	36E
64776	30A	64838	38E	64900	32B	64962	39A
64777	30F	64839	37A	64901	9E	64963	64A
64778	51F	64840	37A	64902	36A	64964	12B
64779	30F	64841	32B	64903	39B	64965	38A
64780	30A	64842	52C	64904	40A	64966	14A
64781	30A	64643	52D	64905	32B	64967	36A
64782	30A	64844	52D	64906	36E	64968	32A
64783	30A	64845	50D	64907	37A	64969	39B
64784	32A	64846	54C	64908	36E	64970	36E
64785	32B	64847	51D	64909	36A	64971	40A
64786	62B	64848	51F	64910	36A	64972	39A
64787	30F	64849	52C	64911	37A	64973	39B
64788	30F	64850	50B	64912	12B	64974	38A
64789	40A	64851	52C (A)	64913	32A	64975	61B
64790	62B	64852	52C	64914	53A	64976	36A
64791	50B	64853	52A	64915	52B	64977	36A
64792	62B	64854	52D	64916	51C	64978	51C
64793	32B	64855	50D	64917	52D	64979	37A
64794	64A	64856	52B	64918	14A	64980	38A
64795	61B	64857	50D	64919	50E	64981	38A
64796	37A	64858	52C	64920	50B	64982	52D

64983	38A	65077	51F	65164	10F	
64984	36A	65078	51F	65165	9G	
64985	37A	65080	52F (SB)	65166	9G	
64986	64A	65082	52C	65167	6D	
64987	36E	65088	51F	65168	9E	
64988	38A	65089	51H	65169	9G	

J1
0–6–0

65002	35A	65090	51A	65170	10F	
65003	34D	65091	51F	65171	9G	
65004	35A	65092	51F	65172	8E	
65005	35A	65095	36A	65173	10F	
65006	35A	65097	51F	65175	10F	
65007	38A	65098	51A	65176	10F	
65008	38A	65099	52C	65177	27E	
65009	38A	65100	51H	65178	9F	
65010	34D	65102	51F	65179	9E	
65013	34D	65103	51H	65180	27E	
65014	38A	65105	50C	65181	8E	
		65110	51A	65182	8E	
		65111	52C (R)	65183	9E	
		65117	36A	65184	9E	

J2
0–6–0

		65118	50B	65185	9F	
65015	38C	65119	51A	65186	9E	
65016	40F	65122	50B	65187	9G	
65017	40F			65188	9F	
65018	38A			65189	10F	
65019	38A	**J10**		65190	9G	
65020	40F	**0–6–0**		65191	9G	
65021	38C			65192	27E	
65022	38A	65126	8E	65193	9F	
65023	38A	65128	27E	65194	9F	
		65130	27E	65195	10F	
		65131	9G	65196	10F	
		65132	9F	65197	9F	
J21		65133	27E	65198	9F	
0–6–0		65134	9G	65199	10F	
		65135	9F	65200	9F	
65025	52C	65136	8E	65201	9E	
65028	51H	65137	9E	65202	9G	
65030	51J	65138	9G	65203	10F	
65033	51A	65139	9G	65204	9E	
65035	52F (R)	65140	9G	65205	9G	
65038	51A	65141	9E	65208	9G	
65039	50C	65142	8E	65209	9F	
65040	51H	65143	6D			
65041	50B	65144	9F			
65042	50C	65145	9F	**J36**		
65043	50A	65146	9F	**0–6–0**		
65047	51H	65147	9G			
65057	51F	65148	9F	65210	65E	
65061	51F	65149	8E	65211	64F	
65062	50B	65151	9G	65213	61B	
65064	51F (W)	65153	8E	65214	65E	
65067	50B	65154	9E	65216*	12B	
65068	51A	65155	8E	65217*	65E	
65070	36E	65156	9G	65218	62A	
65075	50A	65157	9F	65221	65A	
65076	50B	65158	9G	65222*	64E	
		65159	10F	65224*	64A	
		65160	9F	65225	64F	
		65161	9F	65226*	65E	
		65162	10F	65227	65I	
		65163	8E	65228	65A	
				65229	64	

65230	64F
65231	64F
65232	64G
65233*	64E
65234	64F
65235*	64F
65236*	65E
65237	63D
65238	65E
65239	62C
65240	64B
65241	64E
65242	64G
65243*	64B
65244	64B
65245	64E
65246	64E
65247	61A
65248	64F
65249	65E
65250	64F
65251	64A
65252	62C
65253*	62C
65254*	64F
65255	65E
65257	64E
65258	64A
65259	64G
65260	65E
65261	64F
65264	65E
65265	64F
65266	65E
65267	64A
65268*	64E
65270	65A
65271	64C
65273	65A
65274	65C
65275	64E
65276	64F
65277	64F
65278	64F
65279	64G
65280	64F
65281	62C
65282	64F
65283	65C
65285	65E
65286	64A
65287	65E
65288	64A
65290	64E
65291	62A
65292	64A
65293	12B
65295	52C (H)
65296	65A
65297	61B
65298	65C
65300	63D

b5303	64F	65390	32A	65472	32A	65524	32A
65304	12B	65391	31A	65473	30E	65525	31A
65305	64A	65396	32B	65474	31A	65526	31D
65306	64E	65398	32A	65475	31A	65527	31C
65307	62C	65401	32C	65476	30A	65528	30A
65308	65A	65402	30E	65477	31A	65529	31A
65309	62B	65404	32A	65478	32C	65530	31C
65310	64A	65405	31A	65479	32A	65531	30E
65311	64A	65406	31A			65532	31A
65312	12B	65407	32B			65533	31D
65313	63D	65408	32B	**J5**		65534	32A
65314	64F	65413	31A	**0-6-0**		65535	30A
65315	65I	65417	32A			65536	30A
65316	64A	65420	31E	65480	38A	65537	31A
65317	64G	65422	32A	65481	38A	65538	31A
65318	64F	65423	32B	65482	38A	65539	30E
65319	62B	65424	30E	65483	38A	65540	30A
65320	62C	65425	31A	65484	38A	65541	30A
65321	12B	65426	32A	65485	38A	65542	31C
65322	62C	65427	30E	65486	38A	65543	30A
65323	62C	65429	32B	65487	38A	65544	31C
65324	65C	65430	32B	65488	38A	65545	31D
65325	65E	65431	30E	65489	38A	65546	31A
65327	64F	65432	30E	65490	38A	65547	31A
65329	64D	65433	32C	65491	38A	65548	31C
65330	62B	65434	30F	65492	38A	65549	31C
65331	52C (R)	65435	32C	65493	38A	65551	32G
65333	62B	65437	31C	65494	38B	65552	32G
65334	64A	65438	31A	65495	38C	65553	32A
65335	65C	65439	31B	65496	38A	65554	31B
65338	64E	65440	30A	65497	38A	65555	31B
65339	65I	65441	30E	65498	38A	65556	31B
65340	64G	65442	31E	65499	38A	65557	32G
65341	64F	65443	30E			65558	32F
65342	64F	65444	30E			65559	32F
65343	52C	65445	30E	**J17**		65560	32B
65344	64F	65446	30E	**0-6-0**		65561	31A
65345	62A	65447	32B			65562	31D
65346	64F	65448	30E	65500	30A	65563	31A
		65449	30A	65501	31A	65564	30E
		65450	30A	65502	31A	65565	31A
		65451	31A	65503	31A	65566	32C
J15		65452	30A	65504	31D	65567	32G
0-6-0		65453	30A	65505	31B	65568	32A
		65454	30E	65506	31A	65569	32A
65350	31A	65455	30A	65507	32A	65570	32A
65354	30F	65456	30E	65508	30A	65571	31B
65355	32C	65457	31A	65509	32G	65572	31C
65356	31A	65458	30F	65510	32B	65573	31C
65359	31C	65459	32B	65511	30A	65574	32A
65361	30A	65460	32A	65512	32A	65575	31A
65362	31E	65461	31A	65513	32A	65576	31B
65366	31B	65462	32C	65514	32A	65577	31B
65369	30E	65463	30A	65515	31B	65578	32A
65370	30A	65464	30A	65516	32G	65579	31D
65373	32A	65465	30E	65517	31A	65580	31D
65374	32C	65466	30A	65518	31B	65581	32F
65377	32B	65467	30B	65519	31C	65582	31D
65378	31C	65468	30E	65520	31A	65583	31B
65382	32B	65469	32A	65521	31B	65584	31B
65384	30A	65470	32B	65522	30E	65585	31A
65388	30A	65471	32A	65523	30A	65586	32G
65389	32C						

65587	31A	65686	54C	65755	51B	65812	52E
65588	31D	65687	51D	65756	51B	65813	52E
65589	31A	65688	51A	65757	51B	65814	52E
		65689	51E	65758	51B	65815	51C
		65690	53A	65759	51B	65816	51C
J24		65691	51A	65760	51B	65817	54A
0–6–0		65692	51A	65761	51B	65818	51C
		65693	51J	65762	51B	65819	52F
65600	50F	65694	54B	65763	51B	65820	51C
65601	51B	65695	51H	65764	51D	65821	52E
65604	51B	65696	51A	65765	51B	65822	52E
65611	54C	65697	52D	65766	51B	65823	54A
65614	62B	65698	53A	65767	51B	65824	52F (SB)
65615	54C	65699	53A	65768	51B	65825	52E
65617	64A	65700	50A	65769	51B	65826	52E
65619	50A	65702	51A	65770	51B	65827	50C
65621	50G	65705	53C	65771	51D	65828	52F
65622	62B	65706	51F	65772	51B	65829	52F (SB)
65623	64A	65708	50A	65773	51B	65830	51G
65624	50G	65710	51D	65774	51B	65831	52E
65627	50G	65712	53A	65775	51D	65832	54A
65628	50G	65713	53A	65776	51D	65833	54A
65631	50F	65714	53E	65777	51B	65834	52F (SB)
65636	50F	65716	54B	65778	51B	65835	54A
65640	50F	65717	51H	65779	51D	65836	54A
65642	50F	65718	51E			65837	52E
65644	50F	65720	51A			65838	52E
		65723	50A	**J27**		65839	52E
		65725	51J	**0–6–0**		65840	54A
J25		65726	51D			65841	54A
0–6–0		65727	52D	65780	52E	65842	52B
		65728	53C	65781	52F (SB)	65843	54A
65645	51J			65782	51C	65844	50C
65647	53A			65783	52F	65845	50A
65648	51A	**J26**		65784	52E	65846	51C
65650	51A	**0–6–0**		65785	54A	65847	54A
65651	53A			65786	52F	65848	50C
65653	51H	65730	51B	65787	51G	65849	50A
65654	53A	65731	51B	65788	52B	65850	54A
65655	51H	65732	51B	65789	52F	65851	52F
65656	50A	65733	51D	65790	51C	65852	52E
65657	54C	65734	51B	65791	52E	65853	51G
65659	51F	65735	51B	65792	52E	65854	54A
65660	51G	65736	51B	65793	50C	65855	51G
65661	54C	65737	51B	65794	52E	65856	54A
65662	51F	65738	51B	65795	52E	65857	51K
65663	53A	65739	51B	65796	52E	65858	52E
65664	51A	65740	51B	65797	54A	65859	51G
65666	54B	65741	51B	65798	54A	65860	51E
65667	53C	65742	51B	65799	52F	65861	50A
65670	54B	65743	51B	65800	52B	65862	52B
65671	51F	65744	51B	65801	52F	65863	52B
65672	51A	65745	51B	65802	52F	65864	52B
65673	51H	65746	51B	65803	51C	65865	51G
65675	51F	65747	51C	65804	52F	65866	51C
65676	54C	65748	51C	65805	51G	65867	52F
65677	51A	65749	51B	65806	52E	65868	51E
65679	50A	65750	51B	65807	52B	65869	52B
65680	54C	65751	51B	65808	52F (SB)	65870	52F
65683	51F	65752	51B	65809	52F	65871	54A
65685	54C	65753	51B	65810	52F (SB)	65872	54A
		65754	51B	65811	52F	65873	52B

65874	50C	**F2**		67204	30E	67256	53B
65875	50C	**2–4–2T**		67205	30A	67257	54A
65876	52F			67206	30A	67258	54A (D)
65877	52F	67111	34A	67207	30A	67259	52C
65878	54A			67208	30A	67260	54A
65879	52F			67209	30A	67261	52F (SB)
65880	52F	**F3**		67210	30A	67262	50B
65881	50C	**2–4–2T**		67211	30A	67263	54A (D)
65882	50C			67212	30A	67264	54A
65883	50A	67127	32C	67213	30A	67265	52C (H)
65884	54A	67128	32B	67214	30A	67266	50B
65885	50A	67139	32A	67215	30E	67267	54A
65886	52B			67216	32C	67268	52C (H)
65887	51E			67217	30E	67269	30A
65888	50A	**F4**		67218	32D	67270	54A
65889	52B	**2–4–2T**		67219	30E	67271	51C
65890	50A					67272	51A
65891	54A	67151	61A			67273	50F
65892	52F	67152	32G	**F6**		67274	50B
65893	52B	67153	31B	**2–4–2T**		67275	50F
65894	50A	67154	32D			67276	54A
		67155	50F	67220	32B	67277	52C
		67156	32C	67221	31C	67278	51E
		67157	61A	67222	31A	67279	30A
J38		67158	32C	67223	32F	67280	53B
0–6–0		67162	32G	67224	32G	67281	51D (G)
		67163	32C	67225	32G	67282	53B
65900	62C	67164	61A	67226	32F	67283	54A
65901	62A	67165	32C	67227	31C	67284	50D
65902	62A	67166	32C	67228	32G	67286	50C
65903	62A	67167	32C	67229	32A	67287	61A
65904	62A	67171	53A	67230	32B	67288	54B
65905	62C	67174	32C	67231	32C	67289	50D
65906	64E	67175	53A	67232	32A	67290	50B
65907	62A	67176	32A	67233	32F	67291	51C
65908	62A	67177	32C	67234	32F	67292	61C
65909	64E	67178	32A	67235	32F	67293	50B
65910	62A	67182	32C	67236	31E	67294	51F
65911	62A	67184	32C	67237	31E	67295	52F (SB)
65912	64A	67186	32C	67238	31E	67296	52F (R)
65913	62A	67187	31B	67239	32B	67297	54A
65914	64A					67298	54A (D)
65915	64A					67300	54A
65916	62C					67301	53B
65917	64E	**F5**		**G5**		67302	50G
65918	64A	**2–4–2T**		**0–4–4T**		67303	52D
65919	64A					67304	52D
65920	64A	67188	30E	67240	50B	67305	51E
65921	62A	67189	30E	67241	52C	67306	54A (D)
65922	62C	67190	30E	67242	51E	67307	50B
65923	62C	67191	30E	67243	54A	67308	50B
65924	62C	67192	30A	67244	52F (SB)	67309	52A
65925	62A	67193	30A	67245	52C (H)	67310	54A
65926	62C	67194	30E	67246	52F (SB)	67311	53B
65927	64A	67195	30E	67247	54A	67312	51F
65928	62C	67196	30E	67248	52D	67313	52C (H)
65929	64A	67197	30A	67249	52C (H)	67314	51C
65930	62C	67198	30A	67250	50C	67315	52C (A)
65931	62A	67199	32D	67251	54A	67316	51C
65932	62A	67200	30A	67252	54A	67317	51E
65933	62C	67201	32C	67253	50D (P)	67318	51E
65934	62C	67202	30A	67254	53B	67319	50B
		67203	30A	67255	52C	67320	52A

67321	53B
67322	30A
67323	52C
67324	51J
67325	52A
67326	52F (SB)
67327	61A
67328	54A
67329	52A
67330	50F
67331	51C
67332	50F
67333	51A
67334	52F (SB)
67335	50G
67336	54A
67337	50B (I)
67338	51D
67339	52C
67340	53B
67341	52F (SB)
67342	51A
67343	51C
67344	51J
67345	51F
67346	51J (L)
67347	52F (SB)
67348	54A
67349	50F

CI2
4–4–2T

67350	40F
67351	40C
67352	40C
67353	37B
67354	53B
67356	34A
67357	34A
67360	31A
67361	35A
67362	35C
67363	38B
67364	40C
67365	35A
67366	9E
67367	31A
67368	35A
67369	9E
67371	53B
67372	37B
67373	35A
67374	34A
67375	31A
67376	34A
67379	40C
67380	35B
67381	40C
67382	35B
67383	40C
67384	40C
67385	31A

67386	37A
67387	38B
67389	40A
67390	35A
67391	53B
67392	53B
67393	53B
67394	53B
67395	53B
67397	53B
67398	40C

CI3
4–4–2T

67400	6D
67401	39A
67402	39A
67403	39A
67404	39B
67405	39A
67406	39A
67407	39A
67408	39A
67409	36D
67410	39A
67411	36D
67412	39A
67413	6D
67414	6D
67415	39A
67416	39A
67417	39A
67418	34E
67419	39A
67420	34E
67421	39A
67422	39A
67423	39A
67424	39A
67425	39A
67426	39A
67427	39A
67428	6E
67429	6E
67430	6E
67431	39A
67432	6E
67433	6D
67434	36D
67435	6E
67436	6D
67437	39A
67438	39A
67439	39A

CI4
4–4–2T

67440	37A
67441	37A
67442	6E

67443	37A
67444	37A
67445	37A
67446	37A
67447	37C
67448	37C
67449	6E
67450	37C
67451	37A

CI5
4–4–2T

67452	62A
67453	62C
67454	65C
67455	61B
67456	65A
67457	64G
67458	12B
67459	64G
67460	65A
67461	62B
67462	63B
67463	64E
67464	64E
67465	64G
67466	62C
67467	65A
67468	64E
67469	62C
67470	65C
67471	62B
67472	64G
67473	64E
67474	12B
67475	65E
67476	62A
67477	64G
67478	61B
67479	65C
67480	65C
67481	12B

CI6
4–4–2T

67482	65A
67483	62B
67484	62B
67485	65A
67486	62B
67487	65C
67488	65A
67489	62B
67490	62B
67491	62B
67492	64A
67493	62B
67494	64A

67495	**64A**
67496	64A
67497	64A
67498	62B
67499	62B
67500	65A
67501	65A
67502	62B

VI & V3
2–6–2T

67600	65A
67601	65I
67602	65A
67603	65A
67604	65C
67605	64A
67606	64A
67607	64A
67608	64A
67609	64A
67610	64B
67611	65C
67612	65C
67613	65H
67614	65H
67615	64B
67616	65H
67617	64A
67618	65A
67619	65C
67620	64B
67621	65C
67622	65C
67623	65C
67624	64A
67625	65H
67626	65C
67627	65E
67628	65C
67629	64A
67630	64A
67631	65H
67632	65H
67633	65C
67634	52A
67635	52B
67636	52C
67637	52B
67638	51D
67639	51D
67640	52B
67641	52B
67642	52B
67643	65C
67644	65A
67645	52B
67646	52B
67647	51D
67648	65C

67649	64A	67715	34E	67777	51A	
67650	63B	67716	32B	67778	34E	
67651	52B	67717	34E	67779	34E	
67652	52B	67718	34E	67780	34E	
67653	52C	67719	32B	67781	34E	
67654	52B	67720	34E	67782	34E	
67655	65C	67721	30A	67783	34E	
67656	52C	67722	30A	67784	34E	
67657	52C	67723	30A	67785	34E	
67658	52C	67724	30A	67786	34E	
67659	64A	67725	30A	67787	32B	
67660	65E	67726	30A	67788	32A	
67661	65C	67727	30A	67789	32A	
67662	65C	67728	30A	67790	34D	
67663	32A	67729	30A	67791	34D	
67664	32A	67730	30A	67792	34A	
67665	65E	67731	30A	67793	34A	
67666	64A	67732	30A	67794	32A	
67667	61A	67733	30A	67795	32A	
67668	64A	67734	30A	67796	34A	
67669	62C	67735	30A	67797	34A	
67670	64A	67736	30A	67798	32A	
67671	61A	67737	30A	67799		
67672	62C	67738	30A	67800		
67673	65E	67739	30A			
67674	65E	67740	34D			
67675	63B	67741	34D	**J94**		
67676	65C	67742	51A	**0-6-0ST**		
67677	32A	67743	34D			
67678	65C	67744	34D	68006	6F	
67679	32A	67745	34D	68007	51B	
67680	65A	67746	34D	68008	51A	
67681	65C	67747	34E	68009	40B	
67682	51E	67748	34E	68010	52C	
67683	52A	67749	34E	68011	51B	
67684	51D	67750	51A	68012	39A	
67685	51D	67751	34E	68013	40B	
67686	51D	67752	34E	68014	52B	
67687	52A	67753	34E	68015	51A	
67688	52A	67754	51A	68016	54A	
67689	52A	67755	51D	68017	50A	
67690	52A	67756	34E	68018	40B	
67691	51D	67757	34E	68019	52C	
		67758	34E	68020	40B	
		67759	51D	68021	52C	
		67760	34E	68022	40B	
LI		67761	34E	68023	51B	
2-6-4T		67762	34E	68024	52C	
		67763	51D	68025	51A	
67701	30A	67764	51D	68026	40B	
67702	32B	67765	51D	68027	51A	
67703	32B	67766	51D	68028	40B	
67704	32B	67767	34E	68029	52C	
67705	32B	67768	34E	68030	40B	
67706	32B	67769	34E	68031	50A	
67707	34E	67770	34E	68032	50A	
67708	32B	67771	34E	68033	40B	
67709	32B	67772	34E	68034	40B	
67710	32B	67773	34E	68035	52C	
67711	32B	67774	34E	68036	52C	
67712	30A	67775	34E	68037	51B	
67713	30A	67776	34E	68038	52C	
67714	34E					

68039	51A
68040	50A
68041	52C
68042	51C
68043	51A
68044	50A
68045	51A
68046	50A
68047	51A
68048	52C
68049	51B
68050	51A
68051	51A
68052	51A
68053	51C
68054	51C
68055	51C
68056	51C
68057	51C
68058	52C
68059	52C (H)
68060	51B
68061	50A
68062	51B
68063	6E
68064	9E
68065	6F
68066	6F
68067	39A
68068	40B
68069	40B
68070	40B
68071	39A
68072	40B
68073	40B
68074	40B
68075	40B
68076	40B
68077	40B
68078	40B
68079	39A
68080	40B

Y6
0-4-0T

68082	31C
68083	31C

Y7
0-4-0T

68088S	30A
68089	52D

Y8
0-4-0T

68091	50A

Y9	
0-4-0ST	
68092	64A
68093	64A
68094	65E
68095	64A
68096	64A
68097	64A
68098	64A
68099	64A
68100	62B
68101	62C
68102	64A
68103	65A
68104	64E
68105	65A
68106	65E
68107	62B
68108	60A
68109	65A
68110	62B
68111	64A
68112	65G
68113	64E
68114	62B
68115	64A
68116	65E
68117	65E
68118	65A
68119	64A
68120	65E
68121	65E
68122	64A
68123	62B
68124	65A

Y4	
0-4-0T	
68125	30A
68126	30A
68127	30A
68128	30A
68129S	30A

Y1	
0-4-0T	
68130S	32C
68131S	32C
68132S	36A†
68133S	35A
68136S	51A‡
68137	53A

68138	64G
68139	53A
68140	53A
68141	52A
68142	51F
68143	50C
68144	51E
68145	51F
68146	52A
68147	50F
68148	53D
68149	51F
68150	50F
68151	53B
68152S	50A
68153S	51A§

Y3	
0-4-0T	
68154	52A
68155	53D
68156	50C
68157	50F (P)
68158	50C
68159	51J
68160	52A
68161	50C
68162	40B
68163	6E
68164	6E
68165S	36A
68166S	40F
68168S	32C
68169	39A
68171	40F
68172	34E
68173S	32C
68174	30A
68175	34D
68176	39B
68177S	32C
68178S	32C
68179	40B
68180	52A
68181	54B
68182	51F
68183	54B
68184	39B
68185	35A

Y10	
0-4-0T	
68186	32D

Z4	
0-4-2T	
68190	61A
68191	61A

Z5	
0-4-2T	
68192	61A
68193	61A

J62	
0-6-0ST	
68200	6E

J63	
0-6-0T	
68204	40B
68205	40B
68206	40B
68207	40B
68208	40B
68209	40B
68210	40B

J65	
0-6-0T	
68211	32B
68214	32F

J70	
0-6-0T	
68216	32B
68217	31C
68219	32D
68220	31C
68221	32B
68222	31C
68223	31C
68224	32B
68225	31C
68226	30E

J71	
0-6-0T	
68230	50A
68231	51A
68232	53A

68233	51C
68234	52B
68235	51A
68236	51A
68238	50A (N)
68239	51A
68240	50A
68242	53A
68244	51C
68245	52B
68246	50A
68247	52B
68248	51F
68249	51F
68250	50A
68251	52A
68252	53A
68253	50A
68254	51F
68255	51F
68256	52B
68258	51C
68259	51A
68260	51D
68262	52B
68263	51C
68264	52B
68265	52C
68266	54B
68267	52B
68268	50C
68269	51F
68270	52A
68271	52B
68272	54B
68273	52B
68275	50A
68276	51C
68277	53A
68278	52B
68279	51A
68280	50A
68281	51A
68282	50A
68283	52A
68284	52D
68286	50A
68287	54C
68288	53A
68289	54C
68290	51C
68291	51C
68292	50A (N)
68293	50A
68294	50A (N)
68295	51C
68296	53A
68297	50A

† Operates at Ranskill Wagon Works
‡ Operates at Faverdale Wagon Works
§ Geneva P.W. depot

68298	53A
68299	54C
68300	51A
68301	51C
68302	51C
68303	51D
68304	53A
68305	51E
68306	51C
68307	51D
68308	51A
68309	52A
68310	50A
68311	53A
68312	51D
68313	50A
68314	52A
68316	53A

J88
0–6–0T

68320	64A
68321	62A
68322	62A
68323	62A
68324	64E
68325	64A
68326	65A
68327	65A
68328	64B
68329	65E
68330	65A
68331	65E
68332	62A
68333	65A
68334	64A
68335	62A
68336	65A
68337	62A
68338	64A
68339	64B
68340	64A
68341	62A
68342	64A
68343	65E
68344	65E
68345	62C
68346	62C
68347	65A
68348	64A
68349	65A
68350	64E
68351	62C
68352	64A
68353	62A
68354	64E

J73
0–6–0T

68355	51C
68356	50C
68357	50C
68358	51C
68359	51C
68360	53C (AD)
68361	53C (AD)
68362	50C
68363	53C (AD)
68364	51C

J66
0–6–0T

68370S	30A
68371	38D
68372	31A
68373	32B
68374	32B
68375	32B
68375	40A
68377	32G
68378	31D
68379	38D
68380	30A
68381	32A
68382	38D
68383	31A
68385	40A
68387	35A
68388	32A

J77
0–6–0T

68391	51F
68392	50D
68393	50D
68395	50B
68397	52F
68398	52F
68399	50C
68401	53B
68402	53C (AD)
68404	50D
68405	52F
68406	50B
68407	51E
68408	51A
68409	51D
68410	51A
68412	51E
68413	53C (AD)

68414	51D
68417	52F
68420	51E
68421	52D
68422	51D
68423	51A
68424	52F (SB)
68425	51D
68426	52F
68427	52F
68428	52F (SB)
68429	53C (AD)
68430	52B
68431	52F (SB)
68432	51A
68433	50C
68434	50D
68435	53C (AD)
68436	50A
68437	52D
68438	50D
68440	53C (AD)

J83
0–6–0T

68442	65E
68443	65E
68444	65E
68445	65E
68446	62B
68447	65A
68448	64A
68449	64A
68450	64A
68451	62A
68452	62B
68453	62A
68454	64A
68455	62B
68456	62A
68457	64B
68458	62A
68459	64A
68460	64B
68461	65E
68463	64A
68464	64A
68465	62C
68466	62B
68467	62A
68468	65A
68469	64A
68470	62B
68471	64E
68472	64A
68473	64B
68474	64A
68475	65A
68476	65A
68477	64A

68478	64B
68479	65A
68480	65A
68481	64B

J67 & J69
0–6–0T

68490	31C
68491	30A
68492	64A
68493	31C
68494	31C
68495	32A
68496	30A
68497	31E
68498	32B
68499	12B
68500	30A
68501	32A
68502	31C
68503	65C
68504	62A
68505	64A
68507	30A
68508	30A
68509	31A
68510	30A
68511	64A
68512	34D
68513	30A
68514	31C
68515	31C
68516	31A
68517	30A
68518	32B
68519	30A
68520	30A
68521	30A
68522	30E
68523	30A
68524	64E
68525	64A
68526	30A
68527	30A
68528	40F
68529	40A
68530	31A
68531	6E
68532	30A
68533	64E
68534	30A
68535	62A
68536	32G
68537	40A
68538	30A
68540	9E
68541	34D
68542	31D
68543	40F
68544	64E

68545	31C
68546	30A
68547	8D
68548	30A
68549	30A
68550	62A
68551	65A
68552	65A
68553	40A
68554	30A
68555	62A
68556	30F
68557	30F
68558	40A
68559	8E
68560	40F
68561	30F
68562	64A
68563	30A
68565	34C
68566	31D
68567	65C
68568	61B
68569	30A
68570	32A
68571	30A
68572	34C
68573	30A
68574	30A
68575	30A
68576	30A
68577	30A
68578	30E
69579	31A
68581	40F
68583	9E
68584	27E
68585	27E
68586	32A
68587	40A
68588	30A
68589	30A
68590	30A
68591	30A
68592	30A
68593	32B
68594	30A
68595	9E
68596	30F
68597	31D
68598	9E
68599	40A
68600	31D
68601	30A
68602	32A
68603	32A
68605	34D
68606	30A
68607	30A
68608	30A
68609	31A
68610	40A
68611	32C
68612	30A
68613	30A
68616	30E
68617	30A
68618	40A
68619	30A
68621	30A
68623	64A
68625	32D
68626	30A
68628	32D
68629	30E
68630	30E
68631	30A
68632	35A
68633	30A
68635	62C
68636	30A

J68
0–6–0T

68638	30A
68639	30A
68640	32C
68641	32A
68642	30A
68643	30F
68644	30A
68645	31A
68646	30A
68647	30A
68648	30A
68649	30A
68650	30A
68651	32F
68652	30A
68653	30F
68654	31B
68655	40F
68656	31C
68657	40F
68658	40F
68659	40F
68660	30A
68661	30A
68662	30A
68663	30A
68664	31B
68665	30A
68666	30A

J92
0–6–0CT

68667**S**	30A
68668**S**	30A
68669**S**	30A

J72
0–6–0T

68670	53C (AD)
68671	6F
68672	50B
68673	53C (AD)
68674	52A
68675	52A
68676	53C (AD)
68677	50B
68678	54A
68679	51A
68680	52A
68681	50B
68682	52B
68683	51C
68684	51C
68685	51C
68686	53C (AD)
68687	52B
68688	51D
68689	51D
68690	51D
68691	51F
68692	51C
68693	52A
68694	51C
68695	50A
68696	51F
68697	51C
68698	54A
68699	50A
68700	61A
68701	6F
68702	52A
68703	51C
68704	54A
68705	54C
68706	54B
68707	51A
68708	54C
68709	65A
68710	61A
68711	51C
68712	51D
68713	51D
68714	6F
68715	50A
68716	51C
68717	61A
68718	54A
68719	61A
68720	52A
68721	51D
68722	50A
68723	52A
68724	53C (AD)
68725	52B
68726	50A
68727	6F
68728	54C
68729	54B
68730	54C
68731	54B
68732	52A
68733	65A
68734	51C
68735	50A
68736	54C
68737	54C
68738	52B
68739	50A
68740	51D
68741	50A
68742	52B
68743	53C (AD)
68744	52A
68745	50A
68746	53C (AD)
68747	53C (AD)
68748	53A
68749	61A
68750	61A
68751	53C (AD)
68752	53C (AD)
68753	53C (AD)
68754	51D

J52
0–6–0ST

68757	34B
68758	34B
68759	34B
68760	34B
68761	34B
68762	38A
68763	36A
68764	34A
68765	35A
68766	36E
68767	38A
68768	38A
68769	36A
68770	34A
68771	34A
68772	34A
68773	34B
68774	34B
68775	36A
68776	34B
68777	34B
68778	34B
68779	38A
68780	34A
68781	34B
68782**S**	36A
68783	34B
68784	34B
68785	34B
68786	36A
68787	34B

68788	34B	68852	35A	68909	37A	68971	36C
68789	35A	68853	34B	68910	37A	68972	38A
68790	37A	68854	34A	68911	37B	68973	36C
68791	34B	68855	34A	68912	37C	68974	36B
68792	38A	68856	34B	68913	37B	68975	38B
68793	34B	68857	36A	68914	37A	68976	38B
68794	34B	68858	36A	68915	37A	68977	30A
68795	34B	68859	38A	68916	37A	68978	37B
68796	36A	68860	36A	68917	36A	68979	36C
68797	34A	68861	34A	68918	36A	68980	36A
68798	35A	68862	34A	68919	37A	68981	38C
68799	34A	68863	38A	68920	38A	68982	38A
68800	36A	68864	34A	68921	37A	68983	39B
68801	35B	68865	36A	68922	37C	68984	37B
68802	34A	68866	35A	68923	37C	68985	36A
68803	34A	68867	36A	68924	32A	68986	36A
68804	36A	68868	35A	68925	37B	68987	36A
68805	34A	68869	36A	68926	36A	68988	37B
68806	36A	68870	36A	68927	38B	68989	36A
68807	38A	68871	37A	68928	39B	68990	39B
68808	34B	68872	37A	68929	38B	68991	36A
68809	34A	68873	34A	68930	37A		
68810	34A	68874	34A	68931	37A		
68811	34B	68875	38A	68932	37C	**J72**	
68812	38A	68876	35A	68933	37C	**0–6–0T**	
68813	36A	68877	35B	68934	37C		
68814	38A	68878	34A	68935	38A	69001	53C (AD)
68815	34B	68879	35A	68936	36A	69002	53C (AD)
68817	35A	68880	35A	68937	37B	69003	53C (AD)
68818	34A	68881	34A	68938	37A	69004	51A
68819	35A	68882	38A	68939	37A	69005	52A
68820	35A	68883	34B	68940	37C	69006	51D
68821	35A	68884	34A	68941	37C	69007	51F
68822	34A	68885	36A	68942	37C	69008	54B
68823	35A	68886	36A	68943	37C	69009	53C (AD)
68824	35A	68887	38A	68944	37C	69010	53A
68825	34B	68888	34A	68945	36A	69011	53A
68826	34B	68889	34A	68946	36B	69012	32B
68827	34B			68947	37A	69013	32B
68828	34A			68948	37A	69014	36A
68829	34B	**J50**		68949	37A	69015	39B
68830	34A	**0–6–0T**		68950	30A	69016	50E
68831	34A			68951	37A	69017	54C
68832	34A	68890	36B	68952	64A	69018	54A
68833	34B	68891	38A	68953	65A	69019	51D
68834	34B	68892	37C	68954	65A	69020	50A
68835	36A	68893	36A	68955	65A		
68836	36A	68894	38A	68956	65A		
68837	36A	68895	37C	68957	65A	**L3**	
68838	34A	68896	37A	68958	65A	**2–6–4T**	
68839	38A	68897	37C	68959	37C		
68840	35A	68898	37C	68960	36B	69050	38E
68841	36A	68899	32A	68961	36A	69051	36C
68842	36A	68900	37A	68962	36C	69052	9G
68843	36A	68901	37A	68963	30A	69055	34E
68844	34A	68902	37C	68964	36C	69056	34E
68846	35A	68903	37A	68965	30A	69060	34E
68847	36A	68904	37A	68966	37A	69061	34E
68848	37A	68905	32A	68967	30A	69062	9G
68849	36A	68906	37C	68968	36C	69064	35A
68850	35A	68907	37A	68969	37C	69065	34E
68851	34B	68908	37C	68970	36C	69067	34E
						69069	38E

N10
0–6–2T

69090	52A
69091	52A
69092	52A
69093	53A
69094	53A
69095	52C
69096	53A
69097	52A (B)
69098	53A
69099	53A
69100	52A (B)
69101	51J
69102	53A
69104	53A
69105	53A
69106	53A
69107	53A
69108	53A
69109	52A

N13
0–6–2T

69111	53C (AD)
69112	53C
69113	53C
69114	50B
69115	50B
69116	53C
69117	50B
69118	50B
69119	53C

N14
0–6–2T

69120	65A
69124	65A
69125	61A

N15
0–6–2T

69126	65A
69127	65A
69128	61B
69129	61B
69130	64A
69131	65A
69132	62A
69133	64A
69134	64A
69135	62C
69136	62C
69137	64E
69138	65A

69139	12B
69140	64A
69141	64A
69142	64F
69143	65C
69144	64A
69145	65E
69146	64A
69147	64A
69148	64A
69149	64A
69150	62A
69151	65C
69152	64A
69153	62A
69154	62C
69155	12B
69156	64F
69157	65C
69158	64F
69159	64F
69160	62C
69161	65C
69162	64E
69163	65A
69164	62C
69165	65A
69166	65A
69167	64A
69168	64A
69169	64B
69170	65A
69171	65C
69172	64A
69173	64A
69174	12B
69175	64A
69176	65A
69177	65A
69178	65A
69179	65A
69180	65A
69181	65A
69182	65A
69183	65A
69184	65A
69185	12B
69186	64A
69187	64C
69188	65A
69189	65A
69190	65C
69191	65A
69192	62C
69193	65C
69194	65C
69195	65C
69196	65E
69197	12B
69198	65C
69199	65C
69200	64E

69201	61B
69202	62C
69203	65A
69204	62C
69205	65A
69206	65E
69207	65E
69208	65A
69209	65C
69210	65C
69211	62A
69212	65C
69213	65C
69214	65C
69215	12B
69216	64F
69217	65C
69218	12B
69219	64A
69220	64B
69221	62C
69222	65A
69223	62A
69224	62A

N4
0–6–2T

69225	39B
69227	39B
69228	39B
69229	39B
69230	39B
69231	39B
69232	39B
69233	39B
69234	39B
69235	39B
69236	39B
69239	39B
69240	39B
69242	39B
69244	39B
69245	39B
69246	39B

N5
0–6–2T

69250	39A
69252	9E
69253	40A
69254	8E
69255	9E
69256	40F
69257	34E
69258	8E
69259	34E
69260	39A
69261	40F

69262	9G
69263	38E
69264	36B
69265	27E
69266	37B
69267	6E
69268	36D
69269	38E
69270	39A
69271	37B
69272	8E
69273	36E
69274	6D
69275	40A
69276	9F
69277	36E
69278	36D
69279	38D
69280	40F
69281	6D
69282	36E
69283	34E
69284	40E
69285	36D
69286	38E
69287	40A
69288	8E
69289	6F
69290	6E
69291	36D
69292	38D
69293	9G
69294	36E
69295	38D
69296	39A
69297	36B
69298	27E
69299	39A
69300	34E
69301	38D
69302	34E
69303	36D
69304	9E
69305	40B
69306	40C
69307	39A
69308	39A
69309	40B
69310	38E
69311	40A
69312	38A
69313	36E
69314	36B
69315	34E
69316	36B
69317	9F
69318	34E
69319	40E
69320	36D
69321	36E
69322	40B
69323	40E

69324	38A	69387	52B	69463	34B	69524	34A

69324	38A
69325	36D
69326	9E
69327	40E
69328	9F
69329	6E
69330	6E
69331	9F
69332	9F
69333	39A
69334	36D
69335	9G
69336	9E
69337	35A
69338	39A
69339	8E
69340	6E
69341	34E
69342	8E
69343	9E
69344	27E
69345	36D
69346	6E
69347	39A
69348	36D
69349	6E
69350	34E
69351	38D
69352	6E
69353	39A
69354	36E
69355	36E
69356	27E
69357	36D
69358	34E
69359	9F
69360	38E
69361	9E
69362	6E
69363	38D
69364	9E
69365	36D
69366	6E
69367	36D
69368	36D
69369	34E
69370	9E

N8
0–6–2T

69371	52B
69372	52B
69377	53A
69378	54B
69379	53A
69380	52B
69381	53A
69382	53A
69385	53A
69386	53A

69387	52B
69389	53A
69390	52B
69391	54C
69392	53A
69393	53A
69394	54D
69395	54D
69398	53A
69400	54B
69401	53A

N9
0–6–2T

69410	54B
69413	54A
69418	54A
69423	54A
69424	54A
69425	54A
69426	51A
69427	54A
69429	54B

N1
0–6–2T

69430	37B
69431	34B
69432	34B
69433	34B
69434	34B
69435	34B
69436	37B
69437	37B
69439	34B
69440	37B
69441	34B
69442	34B
69443	37C
69444	37B
69445	34B
69446	37B
69447	37C
69448	37C
69449	37C
69450	34B
69451	34B
69452	37A
69453	34B
69454	37C
69455	34B
69456	34B
69457	34B
69458	34B
69459	37C
69460	34B
69461	37A
69462	34B

69463	34B
69464	37C
69465	34B
69466	34B
69467	34B
69468	34B
69469	34B
69470	34B
69471	37B
69472	37B
69473	37B
69474	37C
69475	34B
69476	34B
69477	34B
69478	37C
69479	37C
69480	34B
69481	34B
69482	37C
69483	37C
69484	34C
69485	37C

N2
0–6–2T

69490	34A
69491	34A
69492	34A
69493	34C
69494	34C
69495	34A
69496	34A
69497	34A
69498	34A
69499	34A
69500	65C
69501	38A
69502	34A
69503	65E
69504	34C
69505	34B
69506	34A
69507	65C
69508	65E
69509	65E
69510	65C
69511	65C
69512	34A
69513	34B
69514	65C
69515	34D
69516	34B
69517	34A
69518	65E
69519	34A
69520	34A
69521	34A
69522	34B
69523	34A

69524	34A
69525	34A
69526	34A
69527	34A
69528	34A
69529	34A
69530	34B
69531	34B
69532	34A
69533	34B
69534	34C
69535	34A
69536	34A
69537	34C
69538	34A
69539	34A
69540	34A
69541	34A
69542	34A
69543	34A
69544	34A
69545	34A
69546	34A
69547	34B
69548	34A
69549	34A
69550	38A
69551	34C
69552	38A
69553	65C
69554	34C
69555	38A
69556	34B
69557	34D
69558	34C
69559	34C
69560	38E
69561	34A
69562	65C
69563	65E
69564	65C
69565	65C
69566	34B
69567	34B
69568	34A
69569	34A
69570	34A
69571	34A
69572	34A
69573	34A
69574	34A
69575	34A
69576	34A
69577	34A
69578	34A
69579	34A
69580	34C
69581	34A
69582	34C
69583	34A
69584	34A
69585	34A

69586	34C	69646	30A	69708	32A	**A5**	
69587	34C	69647	30A	69709	32A	**4-6-2T**	
69588	34C	69648	30A	69710	30A	69800	40B
69589	34A	69649	30A	69711	32B	69801	38A
69590	34A	69650	30A	69712	30A	69802	51K
69591	34A	69651	30A	69713	30A	69803	35B
69592	34A	69652	30A	69714	30A	69804	40A
69593	34A	69653	30A	69715	30A	69805	34E
69594	34C	69654	30A	69716	30A	69806	38A
69595	65C	69655	30A	69717	30A	69807	38A
69596	65E	69656	30A	69718	30A	69808	40F
		69657	30A	69719	30A	69809	38A
		69658	30A	69720	30A	69810	38A
N7		69659	30A	69721	30A	69811	51K
0-6-2T		69660	30A	69722	30A	69812	40E
69600	30A	69661	30A	69723	30A	69813	40A
69601	30A	69662	30A	69724	30A	69814	38A
69602	30A	69663	30A	69725	30A	69815	40E
69603	30A	69664	30A	69726	30E	69816	35B
69604	30A	69665	30A	69727	30A	69817	38A
69605	30A	69666	30A	69728	30A	69818	40E
69606	30A	69667	30A	69729	30A	69819	40F
69607	30A	69668	30A	69730	30A	69820	40A
69608	30A	69669	30A	69731	30A	69821	38A
69609	30A	69670	30A	69732	30A	69822	34E
69610	30A	69671	30A	69733	30A	69823	38A
69611	30A	69672	30A			69824	35B
69612	30F	69673	30A			69825	38A
69613	34C	69674	30A	**A7**		69826	38A
69614	30F	69675	30A	**4-62T**		69827	34E
69615	34C	69676	30A	69770	53A	69828	34E
69616	30A	69677	30F	69771	53A	69829	34E
69617	30A	69678	30A	69772	53A	69830	51A
69618	30A	69679	32G	69773	53A	69831	51K
69619	30A	69680	30A	69774	53C	69832	51A
69620	34C	69681	30A	69775	53A	69833	51A
69621	30F	69682	30A	69776	53C	69834	51K
69622	30A	69683	30A	69777	53A	69835	51A
69623	30A	69684	30A	69778	53A	69836	51A
69624	30A	69685	30A	69779	53A	69837	51A
69625	30A	69686	30A	69780	53A	69838	51A
69626	30A	69687	30A	69781	51E	69839	51A
69627	30A	69688	30A	69782	53A	69840	51A
69628	30A	69689	34E	69783	53A	69841	51A
69629	30A	69690	34E	69784	53A	69842	51K
69630	30A	69691	34C	69785	53C		
69631	30A	69692	34E	69786	53A		
69632	34C	69693	30A	69787	51E	**A8**	
69633	30A	69694	34E	69788	53A	**4-6-2T**	
69634	30A	69695	34C	69789	53C	69850	54A
69635	30F	69696	34C			69851	51F
69636	30A	69697	30A			69852	51C
69637	30A	69698	34E	**A6**		69853	54A
69638	30A	69699	34E	**4-6-2T**		69854	53B
69639	34C	69700	30A	69791	50D	69855	53B
69640	34C	69701	30E	69793	50D	69856	51F
69641	30A	69702	30A	69794	50D	69857	54A
69642	30A	69703	32B	69796	50D	69858	50G
69643	30A	69704	30A	69797	50D	69859	53B
69644	34C	69705	30A	69798	53B	69860	50G
69645	30A	69706	32A				
		69707	32A				

69861	50G	69883	51E
69862	51C	69884	51K
69863	51C	69885	50E
69864	50G	69886	50E
69865	50G	69887	54A
69866	53B	69888	50G
69867	50C	69889	51K
69868	51F	69890	50G
69869	51K	69891	51K
69870	51F	69892	51K
69871	51C	69893	51C
69872	51F	69894	53B

69873	53B
69874	54A
69875	51F
69876	53B
69877	50E
69878	53B
69879	50C
69880	53B
69881	50E
69882	50E

SI
0–8–4T

69900	36B
69901	36B
69902	36C

69903	36C
69904	36B
69905	36B

TI
4–8–0T

69910	51B
69911	51B
69912	53A
69913	51B
69914	53A
69915	53A
69916	51B
69917	51B
69918	51E
69919	51B
69920	53A
69921	51B
69922	53A

QI
0–8–0T

69925	65A
69926	31B
69927	65A
69928	40E
69929	40E
69930	36C
69931	50C
69932	36C
69933	50C
69934	36C
69935	36C
69936	36C
69937	36C

UI
2–8–8–2

69999	21C

WD
2–8–0

NOTE : Former W.D. and L.N.E.R. numbers are given in the second column as not all these engines have yet received B.R. numbers.

B.R. No.	Old No.	
90000	63000	38A
90001	63001	52D
90002	63002	38A
90003	63003	31B
90004	63004	62A
90005	63005	31B
90006	63006	53A
90007	63007	53C
90008	63008	53A
90009	63009	53A
90010	63010	53C
90011	63011	53C
90012	63012	51E
90013	63013	31B
90014	63014	51B
90015	63015	31B
90016	63016	51B
90017	63017	62B
90018	63018	31B
90019	63019	62A
90020	63020	65A
90021	63021	53A
90022	63022	53A
90023	63023	31B
90024	63024	31B
90025	63025	38A

B.R. No.	Old No.	
90026	63026	54B
90027	63027	51B
90028	63028	35A
90029	63029	30E
90030	63030	52D
90031	63031	35A
90032	63032	40B
90033	63033	38E
90034	63034	35A
90035	63035	31B
90036	63036	38A
90037	63037	31B
90038	63038	64A
90039	63039	38E
90040	63040	38E
90041	63041	61B
90042	63042	31B
90043	63043	38A
90044	63044	66B
90045	63045	51B
90046	63046	38E
90047	63047	53C
90048	63048	51E
90049	63049	62A
90050	63050	38A
90051	63051	38E
90052	63052	53C
90053	63053	31B
90054	63054	51B
90055	63055	31B
90056	63056	50A
90057	63057	53A
90058	63058	62A
90059	63059	35A
90060	63060	31B
90061	63061	51A
90062	63062	35A

B.R. No.	Old No.	
90063	63063	35A
90064	63064	31B
90065	63065	38E
90066	63066	31B
90067	63067	51E
90068	63068	51B
90069	63069	50A
90070	63070	35A
90071	63071	62B
90072	63072	52D
90073	63073	38A
90074	63074	51B
90075	63075	40B
90076	63076	51B
90077	63077	62B
90078	63078	51A
90079	63079	35A
90080	63080	38E
90081	63081	51B
90082	63082	51E
90083	63083	31B
90084	63084	38A
90085	63085	30E
90086	63086	51E
90087	63087	31B
90088	63088	35A
90089	63089	51B
90090	63090	51B
90091	63091	51B
90092	63092	51E
90093	63093	35A
90094	63094	53C
90095	63095	38E
90096	63096	35A
90097	63097	61B
90098	63098	51B
90099	63099	50A
90100	63100	50A
90101	77000	81A
90102	77001	87K
90103	77003	38A
90104	77004	36B
90105	77005	81A
90106	77006	35A
90107	77007	73C
90108	77008	36B
90109	77010	24B
90110	77012	84G
90111	77013	38A
90112	77014	26F
90113	77015	84G
90114	77016	64A
90115	77017	38D
90116	77018	53C
90117	77019	62C
90118	77020	31B
90119	77022	31B
90120	77023	36B
90121	77024	61B
90122	77025	24B
90123	77026	84G

B.R. No.	Old No.	
90124	77027	25A
90125	77028	66B
90126	77029	24B
90127	77030	73C
90128	77031	62A
90129	77032	38A
90130	77034	35A
90131	77035	31B
90132	77036	51B
90133	77037	40B
90134	77039	65F
90135	77040	6C
90136	77041	38A
90137	77042	38E
90138	77044	24B
90139	77047	38A
90140	77048	25G
90141	77049	84B
99142	77150	73C
90143	77151	6C
90144	77152	36B
90145	77155	62A
90146	77157	36B
90147	77160	65A
90148	77161	83D
90149	77162	65A
90150	77163	36B
90151	77164	35A
90152	77165	66B
90153	77166	36B
90154	77167	36B
90155	77169	51E
90156	77170	35A
90157	77171	25A
90158	77173	35A
90159	77174	24B
90160	77175	53C
90161	77176	36B
90162	77178	40B
90163	77179	25A
90164	77180	73B
90165	77181	35A
90166	77182	36B
90167	77184	86A
90168	77185	62A
90169	77186	35A
90170	77187	62A
90171	77192	24B
90172	77195	51E
90173	77196	87K
90174	77198	65A
90175	77199	31B
90176	77200	82B
90177	77201	62A
90178	77202	24D
90179	77203	85B
90180	77204	35A
90181	77205	25B
90182	77206	62A
90183	77207	24B
90184	77208	51E

B.R. No.	Old No.	
90185	77209	38E
90186	77210	87K
90187	77212	25A
90188	77214	87K
90189	77215	36B
90190	77218	36B
90191	77221	35A
90192	77222	65A
90193	77225	65A
90194	77226	73B
90195	77227	36B
90196	77228	36B
90197	77229	25A
90198	77230	62B
90199	77231	62C
90200	77232	50A
90201	77234	86E
90202	77235	38A
90203	77237	61B
90204	77239	25G
90205	77241	87K
90206	77242	24A
90207	77247	82B
90208	77248	35A
90209	77249	36B
90210	77252	54B
90211	77253	36B
90212	77255	25A
90213	77256	73C
90214	77257	84K
90215	77258	38A
90216	77259	73B
90217	77260	53C
90218	77261	38E
90219	77302	65F
90220	77303	36B
90221	77305	31B
90222	77306	65A
90223	77307	36B
90224	77309	31B
90225	77310	87K
90226	77311	73B
90227	77312	24B
90228	77313	25C
90229	77314	36B
90230	77315	51B
90231	77317	24B
90232	77319	36B
90233	77320	53C
90234	77321	73B
90235	77323	50A
90236	77324	65F
90237	77325	25A
90238	77326	82B
90239	77327	35A
90240	77328	51E
90241	77329	24B
90242	77330	25A
90243	77332	25A
90244	77334	35A
90245	77335	25G

B.R. No.	Old No.	
90246	77338	36B
90247	77340	75A
90248	77342	64A
90249	77348	25A
90250	77350	36B
90251	77351	38A
90252	77352	36B
90253	77353	35A
90254	77355	73B
90255	77356	36B
90256	77358	35A
90257	77359	70B
90258	77362	24B
90259	77364	35A
90260	77365	61B
90261	77368	86A
90262	77371	25C
90263	77372	38E
90264	77374	24B
90265	77375	65A
90266	77378	24D
90267	77379	73C
90268	77380	86G
90269	77381	38D
90270	77386	36B
90271	77388	86C
90272	77390	54B
90273	77392	51B
90274	77393	24B
90275	77394	31B
90276	77395	38D
90277	77398	25E
90278	77399	62C
90279	77401	35A
90280	77402	36B
90281	77404	25C
90282	77406	62A
90283	77407	24B
90284	77408	85A
90285	77411	36B
90286	77413	36B
90287	77414	35A
90288	77415	35A
90289	77416	64A
90290	77418	36B
90291	77419	64A
90292	77421	25A
90293	77424	62C
90294	77425	31B
90295	77426	24C
90296	77428	36B
90297	77429	87K
90298	77431	65A
90299	77432	38D
90300	77433	62A
90301	77434	36B
90302	77436	31B
90303	77439	38A
90304	77440	30E
90305	77441	35A
90306	77442	62C

B.R. No.	Old No.		B.R. No.	Old No.	
90307	77443	87K	90368	78525	38A
90308	77444	25B	90369	78526	38A
90309	77445	54B	90370	78560	25A
90310	77447	25A	90371	78561	24B
90311	77449	36B	90372	78563	25G
90312	70801	82C	90373	78564	51B
90313	70802	65A	90374	78568	24D
90314	70807	24B	90375	78569	73B
90315	70808	87F	90376	78572	64A
90316	70809	25G	90377	78575	51E
90317	70811	75B	90378	78578	53C
90318	70814	25G	90379	78580	25A
90319	70817	62A	90380	78581	25A
90320	70825	24C	90381	78583	25A
90321	70829	25E	90382	78585	53A
90322	70833	25G	90383	78587	36B
90323	70834	38A	90384	78588	31B
90324	70836	82C	90385	78590	25E
90325	70838	25G	90386	78592	66B
90326	70839	25G	90387	78594	24B
90327	70843	81E	90388	78595	26A
90328	70845	24C	90389	78596	73C
90329	70849	25A	90390	78597	73C
90330	70850	38A	90391	78598	38A
90331	70851	24C	90392	78599	31B
90332	70853	25B	90393	78600	31B
90333	70857	25A	90394	78601	38D
90334	70859	25A	90395	78602	25G
90335	70860	24C	90396	78604	25A
90336	70864	25G	90397	78605	25A
90337	70865	25A	90398	78606	24C
90338	70866	26A	90399	78607	24B
90339	70867	25A	90400	78609	36C
90340	70871	36B	90401	78610	36B
90341	70874	25A	90402	78612	24A
90342	70875	25A	90403	78614	38D
90343	70876	82D	90404	78615	25A
90344	70877	51E	90405	78616	51E
90345	70878	25B	90406	78621	25E
90346	77263	35A	90407	78624	25G
90347	77270	25B	90408	78531	73B
90348	77271	24B	90409	78532	53A
90349	77274	35A	90410	78537	36B
90350	77278	62A	90411	78538	38A
90351	77280	25G	90412	78541	25A
90352	77283	54B	90413	78542	85B
90353	77285	25A	90414	78543	25A
90354	77286	75A	90415	78544	25A
90355	77288	86E	90416	78546	24A
90356	77289	82B	90417	78551	25A
90357	77291	24D	90418	78553	38D
90358	77292	38A	90419	78554	26D
90359	77294	87K	90420	78556	24B
90360	77296	75B	90421	78559	36B
90361	77297	25A	90422	63101	31B
90362	77299	25A	90423	63102	51A
90363	78510	25A	90424	63103	50A
90364	78512	26D	90425	63104	31B
90365	78514	38E	90426	63105	51B
90366	78521	84G	90427	63106	52D
90367	78522	24C	90428	63107	35A

B.R. No.	Old No.	
90429	63108	53C
90430	63109	54B
90431	63110	30E
90432	63111	50A
90433	63112	31B
90434	63113	51B
90435	63114	52D
90436	63115	64A
90437	63116	38A
90438	63117	35A
90439	63118	35A
90440	63119	65D
90441	63120	65A
90442	63121	31B
90443	63122	30E
90444	63123	62B
90445	63124	54B
90446	63125	51B
90447	63126	35A
90448	63127	38A
90449	63128	51A
90450	63129	53A
90451	63130	51B
90452	63131	51B
90453	63132	31B
90454	63133	35A
90455	63134	61B
90456	63135	40B
90457	63136	51B
90458	63137	54B
90459	63138	51B
90460	63139	40B
90461	63140	51B
90462	63141	51B
90463	63142	62B
90464	63143	68A
90465	63144	51B
90466	63145	38A
90467	63146	51A
90468	63147	64A
90469	63148	64A
90470	63149	53C
90471	63150	30E
90472	63151	62A
90473	63152	31B
90474	63153	31B
90475	63154	51B
90476	63155	31B
90477	63156	30E
90478	63157	53C
90479	63158	52D
90480	63159	31B
90481	63160	51B
90482	63161	54B
90483	63162	53A
90484	63163	38A
90485	63164	54B
90486	63165	38E
90487	63166	51B
90488	63167	51B
90489	63168	62A

B.R. No.	Old No.	
90490	63169	35A
90491	63170	38A
90492	63171	38A
90493	63172	64A
90494	63173	35A
90495	63174	35A
90496	63175	64A
90497	63176	53C
90498	63177	62A
90499	63178	38A
90500	63179	51B
90501	63180	35A
90502	63181	31B
90503	63182	51B
90504	63183	38E
90505	63184	68A
90506	63185	31B
90507	63186	38E
90508	63187	30E
90509	63188	38E
90510	63189	31B
90511	63190	50A
90512	63191	35A
90513	63192	62C
90514	63193	35A
90515	63194	62B
90516	63195	38E
90517	63196	51B
90518	63197	50A
90519	63198	31B
90520	63199	38E
90521	77050	36B
90522	77051	30E
90523	77052	63A
90524	77053	85C
90525	77054	26A
90526	77055	38D
90527	77056	25B
90528	77057	35A
90529	77058	81F
90530	77059	63A
90531	77060	25E
90532	77061	38A
90533	77062	73B
90534	77063	62A
90535	77064	84G
90536	77066	65F
90537	77067	36B
90538	77068	36B
90539	77070	62A
90540	77071	31B
90541	77072	24C
90542	77073	62C
90543	77074	25D
90544	77075	38A
90545	77076	65A
90546	77077	87K
90547	77078	62A
90548	77079	84G
90549	77080	65D
90550	77081	36B

B.R. No.	Old No.	
90551	77085	38A
90552	77086	73B
90553	77087	62C
90554	77088	35A
90555	77089	64A
90556	77090	73C
90557	77092	24B
90558	77094	73B
90559	77095	35A
90560	77096	62C
90561	77097	84G
90562	77098	70B
90563	77099	86G
90564	77101	73B
90565	77102	86A
90566	77103	73C
90567	77104	53A
90568	77106	87K
90569	77107	62C
90570	77108	70B
90571	77111	53C
90572	77115	84K
90573	77116	82B
90574	77118	38A
90575	77119	62C
90576	77120	24B
90577	77121	35A
90578	77122	25D
90579	77123	87K
90580	77124	31B
90581	77126	25A
90582	77127	31B
90583	77128	36B
90584	77129	24B
90585	77130	66B
90586	77135	53C
90587	77138	36B
90588	77141	25G
90589	77142	82C
90590	77144	36B
90591	77145	25G
90592	77147	24B
90593	77148	25E
90594	77149	36B
90595	77451	24C
90596	77452	36B
90597	77453	36B
90598	77454	36B
90599	77455	24B
90600	77456	62B
90601	77457	31B
90602	77458	31B
90603	77459	51E
90604	77460	70B
90605	77461	51B
90606	77462	38D
90607	77463	25A
90608	77464	31B
90609	77465	50A
90610	77466	24A
90611	77467	54B

B.R. No.	Old No.	
90612	77468	36B
90613	77469	35A
90614	77470	62A
90615	77471	25A
90616	77476	65F
90617	77479	25A
90618	77480	36B
90619	77481	25B
90620	77482	25A
90621	77484	24B
90622	77485	25D
90623	77488	51E
90624	77489	25A
90625	77492	51B
90626	77494	26F
90627	77497	54B
90628	77499	66B
90629	77503	38A
90630	77508	82D
90631	78626	25A
90632	78629	24A
90633	78632	25A
90634	78637	38D
90635	78638	25A
90636	78643	38A
90637	78644	25A
90638	78650	38E
90639	78652	25A
90640	78658	24C
90641	78666	75B
90642	78671	25D
90643	78672	25A
90644	78675	25A
90645	78681	25G
90646	78682	40B
90647	78683	40B
90648	78684	38A
90649	78685	25G
90650	78688	25B
90651	78689	25A
90652	78695	25A
90653	78700	36B
90654	78704	25A
90655	78705	25B
90656	78714	25A
90657	78715	35A
90658	78717	24C
90659	79178	35A
90660	79181	31B
90661	79182	53C
90662	79184	38A
90663	79186	53A
90664	79190	25G
90665	79194	35A
90666	79195	25G
90667	79196	25A
90668	79198	31B
90669	79199	73C
90670	79202	50A
90671	79203	73C
90672	79204	38A

B.R. No.	Old No.	
90673	79205	25A
90674	79206	52D
90675	79207	63A
90676	79208	38A
90677	79209	53C
90678	79210	73C
90679	79213	25A
90680	79214	25B
90681	79215	24C
90682	79219	25A
90683	79220	35A
90684	79221	25G
90685	79224	84D
90686	79225	84K
90687	79226	24B
90688	79227	53C
90689	79228	24C
90690	79229	62A
90691	79232	85B
90692	79233	25A
90693	79234	66B
90694	79235	25B
90695	79239	53A
90696	79242	36B
90697	79243	38A
90698	79244	25G
90699	79254	25G
90700	79259	36B
90701	79261	82D
90702	79262	73C
90703	79263	38A
90704	79264	52D
90705	79265	62C
90706	79266	26A
90707	79268	25E
90708	79269	26A
90709	79271	36B
90710	79272	25A
90711	79273	25G
90712	79274	87K
90713	79275	24A
90714	79276	36B
90715	79278	85A
90716	79279	86E
90717	79280	38A

B.R. No.	Old No.	
90718	79281	73C
90719	79282	25A
90720	79283	26F
90721	79294†	
90722	79298	25A
90723	79301	25D
90724	79302	25E
90725	79303	25A
90726	79304†	
90727	79306	62B
90728	79307	25E
90729	79309	25A
90730	79310	35A
90731	79311	25E
90732	79312	30E

WD 2-10-0

90750	73774	66B
90751	73775	68A
90752	73776	66B
90753	73777	64D
90754	73778	66B
90755	73779	65F
90756	73780	66B
90757	73781	65F
90758	73782	66B
90759	73783	65F
90760	73784	66B
90761	73785	66B
90762	73786	66B
90763	73787	68A
90764	73788	Rugby Plan
90765	73789	65F
90766	73790	66B
90767	73791	68A
90768	73792	64D
90769	73793	68A
90770	73794	66B
90771	73795	66B
90772	73796	66B
90773	73798	68A
90774	73799*	68A

†Not in service.

First published 1950
Reprinted 2005

ISBN 0 7110 3106 1

Published by Ian Allan Publishing

an imprint of Ian Allan Publishing Ltd, Hersham, Surrey, KT12 4RG.

Printed by Ian Allan Printing Ltd, Hersham, Surrey, KT12 4RG.

Code: 0504/B2

Front cover: 'Leader' No 36001 being painted grey in Eastleigh Works yard.
The lining and numbers have still to be applied. No 36001 would be
withdrawn in November 1950. *S. C. Townroe/Colour-Rail (BRS 331)*